MERCHANT SAILING SHIPS 1775~1815

MERCHANT SAILING SHIPS 1775~1815

SOVEREIGNTY OF SAIL

David R MacGregor
MA, FSA, FRHistS

Frontispiece

A British brig heeling to the wind, a detail from a painting by Robert Salmon. The spanker is hooped to the mast and there is also a trysail gaff on the foremast. All the deck fittings, the long boat and inboard bulwarks are painted green, the outside of the hull is black with a wide white band. The flag on the foremast is a white cross on a blue ground. There is a triple dolphin striker; abaft it the spritsail yard has bobstays above and below and therefore no sail could be set. The yard is employed to spread the jibboom guys. Later the yard was replaced by a whisker boom that was hinged or secured on each cathead. (David Geider Gallery)

By the same author

The Tea Clippers (1952; reprinted 1972)
The Tea Clippers 1833–1875 (1983, enlarged and revised edition)
The China Bird (1961)
Fast Sailing Ships 1775–1875 (1973)
Square Rigged Sailing Ships (1977)
Clipper Ships (1979)
Merchant Sailing Ships 1775–1815 (1980)
Merchant Sailing Ships 1815–1850 (1984)
Schooners in Four Centuries (1982)
Merchant Sailing Ships 1850–1875 (1984)

Plans drawn by the author
Additional drawings by Paul A Roberts and T W Ward

First published in 1985 by Conway Maritime Press Ltd
24 Bride Lane, Fleet Street, London EC4Y 8DR

ISBN 0 85177 323 0

Designed by Tony Garrett
Typesetting and page make-up by Witwell Ltd, Liverpool
Printed and bound by Cambridge University Press

CONTENTS

Dedicated to

Bill and Joan Ward
who like and understand
ships and boats

PREFACES

PREFACE TO THE FIRST EDITION

Clipper ships and especially tea clippers are the types of ships with which people always connect me, so I feel that the present book is a new departure as I am discussing many craft which had no pretensions to speed. To some extent the present volume was part of a larger work covering the entire range of merchant ship design between 1815 and 1875, the text and drawings for which were completed in 1969. But it proved too large for a single volume, and so the matter on fast-sailing ships was extracted and was also extended back in time to complete a full century from 1775. The result of this was a book under the title of *Fast Sailing Ships*. Meanwhile the correlative text on the other types of merchant shipping – 'slow-sailing ships' it has been dubbed – needed to be taken back in time and the year 1775 seemed a good date to begin.

Much new research had to be conducted to cover the forty years prior to 1815 and any existing text was entirely re-written and expanded, while practically none of the present drawings had been completed in 1969. Once again, the collection of plans at the National Maritime Museum has been of great value, but many reconstructions of sail plans have been necessary, owing to the fact that such plans were rarely drawn then.

In my previous book concerned with the study of hull-form – *Fast Sailing Ships* – there was a limited field to evaluate. These limits were imposed in such a manner that only ships whose hull-form had measured up to the correct clipper characteristics could be certain of a mention. The wholesale destruction of records, plans and models meant that the hull-form of many ships could not be assessed, and it may be that worthy contenders for the title of 'clipper' were thereby omitted. But this only narrowed the field and made the task that much easier by leaving fewer ships to appraise.

The reverse is now the case because the entire range of merchant ship design is available for inspection and comment. Clippers are generally omitted, except when a comparison is useful, but everything else is included.

Fortunately a limiting factor has arisen and this is the matter of plan material. Just as in *Fast Sailing Ships*, so here, the discussion is for the most part confined to vessels for which plans or models have survived, and as vessels of non-clipper form often excited less interest than ships built for speed, so there is often a shortage of plan material. This is most notable for the smallest classes of craft such as schooners and sloops, and it has been a great problem to complete sets of plans for them.

The Foreword to *Fast Sailing Ships* was written by Howard I Chapelle, the eminent American naval architect and historian, whose study of ship form was published in a number of important volumes. His work influenced me greatly and I studied his techniques of draughtsmanship avidly. We corresponded for twenty-five years and met whenever possible. His conversation on shipbuilding would begin just where the discussion had ended months or years before, while the preambles about one's health were switched to the last few minutes before departure. By examining ship plans he was able to demolish many long-held myths about ship development, and the so-called influences of one country on another. His death in 1975 was a bitter loss.

An important work on eighteenth century ships is the folio book of plans published at Stockholm in 1768 by Chapman, an Englishman in the Swedish Navy. These plans are referred to briefly by writers, but it seemed a good opportunity to employ them here as a basis for establishing the types of merchant ships in existence. This has been done in Chapter 2 and references back to this appraisal are given when appropriate. Chapters 2 and 3 describe merchant ships in some detail; Chapter 4 covers East Indiamen, which seemed worthy of separate treatment. Where available, plans are reproduced of American and French ships in addition to English.

The present book takes the story to 1815 when an era of peace was about to commence. Later volumes in this series should continue this theme with the same degree of detail over the ensuing sixty years, during which the sailing ship witnessed some remarkable developments. No apologies are given for not defining tonnage measurement methods, innovations in construction or the criteria for hull analysis, as these were dealt with in some detail in *Fast Sailing Ships*, to which the Author refers constantly.

David R MacGregor
Barnes 1980

PREFACE AND ACKNOWLEDGEMENTS TO THE SECOND EDITION

The first edition was published in 1980 by Argus Books and was in small quarto size. Despite that, subsequent volumes of the series under the Conway Maritime Press imprint have been in a larger format which has done justice to the plans and illustrations. Now that the first volume is being reprinted in a second edition, the same large format has been adopted. This new edition has been carefully revised and new material added to the text; there are about twenty new plans including those of the schooner *Helena* and a bilander from the Chapman Collection. The number of other illustrations has been considerably increased, and there are some shipbuilders' lists in the Appendices. The second edition is now thoroughly comparable in size and content with the other volumes in this series.

Words are inadequate to express the debt I owe to the late Howard I Chapelle, the eminent American naval architect, historian and author, for the encouragement, advice and stimulus which he gave me over many years. I was greatly influenced by his techniques of draughtsmanship, his method of tracing old plans, the way he took lines off a half-model and above all for his analysis of a ship's form.

At the Science Museum in London, Basil W Bathe, who retired from the post of Curator of Shipping in December 1977, gave much encouragement and advice over many years, and provided excellent facilities to study the Museum's collection. He also read through parts of the manuscript for the first edition.

The National Maritime Museum at Greenwich is the principal source for ship plans used here, and all members of the staff have assisted me over many years. Those formerly at the Museum, such as the late George P B Naish, Arthur H Waite, and the late Arthur L Tucker in the Draught Room, and Michael S Robinson in the Print Room deserve special mention. Latterly, Alan P McGowan and David J Lyon assisted greatly in the search for plans and models, and Bernard Carter and the late George A Osbon with paintings and photographs. In the past, Alan W H Pearsall advised on manuscripts.

A good source for books on shipbuilding was the Scott Collection at the Royal Institution of Naval Architects; but alas, the majority of the books were sold a few years ago and dispersed, which is a major tragedy for those researching into shipbuilding history and its development.

Much of what is written here has resulted from discussions in earlier years with William Salisbury who, like myself, has always favoured the use of plans, not only as illustrative material, but as the basis for research. His methods of taking lines off models and converting them into plans have been of particular benefit to me.

While on the matter of plans, I should like to thank Paul A Roberts for all those reproduced here which he drew at my request and under my direction. His clarity of line and attention to detail are noteworthy, and I am most grateful for all his hard work. A few of William Ward's delightful but accurate freehand drawings are also reproduced, and his drawing of Steel's Collier is a particularly praiseworthy piece of construction.

For permission to examine their records and copy plans, I am especially grateful to John C G Hill of Charles Hill & Sons who made the collection of Hilhouse plans freely available to me; also to Michael Stammers, Curator of Shipping, Merseyside County Museums, who did the same in respect of the Brocklebank Plans.

One important source of plans was Chapman's magnificent series of plates reproduced in *Architectura Navalis Mercatoria* and I am most grateful to David I Moor for arranging to get these photographed.

I should like to acknowledge the assistance given me by various friends and collectors: the late John Lyman for advice on unusual and defunct rigs; the late Grahame Farr for data on West Country shipping; Robert S Craig for suggestions on the economic history of shipping; Roger Finch for advice on colliers; the late Harold Wyllie for plans of Enderby whalers and other merchant ships; and James Henderson for early Aberdeen ships.

A number of Museums and their staff have rendered assistance: Miss Dora M Walker of the Whitby Literary and Philosophical Society which maintains the Whitby Museum; Henning Henningsen when he was Director of the Maritime Museum at Kronborg, Denmark; John Lochhead of the Mariner's Museum, Newport News; the Scheepwart Museum, Amsterdam; Dr Boye Meyer-Friese of the Altonaer Museum, Hamburg; and the curator of shipping at the Peabody Museum, Salem, and Stephanie Jones for particulars on Whitby shipping.

In the search for illustrations I have been able to make use of my own collection, but I should like to give warm thanks to David Clement for kindly allowing me to search through his own collection; also to Frode Holm-Petersen, John Shedd of Model Shipways and Henry S Streeter. Bertram Newbury of the Parker Gallery, Paul Mason of the Paul Mason Gallery and John Sabin of the Richard Green Gallery generously allowed me to reproduce paintings from their collections.

In the matter of photographing the plans and some of the illustrations, I am grateful for the help of Kingprint Ltd and of Kingston Photographic. Joanne Fairney typed the original manuscript some years ago and I have added to this. My wife has greatly assisted me in checking proofs and typing the index and so has Janet Bennett.

David R MacGregor
Barnes, London 1984

LARGER SCALE COPIES OF THE PLANS REPRODUCED IN THIS BOOK CAN BE OBTAINED ON APPLICATION TO THE AUTHOR AT 99 LONSDALE ROAD, LONDON SW13.

Fig 1. Ships beating up the River Thames off Greenwich, as seen from the Isle of Dogs. Judging by the way the branches are bending, there is a strong south-westerly wind. The artist is Robert Dodd and the picture is dated 1792. (Richard Green Gallery)

1

1 INVENTION AND TRADE

INTRODUCTION

The prelude to the century in which these ships were built was a long period of war in different parts of the world, during which British resources were taxed to their limit. As on other occasions, the ability of the nation to sustain its role was determined by the success or otherwise of the Royal Navy both as a fighting machine and as a protector of convoys. Considerable ingenuity was displayed in obtaining raw materials to build and equip the warships and merchantmen. The ever present shortage of timber and the closure of normal sources of supply for imported wood meant that the world had to be scoured for suitable timber, not least for use in masts and spars. Timber was imported from Canada, the West Indies, Africa and India for use in the hard-pressed shipyards and naval dockyards. Fortunately the new mechanical skills of the industrial revolution permitted more economical use of manpower in many industries, and the growing use of iron enabled timber to be conserved to certain cases. Shipbuilders were less concerned with new developments than with the productions of efficient vessels to form adequate gun platforms or to carry the maximum amount of cargo. Safety and good weatherly qualities were naturally required, but the proven forms of design were generally preferred to innovations.

Thanks to the purchase into the Royal Navy of countless merchantmen for use as transports or survey vessels, today we have a fair idea of what some of these craft were like, because it was Admiralty practice to take off their lines. The resultant plans augment the few published drawings of merchant ships and other surviving models and drawings, and their preservation at the National Maritime Museum, Greenwich, is a matter for satisfaction. Although the overall trend during the half century from 1775 indicates a general sameness in merchant ship design, a detailed study of the kind undertaken here throws up some improvements and variations on the standard type of vessel. Even this so-called standard is as yet improperly defined and delineated, although in the past its existence has been taken for granted.

The plans of merchantmen given here represent some

examples of ships that were in operation during these years of war. In looking at the plans it is hard to realize that steam power was becoming an established force on land and was about to be installed in ships.

SHIPBUILDING

The eighteenth century was notable for the rise of the north-east coast ports of Hull, Scarborough, Whitby, Sunderland, Shields and Newcastle as shipbuilding centres. In the forefront of these was Whitby. By 1751, shipowning, too, was on the increase there, so that one ship in every five that entered London from the Baltic was Whitby-owned, and they were mostly ships of the largest size measuring 300 to 500 tons.[1] The likelihood is that the majority were also built in the port. The north-east ports specialized in building bulk cargo carriers.

Fig 2. Brigs and other craft dried out in Tenby Harbour, South Wales, at low water, showing their need for fairly flat bottoms. An etching signed and dated 'C. Norris 12 Apl 1812'. (Etchings of Tenby *by Charles Norris 1812*)

London concentrated more and more on building larger ships and continued to hold the monopoly for building East Indiamen and the larger West Indiamen. Many of the biggest ships built in the outports were owned in London.

The American Colonies provided a growing source of ships up to the outbreak of the War of Independence, and in 1774 it was estimated that nearly one-third of British ships had been built in America, that is 2342 ships out of a total of 7694.[2] The shipbuilding industry in Great Britain was therefore stimulated after 1775 by the removal of the American supply, although in due course Canadian yards were to take over in the supply of cheaply constructed shipping.

Another avenue by which British shipping was augmented was the capture of prizes during the various wars. For instance, in the period 1756–63, the prizes added to the merchant fleet number 1855.[3] This can only have depressed the native shipbuilding industry. The annual volumes of *Lloyd's Register* confirm the large number of prizes owned in the country.

In the matter of ships built, London, which produced the largest tonnage of ships in 1790–91, was supplanted in 1804–5 by Newcastle and Sunderland, as the following table shows.[4]

2

NUMBER AND TONNAGE OF SHIPS BUILT AT TWELVE SELECTED BRITISH PORTS 1790-1 AND 1804-5, FOLLOWED BY TOTALS OF ALL PORTS

	Number of Vessels Built 1790-1				
Place of build	**Under 100**	**100-200**	**Above 200**	**Total No**	**Total tons**
Whitby	6	12	31	49	11,754
London	84	10	25	119	16,372
Beaumaris	38	3	1	42	1782
Bristol	21	1	9	31	3071
Chester	11	4	1	16	1488
Hull	48	23	11	82	8193
Lancaster	14	2	1	17	1323
Liverpool	26	23	10	59	6710
Newcastle	10	16	33	59	12,444
Plymouth	37	4	1	42	2400
Sunderland	4	14	6	24	3951
Whitehaven	10	16	5	31	3630
Total English ports (62)	793	210	151	1154	104,010
Total Scottish ports (21)	201	34	17	252	18,817
Total Britain (83)	994	244	168	1406	122,827

	Number of Vessels Built 1804-5				
Place of build	**Under 100**	**100-200**	**Above 200**	**Total No**	**Total tons**
Whitby	10	11	22	43	9950
London	77	5	15	97	12,680
Beaumaris	55	11	—	66	3620
Bristol	4	1	3	8	1623
Chester	11	5	3	19	2498
Hull	46	19	17	82	10,839
Lancaster	6	2	3	11	1469
Liverpool	23	5	7	35	4154
Newcastle	6	18	37	61	15,054
Plymouth	13	3	1	17	1266
Sunderland	5	65	17	87	14,198
Whitehaven	8	21	12	41	6750
Total English ports (62)	743	267	165	1175	127,901
Total Scottish ports (21)	175	60	16	251	23,306
Total Britain (83)	918	327	181	1426	151,207

Fig 3. A small Spanish brig lies on the slips, ready for launching bow first, which was a practice frequently adopted in Europe. (From Jean Baugean, Recueil de Petites Marines, *1817, plate 117)*

3

In 1804, a total of 9161 shipwrights and caulkers were employed in the shipyards of Great Britain. Some of the ports with the largest numbers of such men were as follows:[5]

Port	**Number of Shipwrights and Caulkers in 1804**
Leith	362
Shields	1301
Sunderland	656
Whitby	265
Hull	334
London	1283
Liverpool	487
Greenock	309

Ships of larger tonnage were becoming more common as the century advanced. East Indiamen of 700 tons appeared in 1764, the 800-ton level was reached by 1780, and 1200 tons by 1793. In the Baltic trade, where large ships were required to transport timber, many of 400 to 500 tons appeared in the 1760s, as well as a few of 600 tons and over.

With the increase in size came another increase, which was in the amount of tonnage separating two-masted from three-masted vessels. At the beginning of the eighteenth century, two-masted vessels such as snows and brigantines were usually less than 110 tons, whereas by 1775 the amount separating two- and three-masters was about 150 tons for London-owned ships or about 200 tons for ships owned in north-east ports.[6] The question of length must also have been a prime consideration and, from the examples quoted in later chapters, it will be seen that there were some vessels in the 150–200 tons range which had only one mast.

In his excellent work entitled *The Rise of the English Shipping Industry*, Ralph Davis has collected some interesting statistics concerning the manning of ships in the eighteenth century, which show how the numbers of crew were steadily being reduced. Ships trading in the North Sea and Baltic where pirates were absent, carried small crews than those in the Mediterranean trade. Taking the example of a 200-ton ship owned in London, a passage to Riga and St. Petersburg required a crew of 15 in 1725, but 10 in 1765. On a passage to Jamaica, the crew was reduced from 23 to 14 for the same years. Excluding East Indiamen, merchant ships of over 300 tons required a smaller crew per ton than smaller vessels. Ralph Davis makes the arresting statement, 'This drastic reduction in crew size in the middle decades of the eighteenth century bespeaks a technical advance of some magnitude.'[7]

The present book begins in 1775 when the improved efficiency in manning had already made its mark, but it is difficult to attribute the reduction in numbers to any vital changes in the eighteenth century comparable with those that occurred in the nineteenth. The reduction in armament due to efficient convoy systems was undoubtedly of prime importance, but did the design of ships in 1775 really permit a reduction in crew from those needed to man a ship built in 1725? Both ships might have been sailing side by side in 1780, but would the older ship have had a larger crew? The operation of pumps had undoubtedly improved and so had windlasses to a lesser extent, but rigging was still very elastic and required constantly to be set up or slackened off. The bulk cargo carriers produced in English north-east ports, Bristol and elsewhere were given full ends and flat floors. Speaking of the North-Country colliers, Lt James Cook said that they were well-suited to ocean voyages, could take the ground, could beat to windward, and were safe in all weathers. Efficient ships would certainly require smaller crews. But better loading and discharge facilities at ports, or the availability of organized shore labour would reduce a crew merely to the number necessary to man the sails and work the anchors.

Fig 4. Could this represent the earliest five-masted barque? Named Experiment *on the drawing, she was certainly that, with her catamaran hull and her unique rig. I have not traced her yet.* (Chapman Collection, Sjöhistoriska Museum, Stockholm)

4

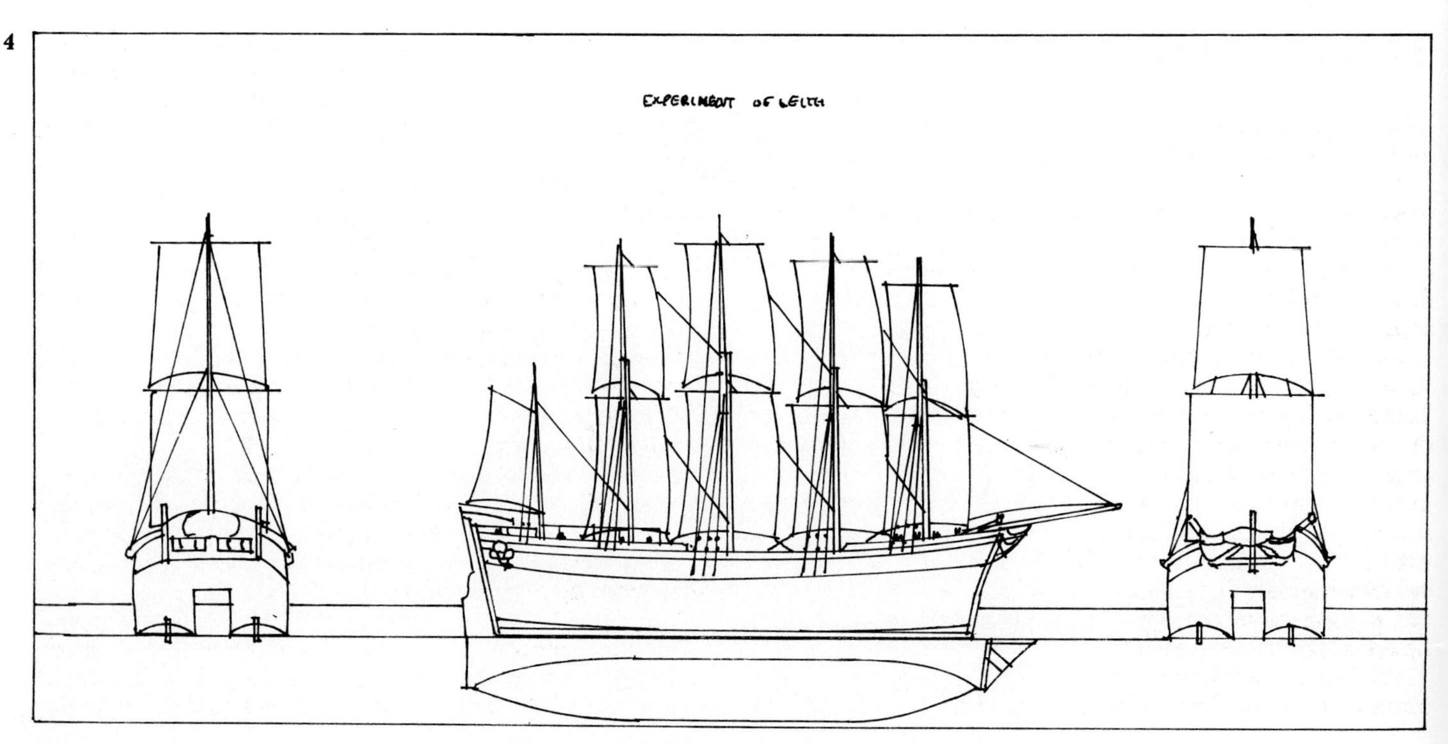

5

Fig 5. *This scene, drawn and etched by J M W Turner, was published in 1808 and depicts a snow and other vessels in stormy weather. Compressed version of an oil painting at Petworth entitled* Ships Bearing up for Anchorage (the Egremont Seapiece). *Reproduced from an autotype facsimile.* (MacGregor Collection)

THE ENGINEER

The iron masters and mechanical engineers of the eighteenth and early nineteenth centuries achieved tremendous progress in their technical skills. Thanks to an abundance of coal, the rapid development of the steam engine and great improvements in the manufacture of iron, enormous strides were made in industrial development. Following James Watt's important introduction of the separate condenser, patented in 1769, the steam engine achieved rapid success in its application of power to a variety of commercial uses. Between 1775 and 1800 Matthew Boulton and James Watt installed 496 engines, all of which were beam engines.[8] Steam engines superseded wind, water and animal power in many industries, and greatly assisted in the manufacture of iron. Early in the nineteenth century, Richard Trevithick developed the high pressure steam engine working horizontally which, with various improvements, persisted in this form for a century. He placed such an engine in a locomotive several years before George Stephenson.[9]

All these advances found equal progress in the manufacture of iron which was widely employed in machinery and structures of all kinds. Specialized machine tools were seen for the first time, such as that installed at Portsmouth in 1808 to make blocks for the Royal Navy. By the same date, many other types of power-driven woodworking machinery were in operation, including the circular saw, rotary planer and all-metal lathe. There was always a great shortage of skilled engineers, due to the absence of training facilities and a natural reluctance to broadcast hard-won knowledge. Data on the strength of materials was the stumbling block, and many disasters occurred through the lack of it, but more research on this subject had been carried out in Europe and published by such men as L Euler, who also wrote on shipbuilding and the science of naval architecture.

The application of these new skills to the shipping industry was gradual. The use of iron extended to small structural members in the hull, to the improved casting of guns, to the wider use of chain for cables and rigging. In the

6

Fig 6. In contrast to the last picture, there is a lack of wind here. The print is entitled 'North Country Shipping: in a Calm off Flamborough Head'. It was published by the artist, Robert Dodd (1748–1815), on 30 March 1787. There are no dolphin strikers to be seen. (Parker Gallery)

shipyards, various mechanical tools were adopted, although the shipwright for long prized his personal skill. Considerable thought was given to the extension of the canal system and the dredging of rivers to provide more efficient communication. An iron canal boat was built in 1787 at Willey, Shropshire;[10] in her construction the new technical skills would have been used, as well as machinery not normally employed in building wooden boats.

Simultaneously with the harnessing of steam power for stationary engines, experiments were being conducted to provide the motive power for ships. In France, atmospheric engines were fitted to several boats during the 1770s with varying degrees of success, and in the same decade similar projects were being carried out in America by John Fitch and James Rumsey. The first employment of steam power in Great Britain was affected in 1788 with a Newcomen atmospheric engine made by William Symington and fitted to a twin-hulled boat on the Forth and Clyde Canal. William Symington, sponsored by Lord Dundas, built the *Charlotte Dundas* in 1801 to tow barges on this canal. She had a wooden hull. William Baker has described her as 'probably the first practical steamboat'.[11] On the other hand he labels as 'the first commercially successful steamboat' Robert Fulton's *North River*, built in 1807 near New York. In the past this vessel has usually been called *Clermont*. She was equipped with one of Boulton and Watt's exported engines. Other steamers followed her.[12]

Back in Scotland, Henry Bell was planning to build a steamer on the Clyde. Christened *Comet*, she was built in 1812 by John Wood & Co of Glasgow with an engine made by John Robertson, and the interest she created had, by 1815, produced ten steamers operating as packets on the Clyde. Other engineers emulated their success with short sea services along the coast and to the Continent. Apart from passenger-carrying, one of the earliest commercial uses to which steamers were put was the job of towing barges or sailing ships. Indeed some observers, while admitting their great use in this respect, thought they would never seriously compete with sailing ships. The East Indiaman, *Farquharson*, referred to in Chapter Four, was towed down the Thames to Gravesend by two steamers at the commencement of her maiden passage in 1820.

Thus, while sailing ships were continuing to develop throughout the nineteenth century until their final demise, the progress of steam ships was forging slowly ahead, in spite of many poorly-financed and ill-conceived schemes. However, the vision of the engineers and other entrepreneurs carried the steamer to ultimate success. It was this same surge in mechanical inventiveness which, in

7

Fig 7. This painting by Robert Salmon shows the slaver Kitty *off Liverpool, where she was built in 1784. Of 366 tons, she could carry 505 slaves. She was armed with 20 9-pounders and 2 18-pounder carronades. In 1795 she beat off a French privateer off Old Calabar. In 1805, she was almost rebuilt. She could undoubtedly cross royal yards, judging by the stays from the mast heads. She was still afloat in 1809.* (Parker Gallery)

spite of long wars and commercial depression, eventually introduced a new look in the shipping industry, although the years of trade protection formed a major stumbling-block to new ideas.

THE BRITISH NAVIGATION LAWS

Discriminatory measures for the promotion of English trade and shipping had their origin in Acts of the fourteenth century, which were revised and extended by further legislation with the passage of time. During the seventeenth century, new methods were devised for developing English trade at the expense of foreign shipping - particularly the Dutch - and these measures resulted in the Commonwealth Navigation Ordinance of 1651.[13] This Act lapsed at the Restoration of Charles II, together with other Cromwellian legislation, but was redrafted and re-enacted in a more comprehensive form in 1660 as 'an Act for the encouraging and increasing of shipping and navigation' and the clauses remained generally in force for 189 years.[14] The term 'Navigation Laws' is generally employed to describe the Act of 1660 and the additional legislation passed between 1660 and 1696. A considerable volume of written matter exists on the subject, some of which comments in great detail on the Acts and their modifications, but less has been written on the effects of the Acts during the last few decades of their existence.

In 1696 an Act regulating colonial trade included the first attempt at registering shipping, although only ships engaged in trade with the colonies were obliged to register.[15] Brief particulars were needed to provide the

8

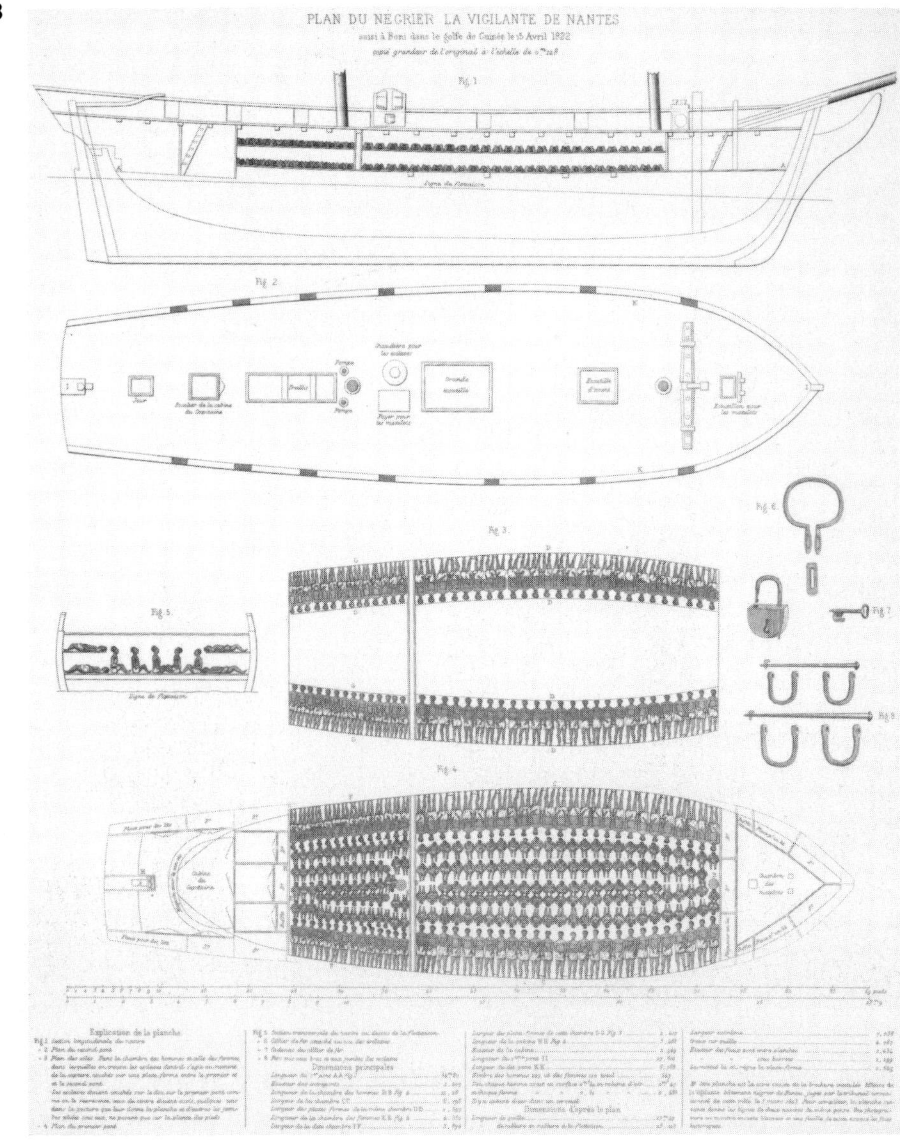

Fig 8. This plan shows the arrangements for the human cargo on the slaver Vigilante *of Nantes which was captured in 1822. This drawing appeared as plate 194 in* Souvenirs de Marine *by Admiral Pâris.*

customs officials with proof of English build and ownership. This legislation was extended in 1786 to cover the registration of all British ships of fifteen tons and upwards, in an Act for 'the further increase and encouragement of shipping and navigation'. By this Act the customs house registers of shipping were created and consequently many shipping statistics date from this time. The provenance of British-built ships was confirmed afresh by this Act, sometimes referred to as the 'Registry Act', which stated that no foreign-built ships, except prizes of war, were entitled to the privileges of a British-built ship, although foreign-built ships already owned by British subjects were not to be deprived of the privileges they then enjoyed.[16] To be British built meant to have been built in Great Britain, Ireland, the Channel Islands, Isle of Man or any British possessions.

These British built and owned ships, of which the master and three-quarters of the crew had to be British, enjoyed the following trade monopoly at the opening of the nineteenth century:

(1) To and from British possessions outside Europe, the export and import of all goods was in British ships. From these same countries a specified list of commodities which included tobacco, sugar and corn could only be exported into Great Britain or some other British possession.

(2) From countries outside Europe, the import of all goods, with some exceptions, was to be in British ships; these goods had to be taken direct to Great Britain and could not be trans-shipped en route.

(3) Imports from Europe, covering a wide range of goods, including the chief products of the Baltic and the Mediterranean and all the products of Russia and Turkey, were to be in British ships. Such goods could be imported by ships owned by the country of origin, but this was discouraged by heavy import duties.

(4) The coasting trade was preserved for British built and owned ships exclusively.

(5) Certain exports such as coal and corn brought a lower duty if exported in British built ships.[17]

9

Fig 9. An English transport loading military stores. She has a dolphin striker, sets a spritsail and still uses large four-sided staysails between the masts, including a main middle staysail. The number 61 might enable her to be identified. (Jean Baugean, Collection de Toutes les Espèces de Bâtiments de Guerre et de Bâtiments Marchands, *1814, plate 32)*

VARIOUS OCEAN TRADES

The slave trade was practised by Great Britain, Holland, Spain, Portugal, Denmark and France – that is to say, by all countries with possessions in the West Indies. After 1783, America imported slaves direct herself. Although the trade was of a speculative nature, great profits could be made. Goods were taken to the African coast and exchanged for slaves, who were then carried to the West Indies and sold there for work in the plantations. There has been some discussion in recent years as to whether these slave ships returned to England with regular cargoes or rice, tobacco and sugar or whether they usually sailed back in ballast.[18] Perhaps, in this study on the design and construction of ships, it is unnecessary to reach a definite conclusion on what was carried in the holds of slavers on the last leg of this 'triangular trade'. However, there seems little doubt that it was the specific West Indiamen that carried most of the cargoes in a direct two-way trade to and from England, and they rarely deviated from it. The same conditions applied to French West Indiamen in the direct (*droiture*) trade with their West Indian possessions. The lure of high profits kept the slave trade alive but expenses were heavy. The cost of fitting out a French slaver was three times that for a normal West Indiaman because two-thirds of the cost was the purchase of goods used in exchange for the slaves. The value of a slaver and a West Indiaman was no different. In Great Britain, a net profit of £13,270 earned in 1805 by the *Fortune* of Liverpool was considered by the owners as a poor return on their investment, whereas that of £24,430 net earned in 1803–4 by the *Enterprize* of Liverpool was held to be satisfactory.[19]

An Act of 1788 provided that the height in the slave deck must not be less than five feet, but prior to this an intermediate platform had been erected in the 'tween decks to provide an additional deck on which to place the slaves,

10

Fig 10. The Dutch whaler De Goede Hoop *under sail with a stern somewhat of the kind called a 'hagboat' by Chapman, in which the wales are taken round to the sternpost and there is a transom above. Unlike Chapman's plans, she has an 'outside' rudder more like that found on a flute.* (*G Groenewegen* Verzameling van Vier tachting Stuks Hollandsche Schepen, *1789, plate E11*)

thus doubling the potential number to be carried. The same Act limited the number of negroes carried to the proportion of five males for every three tons in ships not exceeding 160 tons, which infers that this was the regular size, but it must have been on the increase as the Act of 1795 referred to ships not exceeding 201 tons.

The Parliamentary regulating acts had the effect of reducing the slave-per-ton ratio of British ships in the Jamaica trade from 2.6 before 1788 to 1 slave per ton after 1799. The average size of ships increased steadily in the last 25 years of this trade, as the following figures show:

AVERAGE TOTALS OF SLAVES, SHIPS AND TONNAGE PER VESSEL IN SHIPS REACHING JAMAICA 1782-1808[20]

(These are selected examples of ships with complete records)

Years of arrival	No of ships	No of slaves	Tons	Slaves-per-ton	Crew
1782–88	130	396	172	2.6	34
1792–99	268	328	236	1.4	31
1800–08	283	289	294	1.0	31

During these 26 years, the sample of 681 ships above carried a total of 220,985 slaves to Jamaica. On the whole, ships in the 100 to 200 tons range were preferred because they could easily get up the rivers and along the coast to obtain their cargoes. British ships were spending an average of 114 days on the coast at the end of the eighteenth century, and an average passage across to Jamaica took 60 to 70 days at this date, depending of course on the places of departure and arrival. In the 1790s, the mortality rate on British ships on the 'middle passage' was 56 deaths for every 1000 persons on board, which was a reduction of the mortality rate earlier in the century. French, Dutch and Danish ships suffered deaths of about two or three times as high in the period before 1788. Certainly British slavers became more specialized in design and could therefore operate more efficiently with a reduced rate of mortality.[21]

In England, the principal slaving ports were London, Bristol and Liverpool; in Holland, Amsterdam was the centre; in France there were Nantes, Bordeaux and Marseilles. After 1807, when the trade was made illegal in Great Britain, efforts were made to induce other countries to abolish the slave trade. France and Holland agreed to do so as from 1818, Spain acquiesced in 1820 and Portugal ten years later, but only after receiving a huge compensation. Some of the countries turned a blind eye to the continued activities of the slavers. In such conditions, speed to elude capture became of paramount importance to the slaver, with the result that many extremely sharp-bodied vessels were built, of a style quite different from that adopted for the regular slaving vessel when the trade was legal.

Some 500 ships sailed from Liverpool in the years 1785–87, either in the African slave trade or the West Indies trade, and together they amounted to 12 per cent of all the

Fig 11. A painting by Robert Willoughby of the Hull whaler Molly *in two positions. The mast doublings, yards and mast heads above the topgallant rigging are all painted black. In the right-hand view under sail, the whale boats have been lowered and are attacking a whale on the left. The* Molly *was built as an ordinary merchant ship in 1759 with a tonnage of 290, and only joined the whaling fleet in 1775. She was burned by the French in 1806.* (Parker Gallery)

non-coastwise ships departing from that port. The number of ships was divided about evenly, although the slavers were more heavily manned. In spite of the wide publicity achieved by both trades, they only accounted for a minor share of Liverpool shipping. However, Liverpool did build a large number of slavers and so gave employment to the local shipyards.[22]

People also endured cramped conditions in the Atlantic emigrant trade, where the ships had to sail westward against the prevailing winds. In some ships, terrible casualties were suffered, the indifference by unscrupulous masters and owners being intensified because the emigrants had already paid their passage money in advance. Some emigrant ships from Rotterdam and other north European ports in the middle of the eighteenth century must have been floating pest houses.[23]

Another type of ship crossing the North Atlantic was the merchantman hired or purchased by the Navy Board as a transport during the American War of Independence 1775-83. The rate for hiring ships in peacetime was 9s per ton, but this was increased in 1775 to 10s per ton. By 1783 the figure had risen steadily to 13s per ton. The total cost of freight in 1776 was £703,148.[24] Large numbers of transports and victuallers were needed and 347 vessels were employed by December 1776, with a tonnage of 102,063.[25] The number included many hired Dutch ships.

The War of Independence made severe inroads into the British shipping industry which at the commencement of hostilities had an estimated number of 6000 vessels in overseas trade, with a tonnage of some 600,000. During the War, it has been estimated that 3386 vessels were captured, of which 495 were re-captured, 507 ransomed and 2384 remained in the enemy's hands.[26] By the end of 1782, the lack of ships in the transport service had brought the conduct of the war to crisis point, and only peace in the following year prevented a catastrophe.

Whitby contributed many ships to the transport service in these years and in 1779, out of 251 ships belonging to the port, between 70 and 80 were serving as transports. The story was repeated during the Napoleonic Wars, and from an analysis of the 1807 edition of *Lloyds Register* (underwriters) Stephanie Jones has shown that out of 221 transports surveyed at 63 different ports in the years 1799-1807, no less than 23.7 per cent of the tonnage was built at Whitby.[27] The rates of hire had risen dramatically by 1795 to £3.3s per ton, but by 1805 they had fallen to £1 per ton.[28] Such high rates gave good remuneration to the

12

Fig 12. A fleet of East Indiamen making sail in the Downs, perhaps during wartime, when they sailed in convoy. The date must be about 1790, because, although the mizen yard has been superseded by a gaff, dolphin strikers are not yet fitted. The painting was by Robert Dodd. (Rutland Gallery)

owners who were often in no hurry to withdraw their ships from the transport service.

In the Arctic whaling trade, a subsidy of £1 per ton for each ship was first introduced in 1733; this was doubled in 1749, and remained, with varying rates, until discontinued in 1824. A subsidy of £2 per ton greatly stimulated trade, but it was the termination of War in 1783 and the re-introduction of the £2 subsidy that sent the Arctic whaling trade into boom conditions making it reach its zenith in 1788 when 216 English and 31 Scottish ships participated. Of these, London despatched 91 ships, Hull 36, Liverpool 21, Whitby and Newcastle 20 each, Yarmouth and Sunderland 8 each, King's Lynn and Leith 6 each, and a further 14 ports 5 each or less.[29]

Thanks to changes in women's fashions, the need for whalebone decreased by about 1800, and the impressment of whaling crews and the difficulties of sending out ships during the long years of war brought a decline in the business. By 1813 the price of whale oil had risen from £27 per tun in 1808 to £50 per tun. There was to be another boom starting in 1816 after the signing of peace. By this time Hull accounted for over half the English fleet, and Scottish ports had supplanted most English ports after London.[30]

The last quarter of the eighteenth century saw a big increase in the number of whales caught. Whereas four or five whales per ship per voyage had been consider normal, an average catch was ten to fifteen by 1800. The Scoresbys, father and son, were amongst some of the more experienced captains from the port of Whitby who helped the expansion of the whaling trade in this port. But because of the increasing size of the catches, the whalers had to go further north into the ice fields in their search for whales. In spite of the high cost of fitting out a ship and the dangers of the voyage, large profits were undoubtedly made. For example, the Whitby whaler *Henrietta*, built in 1777 of 251 tons, cost £3294 18s 9d which included her outfit. Subsequent repairs and refits cost a further £1152 10s. From 1777 to 1820, when she was sold to Aberdeen owners, the total net profit distributed to shareholders was £53,553 18s 3d. Comparing her catches with those of other whalers, we find that they may be regarded as slightly above the average, but by no means exceptional. This suggests that the shareholders in a whaler stood to gain high dividends at the beginning of the nineteenth century.[31]

The cost of building whalers at Whitby is compared here:

PRICES FOR BUILDING AND FITTING OUT SOME WHALERS AT WHITBY[32]

Date	Name	Tons	Price	Price per ton
1777	*Henrietta*	251	£3295	£13 2s 6d
1784	*Aurora*	300	£4771	£15 18s 0d (secondhand)
1803	*Resolution*	291	£7791	£26 15s 6d
1818	*Fame*	300	£5980	£19 18s 8d

The Dutch had been very active in pursuing the whale in northern waters, but their fishery began to decline in about 1770 when they were annually sending out 134 ships on average. During the American War of Independence this number was halved. In 1798, British cruisers captured most of the Dutch whaling fleet.

Of other north European nations, the French attempted to revive the trade in 1784 and, two years later, invited some Nantucket whaling families, including William Rotch, to settle at Dunkirk in order to carry on the business. The improvement was curtailed by the Revolution. In 1794,

Hamburg dispatched twenty-five ships, and smaller fleets sailed from ports on the rivers Elbe and Weser. The Danes and Norwegians also sent out small fleets.[33]

Other whaling ships were ranging the Southern Atlantic and Indian Oceans, and in 1789 the *Emelia* of London, owned by Enderby & Sons who remained the leaders in the Southern Whale Fishery in England, rounded Cape Horn and became the first ship to kill a sperm whale in the Pacific, close to the Chilean coast. Of nine whalers in the Pacific in 1792, four came from Dunkirk, two from Nantucket, two from London and one from New Bedford. Great Britain was doing its utmost, by employing bounties and engaging Nantucket masters, to wrest the southern whale fishery from America, and she almost accomplished it. Because of the outbreak of the Revolution in France, William Rotch removed his headquarters from Dunkirk and established himself at New Bedford in 1795. It was partly through his enthusiasm that America regained her lead in the whaling trade.[34]

TRADE TO INDIA AND THE EAST

Throughout the eighteenth century, the Honourable East India Company enjoyed a complete monopoly for all British trade that existed to eastward of the Cape of Good Hope. However, such a monopoly over a long period inevitably produced mismanagement and abuses. The Court of Directors were in charge at East India house, and under them were various committees, including the Committee of Shipping which dealt with such matters and gave recommendations to the directors. The correspondence appears to have been voluminous.

Shortly before the 1770s, it was claimed that East Indiamen were consuming too much timber in their construction, to the detriment of the Royal Navy. At a Parliamentary enquiry in 1771, Gabriel Snodgrass, who had been surveyor to the Company since 1757, gave evidence and refuted this claim. He said that formerly the ships had been too narrow for their depth, and that their scantlings were too light for their size; as a result, they were fit to make only four voyages before being worn out, and that repairs at the end of each voyage consumed much timber. However, he added that Indiamen were already being built broader for the same depth of hold, and of larger scantlings commensurate with their tonnage; the result was

13

Fig 13. Entitled 'Method of Fixing the Masts in the Royal Navy, and in the Merchant Service' as explained underneath. David Steel, The Art of Making Masts, Yards ... *1816, 8vo ed, facing p 84*

that repairs at the end of each voyage were reduced so that less timber was used. It was to even greater advantage that they could now withstand six voyages instead of four, there was thus a good saving in timber consumption.[35]

Snodgrass was of the opinion that three men-of-war could be built in a merchant's yard for the same amount of timber as two built in a Naval yard, and said how unfortunate it was that large Indiamen were compared to 60-gun ships when they had only the scantlings of 32-gun frigates.[36] Although he thought that alterations could be made in the topsides of men-of-war, he had not then proposed the reduction of tumblehome and the substitution of straighter sides, raising the deck level, and inserting diagonal riders in the hold, which his famous pairs of cross-sectional drawings later brought to public notice. His work receives further comment in Chapter 4.

At the time when he gave evidence to the Committee of the House of Commons, Gabriel Snodgrass handed in a copy of another paper, a report which he had made to the then Deputy Chairman of the East India Company. In this he answered a number of questions, one of which concerned ways of reducing the amount of timber used in the construction of Indiamen. His answer was very simple:

> [Do] not build any more ships until their number is reduced, so as to have none lay by, waiting for their turns a whole season; for it is better to have too few than too many, as a supply may easily be had on any emergency; and then each ship might make eight voyages in twelve or fourteen years, in the room of four voyages, and the tonnage of shipping by this means, reduced from sixty to forty thousand tons: this would save more than one-half of the timber now consumed.[37]

It is difficult to say how much attention was given to Snodgrass's reports, but in the next year, 1772, a Parliamentary Committee was appointed to inquire into the affairs of the East India Company. As the Introduction to the *List of Marine Records* states:[38]

> This Committee remarked that a larger number of ships were taken up than were required by the Company's trade, and they showed that, during the years 1753 to 1772, inclusively, the Company employed 175,086 tons of shipping, builders' measurement, for the importation of 139,627 tons of merchandise, so that the tons of shipping exceeded the tons of merchandise brought home by the amount of 35,459 tons. It was further shown that at the date of their enquiry the Company had an excess of shipping entertained in their service to the extent of 26,360 tons. At this time the Company had 87 ships in their employ, whereas it appeared that 55 ships would be more than sufficient for their trade, and they possessed therefore an excess of 32 vessels, which entailed a wholly unnecessary charge to the amount of 73,904*l.* per annum.

An Act was passed in 1772 preventing the Company from building any more ships after 18 March in that year, and the Court of Directors also decided not to authorize the building of any new ship until the 'tonnage of all the ships employed by them should be reduced to 45,000 tons'.[39]

> In October 1784 the number of ships abroad and at home in the Company's service was 66, whereas the Court considered that not less than 70 were required for the proper accommodation of the trade, and they therefore obtained permission to commence the construction forthwith of six ships of about 755 tons burthen each for that service, and six more ships were to be built for the season 1786. In November 1785 it was deemed expedient to have three sets of shipping, comprising about 30 ships in each set, and leave was accordingly given for the construction of eight more new ships.
>
> Under a bye-law of 1773 the employment of ships for more than four voyages was prohibited, but in May 1790 the Court resolved that, from past experience, ships would run three voyages without stripping off their sheathing; and, if the practice should become general, ships which made the outfit of the fourth voyage the repairing voyage, might with great safety perform six voyages. The bye-law was accordingly suspended, and agreements were entered into with the owners for their ships to perform six, instead of only four voyages. . .[40]

> In 1810 an Act was passed authorizing the Company to engage ships beyond eight voyages, if on repair they should be found fit for the service; also, to take up, by private contract, ships employed in carrying convicts or stores to New South Wales, to bring home cargoes from China or India.[41]

During 1795 a decision was taken by the Court of Directors to permit ships built in India to be chartered by the Company, and an Act of Parliament was passed in that year permitting ships that were not British-built or registered, but built within the Company's territories, to bring goods to Great Britain and also to export them to India. Originally a war-time relaxation of the Navigation Acts, it was subsequently extended.[42]

The freight rates at which the Company chartered the

14

ships were constantly being forced up by the ships' husbands to gain as much profit as possible for themselves and their owners. The Company invited tenders in order to obtain competitive prices, but the husbands obviously agreed a rate amongst themselves to force the hand of the Directors.

> Towards the close of the American war, the Directors complained bitterly of the oppressive terms of owners for the hire of their shipping, to which, however, they were forced of necessity to submit. The freights were in this year at the then unexampled rate of £47 per ton, an increase of no less than £9 per ton on the rate of the year immediately preceding. In 1783, the first year of peace, the owners demanded £37 per ton, which was about the price in 1780, when war still raged. The Directors offered £32, and after much altercation the owners consented to take £35. The Directors then advertised for other ships, whereupon 28 ships were tendered at rates much below the last-named price. The report of the Company's Inspecting Officer on the ships tendered was, however, generally unfavourable, many of them being of a foreign build, others of a slight and weak structure, and some nearly worn out. In the interim the old owners had tendered their vessels at £33 per ton, and as this rate was not very much in excess of that at which the other ships had been offered, their tender was accepted, but at the same time the Committee of Shipping was directed to prepare an estimate of the expense of building, outfit, and other charges of an East India ship, fit for sea, to be laid before the Court on the 1st of May in each year.[43]

Fig 14. A painting by Thomas Luny of the East Indiaman King George *seen in three positions off Blackwall in the River Thames. On the right she is hoisting her topsails, in the centre she is getting under way, and on the left she has the topgallants set. She has retained the long mizen yard but no sail is set forward of the mast. This ship was of 755 tons and made her first voyage in 1784, to Bombay.* (Richard Green Gallery)

It was only after strenuous efforts over a number of years that the Directors succeeded in holding down the freight rate during peace time. In the years 1793–1810, ships' husbands would tender at the 'peace rate' of between £19 and £22 per ton, on top of which there would be substantial war time allowances of £20 to £30. In this table, compiled in 1809, George Millett compares Regular and Extra ships to prove that the latter saved the Company considerable sum of money:[44]

The following statement is calculated to show the difference in the price of freight, between the average of three regular and three extra ships from India, of the season 1807–8:

	Average chartered Tonnage	Actual Tonnage delivered	Freight per Ton with extra wages			Rate per Ton of demorage abroad			Rate per Ton for Convoy out and home			Rate per Ton for protracted Voyage			Average Freight and demorage per Ton		
			£	s	d	£	s	d	£	s	d	£	s	d	£	s	d
Regular	817	696	45	19	11	3	7	5	0	15	0	—			50	2	4
Extra	593	663	26	5	0	0	17	0	0	18	9	2	8	1	30	9	0
Difference	225	33	19	14	11	2	10	3	0	3	9	2	8	1	19	13	4

Hence it appears, that the three regular ships are, upon an average, chartered at 225 tons each more than the extra ships; yet they deliver only, upon an average, 33 tons more cargo.

This arises from the circumstances of the regular ships being allowed full freight for about one hundred tons of kintledge, the extra ship has no such allowances: the former seldom carries any surplus tonnage, the latter is generally capable of carrying one hundred tons, being much less encumbered with the establishment of men, stores and privilege to the captains and officer:

To give a variation on London and the Thames, here is a tender submitted for an extra ship built at Topsham, South Devon, in which the Wigram family obviously had an interest:

Gentlemen, London, 12th November 1806.

I beg leave to offer for your service the ship *Retreat*, Captain William Hay, of about 505 tons, builder's measurement, built at Topsham, in the year 1801, with three decks and raised forecastle, and now in the river Thames, subject, in all respects (including the fifty-sixth clause respecting average) to the terms and conditions stated in the printed paper, which I received from the office of the Clerk to your Committee of Shipping, in consequence of your advertisement of the 31st ultimo.

The rates at which I tender the ship are, *viz.*

A permanent peace freight, for the whole number of voyages for which the ship may be engaged of £15 per ton, without kintledge, for as much as the ship can, in the opinion of the Master Attendant, or other proper officer belonging to the Company, conveniently and safely take on board, under the several conditions expressed in the forty-sixth clause of the terms above-mentioned.

An additional freight of £1 10s per ton for sugar in boxes, on each voyage.

A further allowance of £12 per ton on the chartered tonnage, for the first voyage, for the additional expences occasioned by war, under the several conditions expressed in the sixty-second clause of the terms before-mentioned.

And such sum for war contingencies, for each subsequent voyage in war, as the Court of Directors shall think proper to allow, under the conditions prescribed in the sixty-third clause of the terms before-mentioned.

I am, Gentlemen,
Your most obedient servant,
for Sir Rob Wigram
John Wigram

Owners' Names,
Charles Hay, Esq
J Hay, Esq
Robert Wigram, Esq
William Wigram, Esq
S[t]ephen Holden, Esq

The Honorable Court of Directors.

Ownership of the East Indiamen was in fractions, and the price rose steadily. By the 1770s, a $\frac{1}{16}$ share in a 700-ton ship cost £1000 or more; by the first decade of the 19th-century, a $\frac{1}{16}$ share in a ship of 1200 tons cost over £2000.[46]

In those days timber and everything connected with it was the life of a ship; the way in which it was felled, converted and taken from the forest to the shipyard was all-important. Here is an interesting letter on the subject which was included amongst a series of papers connected with Gabriel Snodgrass, as published in the *European Magazine*:[47]

Copy of a Letter from Mr Ferguson, Assistant Surveyor of East-India Shipping, to Gab[riel] Snodgrass, Esq

Liverpool, September 12, 1797

Sir,

I ARRIVED here yesterday with Mr Humble. On Sunday we stopped at Wolseley Bridge, and were most part of the day in the wood belonging to Sir William Wolseley, of whom Mr Humble has made a purchase of oak timber to the amount of nine thousand five hundred pounds; and he is converting it in the wood, where I saw floor timbers, long timbers, lower and middle futtocks, &c. &c. all converted, ready to be put into their places: he sells the waste on the spot, therefore takes only the neat timber to Liverpool, by which he must make a wonderful saving both of land and water carriage. The wood is about one mile from the bridge, where there is a good wharf: it is shipped in barges, and goes between ninety and a hundred miles on the canals to Liverpool.

I am, Sir,
Your most humble servant,
Gilbert Ferguson

Gabriel Snodgrass, Esq

This book is concerned more with the design and construction of the ships than with a quantative analysis of the shipping industry. Succeeding chapters will keep to this programme and in doing so will refer to trades outlined above and to others so far not mentioned. But a final word on investment in ships in the 18th century: a Parliamentary Paper recorded that in 1792 England and Scotland owned 1,365,000 tons of merchant ships, which a correspondent to Gore's *Liverpool Advertiser* on 5 October of that year valued at £8 8s per ton, thus giving a total capital value of the shipping at £11,466,000. At that time, the annual gross profit on merchant shipping was estimated to be 18 per cent on the capital employed: of this 12 per cent was allotted to repairs, maintenance and the like, leaving 6 per cent or £687,960 net profit per annum for distribution to all the country's shareholders.[48]

Fig 15. An interesting engraving by Jean Baugean of two sawyers at work, with the log balanced on trestles. The caption calls them 'galley slaves' (galeriens) *and a chain from the right foot of the man on the ground may be seen ascending to the top of the log, so perhaps the men were chained together.* (Baugean, Recueil de Petites Marines, *1817, plate 24*)

15

16

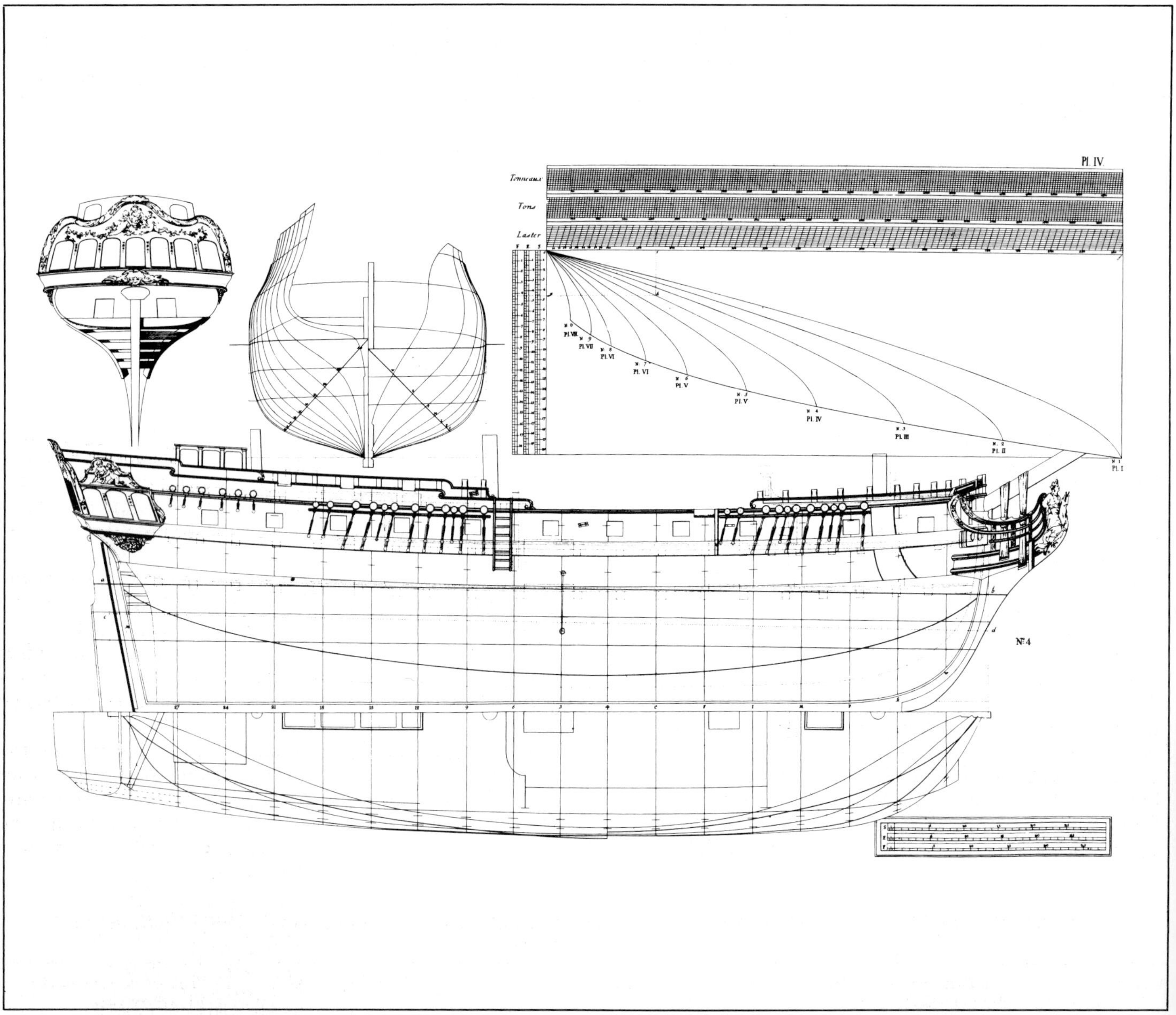

Fig 16. Frigate. *Lines plan, reproduced from plate IV in* Architectura Navalis Mercatoria *(1768) by Fredrik af Chapman. Dimensions given in the English index to the plans: 124ft 2in (length between perpendiculars), 33ft 8 in (moulded breadth), 17ft 6in (draught of water), 572 tons burthen at 18ft 3in draught.*

2

SQUARE RIG AND FORE AND AFT 1775-1793

CLASSIFICATION OF HULL-FORM

Up to the end of the eighteenth century, ship types were classified according to their hulls and it was not until the nineteenth century that the rig became the means of describing a ship. In his book of ship draughts entitled *Architectura Navalis Mercatoria*, published in 1768 at Stockholm, Fredrik af Chapman divided the principal types of merchant ship hulls with which he was familiar into five classes, naming them Frigate, Hagboat, Pink, Cat and Bark, and indicated that each could be rigged as ship, snow, brigantine, schooner or sloop. Later sections of the work cover 'Vessels of small Draught of Water', the majority having a bark's hull; 'Packet Boats'; 'Pleasure Vessels'; Ships Boats; Privateers; 'Vessels used by Different Nations', which include a variety of interesting types. The table of contents was printed in Swedish, English and French, and it is instructive to compare the three for varying translations of types and rigs, which afford extra opportunities for defining the diverse number of rig and hull variations known, and which contemporary dictionaries almost took for granted.[1]

It has always been a problem to evaluate properly the information contained in plates I to XXVI which cover the five classes of Merchant Ships, and so the adjacent table has been compiled in an attempt to consolidate the chief points of identification. The Flute is also included and, later in this section, some paragraphs deal with 'Other Round Sterned Ships'.

Sterns were classified as either square or round, and the definition is really based on the termination of the lower wales: if they ended at the outer edge of the counter or wing transom, the stern was square; if they ended at the sternpost, it was round. But many round-sterned ships had

DEFINITION AND IDENTIFICATION OF SHIP TYPES FROM PLANS IN CHAPMAN'S *ARCHITECTURA NAVALIS MERCATORIA*

Class	Maximum Size (ft ins)	Bows	Stern	Midship section	Waterlines in half-breadth plan
FRIGATE	160 0 L, 41 5 B, 1275 tons B	full head, cheeks, rails, figure head	sqaure tuck, quarter galleries, wales go to wing transom or tuck	deadrise varies from small to big, slack bilges, round sides	moderately fine entrance and run
BARK	150 9 L, 38 0 B, 1250 tons B	plain stem, no head	square tuck, wales go to wing transom or tuck	flat floors, hard bilges, vertical sides	full entrance and run
FLUTE	128 3 L, 29 7 B, 700 tons B	plain stem, no head	round stern, square taff-rail, wales go to stern-post, outside rudder	small deadrise, slack bilges, big tumblehome all round	full entrance, parallel sides, finer run
PINK	109 2 L, 29 6 B, 434 tons B	full head, cheeks, rails, figure head	round stern, square taff-rail or narrow lute, wales go to sternpost	hollow garboards, big deadrise, slack bilges, round sides	fine entrance and run
CAT	151 9 L, 37 6 B, 1120 tons B	plain stem, no head	round stern, square taff-rail, wales go to stern-post, narrow stern	small deadrise, vertical sides	full entrance, finer run
HAGBOAT	156 2 L, 38 11 B, 1159 tons B	full head, cheeks, rails figure head	round stern, square taff-rail, quarter galleries, wales go to sternpost	small deadrise, vertical sides	moderately fine entrance and run

Note: Maximum Size refers to the largest measurements of each type given by Chapman in his list of plates. L = length (in English feet) between perpendiculars; B = moulded breadth (in English feet); tons B = tons burthen *ie* om tons plus cargo capacity of approx 50 per cent, with tonnage converted to English (1 last = 2.397 tons[2])

17

Fig 17. Starboard quarter view of the frigate from plate III in Chapman's book. The wales terminate at the tuck or wing transom, and there are two hinged ports in the square stern.

a square upper counter and square taffrail and, between them, a structure containing two or more large stern windows, the whole finished at the sides by ornamental quarter pieces. The ways of supporting this adequately, especially if the upper part of the hull was narrow, as in a pink, led to various constructional problems, and the solutions gave rise to different sterns. That of the hagboat seems one of the more logical conclusions reached.

Another difference between square and round-sterned ships lies in the method of framing. All square-sterned ships had transoms between the sternpost and aftermost frame, whereas round-sterned ships had vertical cant frames continuing up to the sternpost as at the bow. The transoms of square-sterned ships were covered by thwartship planking laid either parallel with or diagonally to the waterline. This was called a 'square tuck'. It often extended below the waterline. The drawback to this system was the difficulty of providing adequate joints where the planks met on two different planes. In England, a compromise was reached as early as about 1620[3] whereby the transoms were curved slightly forward at their outer ends to give a smooth junction with the aftermost frame, thus permitting the side planking to run smoothly up to the sternpost and to the cross seam along the lower counter. This produced a modified form of round stern. After the middle of the seventeenth century, this form was common practice in

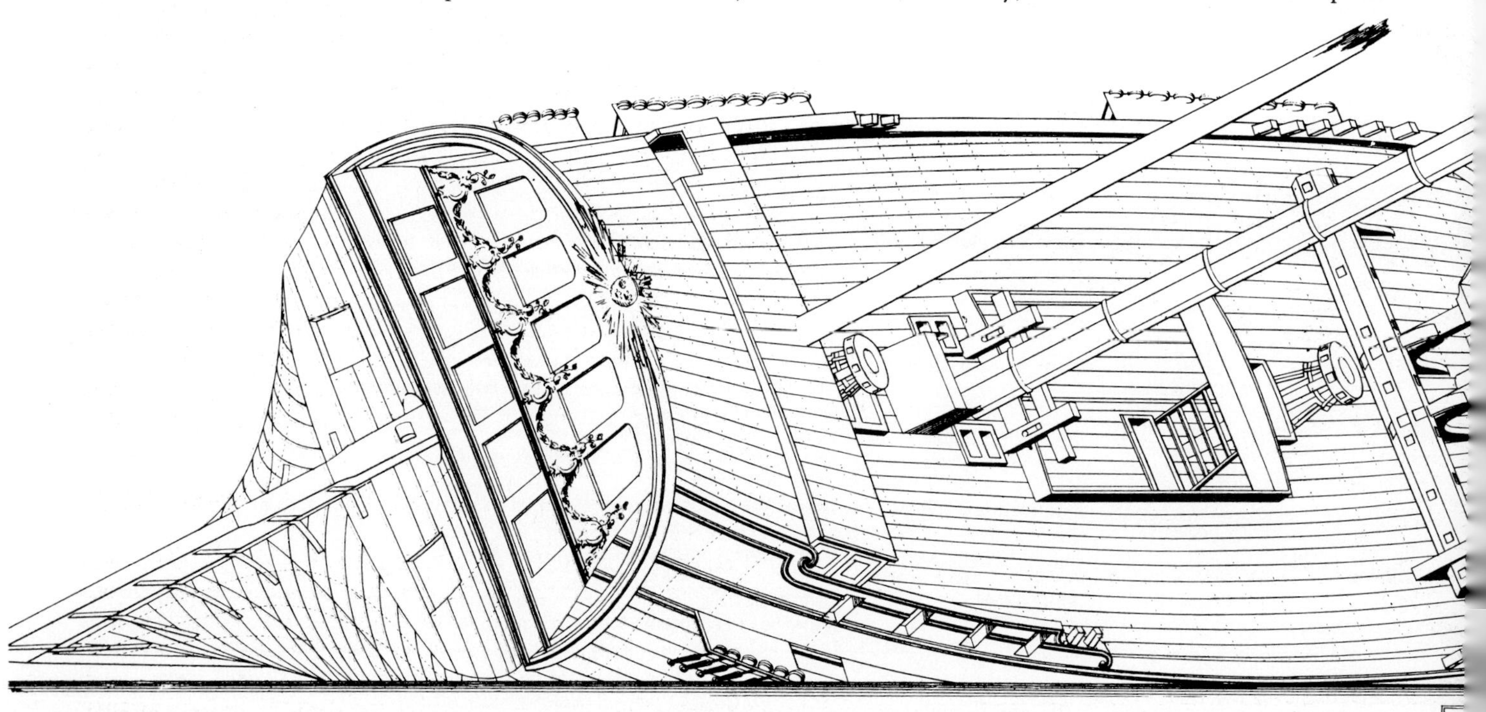

18

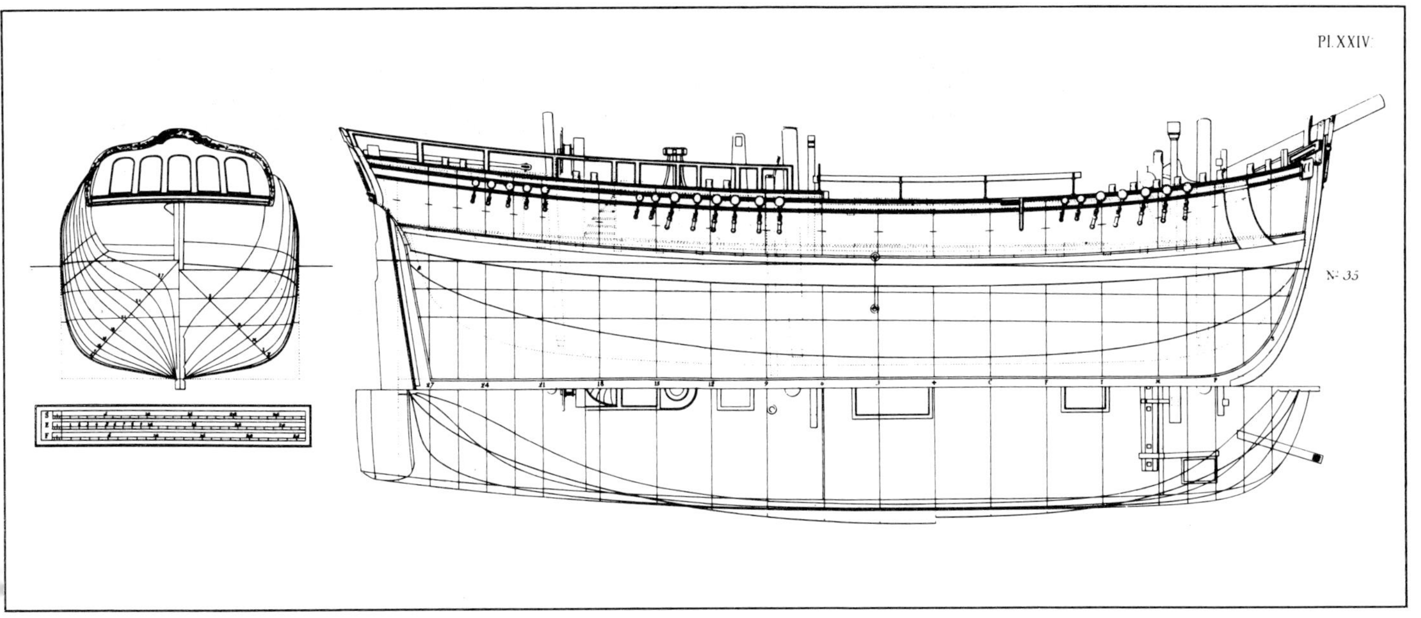

Fig 18. Bark. *Lines plan, reproduced from plate XXIV No 35 in* Architectura Navalis Mercatoria *(1768) by Fredrik af Chapman. Dimensions in the English index: 103ft 10in (length between perpendiculars) 27ft 0in (moulded breadth), 14ft 3in (draught of water), 455 tons burthen at 15ft draught. This is the smallest bark given by Chapman to have three masts.*

Fig 19. Starboard quarter view of the bark from plate XXI in Architectura Navalis Mercatoria. *This illustrates the largest bark of which Chapman gives plans, and she is of 1257 tons burthen. In addition to the large windlass, there are two capstans.*

19

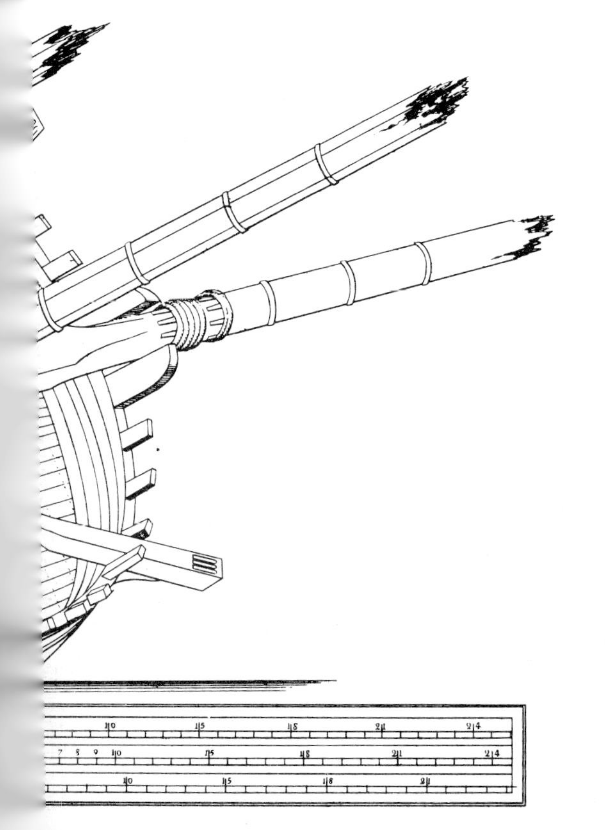

English ships, although cutters often continued to be built with a square tuck.

On the Continent, the square tuck continued for much longer. The French built a few ships with sterns after the English fashion in the last quarter of the seventeenth century, but did not really adopt this method until the beginning of the next. The Dutch took about a century to adopt the English practice, and the Baltic countries followed Dutch practice.[4]

There now follows an appraisal of Chapman's six classes of hulls, to which is added a section concerning other round-sterned ships.

FRIGATE Lines plan figure 16 (Chapman III): Perspective figure 17

In Chapman's plans, the majority of the frigates and barks retain the square tuck stern albeit in a shallow form. The perspective drawings of the frigate (plate III) and a bark (plate XXI) both show the outer side planking butting against the thwartship planking of the transom. The perspective of the English East Indiaman (plate LI) shows the other method. The frigates in plate III and plate V figure 6 also appear to have the English type of a lower counter, as also do the three barks on plate XXVIII.

Chapman gives several examples of the frigate, but they nearly always have three masts, the only exceptions being a snow, a schooner and a sloop. One of the 'Packet Boats' is a frigate, and so is one the 'Pleasure Vessels for Sailing'; the first seven examples of the privateers are also frigates. Some of the privateers have very fine lines with hollow garboards and steep deadrise.

BARK Lines plan figure 18 (Chapman plate XXI); perspective figure 19

The type of stern shown in Chapman's plans was discussed above in the section on frigates which, with the exceptions noted, was not the practice in England. The Whitby collier barks, to judge from plans in the Admiralty Draughts, employed the normal English modified round stern, with the side planking curved under the quarter to butt against the cross seam on the lower counter. Several of the barks in

20

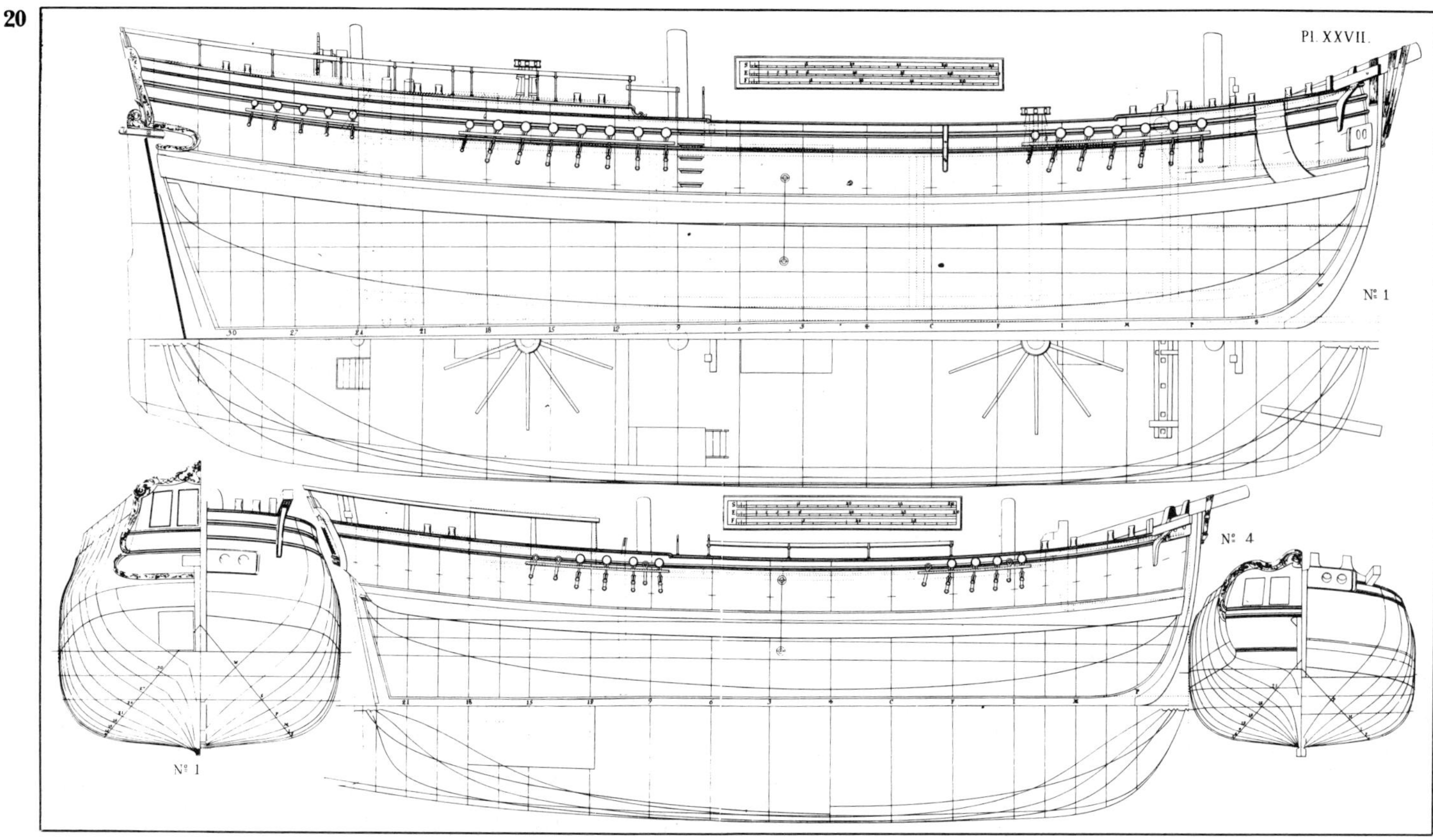

Fig 20. Flute *(upper plan No 1). Reproduced from plate XXVII in* Architectura Navalis Mercatoria, *rigged as a ship. Dimensions in the English index: 128ft 0in (length between perpendiculars), 29ft 7in (moulded breadth), 11ft 9in (draught of water), 618 tons burthen at 14ft 1in draught. There are two large stern ports for loading timber and the forward capstan is installed for this purpose.*

Bark *(lower plan No 4). Also reproduced from plate XXVII in the same work and rigged as a schooner. Dimensions in the English index: 80ft 0in (length between perpendiculars), 21ft 6in (moulded breadth), 8ft 0in (draught of water), 159 tons burthen at 9ft draught. Both the plans in this figure are for shallow draught vessels.*

Chapman's plans have timber ports cut in the stern, and amongst those of shallow draft, two exceptionally have heads and figureheads.

It is generally considered that in northern Europe the hull-form of a bark, with the exception of the stern details discussed, was of the kind illustrated by Chapman and made it especially suitable for the carriage of bulk cargoes. Two of his barks have three decks. Many were built with one, two or three masts. William Falconer gave three meanings to the word:

> *Bark*, a general name given to small ships: it is however peculiarly appropriated by seamen to those which carry three masts without a mizen topsail. Our northern mariners, who are trained in the coal-trade, apply this distinction to a broad-sterned ship, which carries no ornamental figure on the stem or prow.[5]

This definition is already shading from classification by hull-form towards that of rig as adopted in the nineteenth century. The section on 'Sails and Rigging' here describes the bark (or barque) rig at this period. No illustration is given by Falconer, but the rig must have been well established by 1775.

Lescallier's dictionary of 1777 gives two principal meanings: either a merchant ship without head or quarter galleries; or a Mediterranean vessel. The spelling of the latter is 'barque'. After 1815, it became the exception to find a ship or barque without a head even though they were full bodied, bulk cargo carriers.

The liking of the Admiralty for the Whitby collier barks as sturdy, reliable exploration ships was a good indication of their design qualities, and several are discussed in greater detail elsewhere in this chapter.

FLUTE Lines plan figure 20 (Chapman plate XXVII)
In the seventeenth century, the flute was the principal merchant vessel in Holland. It was flat-bottomed with full ends, considerable tumblehome giving pear-shaped cross sections even at the stern, and sterns rounded as high up as main deck level; above this the stern was square, but very narrow. The rudder head was outside the ship, and the lower counter was concave where the tiller passed through an oblong helm port. A carved quarter piece surrounded the lower counter. The wales were taken over the full quarters to finish against the sternpost. Flutes could have elaborate heads or plain stems without gammon knees, depending on their intended trade. In England they usually went by the name of 'fly-boat'.

Flutes were particularly suitable for carrying bulk cargoes. Their great length made them ideal for loading timber, and ports were cut in the bow or stern for this purpose. Plate XXVII No 1 in Chapman shows such a vessel (Figure 20). They were also employed as whalers and on long ocean voyages to India. The engraving in Falconer (1769) is of a seventeenth century flute with its high narrow

22

Fig 22. 'Dutch flute close-hauled on the starboard tack' is the title of Jean Baugean's engraving, translated. The topgallants are ready for hoisting and all the other sails are set. (Collection de . . . Bâtiments de Guerre et de Bâtiments Marchands, *1814, plate 8*)

Fig 23. A flute flying a British ensign. This is a detail from a painting by Francis Holman of ships off Great Yarmouth; the flute is on the right-hand side. Two gun barrels are projecting from ports on the quarter, and abaft them are three stern windows. (Parker Gallery)

23

21

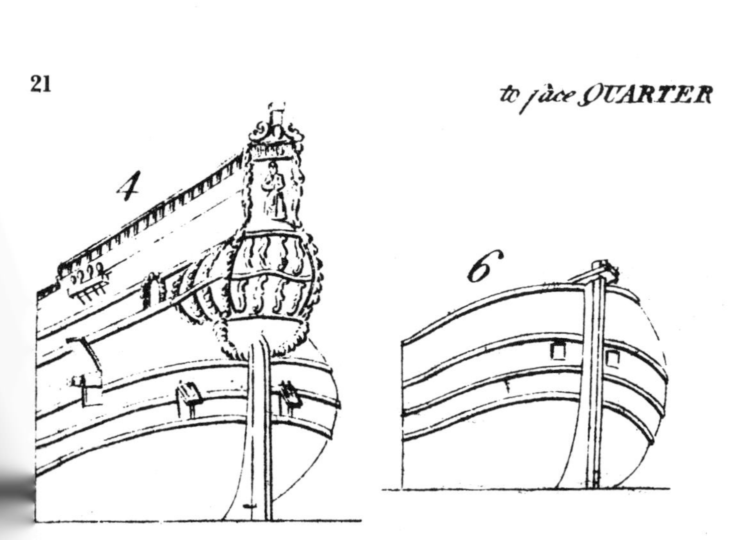

Fig 21. Two sterns from Falconer's Universal Dictionary of the Marine *(1780) plate VIII. No 4 is 'the stern and quarter of a Dutch flight'. No 6 is 'the quarter of a Dutch dogger or galliot'. And Falconer adds: 'The sterns of Dutch doggers and galliots are indeed singular, and like those of no other modern vessel . . .'*

stern. It is matched by the description under the entry 'Fly-Boat or Flight' which reads in part: 'It is distinguished by a stern remarkably high, resembling a Gothic turret, and by a very broad buttock below'.[6]

During the eighteenth century, the tumblehome of the flute was reduced, which widened the decks and in turn made the stern broader. Chapman's book (1768) has only two plans of flutes, but both are long shallow-draft vessels with three masts, plain bows and not much sheer. Lescallier (1777) gives for an engraving of a flute, a galliot with a round stern; in the text he says they carry from 300 to 1000 tons. Groenewegen (1789) does not have a single engraving entitled 'Flute', although his book of eighty-four plates was published in Rotterdam - sure evidence that the flute was extinct.[7] But he does portray *bootschips*, pinks, *kat* and two views of a *Greenlandsvaarder*.

The craft which developed from the flute during the eighteenth century went by such names in Holland as *bootschip*, and *hekboot* and kat, from which come hagboat, and cat.

PINK Lines plan figure 24 (Chapman plate XIII)
Most of Chapman's plans of pinks illustrate fine-lined vessels, but the larger three-masted pinks have sterns like cats. It is only in the smaller ones appearing on his plate XIV that the extreme form of pink stern appears with the long overhanging counter and narrow lute. Commenting on the pink, John Stevens writes: 'Many English merchantmen were "pink-sterned". This differed from the Dutch flute stern in that the buttocks were fined away under the quarters so as not to have a coarse "run". Pinks are shown in illustrations of the Seven Year's War, when they outnumbered conventional square-sterned transports.'[8]
In the extreme versions, the rudder head pivoted in a wide opening in the overhanging counter and the tiller came straight over the quarter deck or poop. The term 'pink' is of Dutch origin dating from the middle ages.

In Mungo Murray's *Shipbuilding*, first published in 1754, there are the bow and stern profiles, body plan and table of offsets of the pink *Bonetta* of 398 tons.[9] These were drawn out and published by William Salisbury.[10] There was not much rise of floor but very rounded slack bilges constructed on arcs of circles and with considerable tumblehome; the lines were comparatively fine, and the very narrow lute stern is there. Dimensions scaled off Salisbury's plan give length of keel and fore rake 104ft and maximum breadth 28ft. There is no head. This plain stem and narrow lute contradicts some of the features combined on Chapman's plans. The *Bonetta's* quarter deck steps down at the after end to accommodate the rudder head.

Also listed by Chapman as a pink is the ketch-rigged vessel in plate XXX figure 1, which is extremely broad with a proportion of beams to length barely exceeding 3:1. She has a plain bow, moderately fine entrance and run, good rise of floor and slack bilges. But there is no counter overhanging the rudder head, although an oblong helm port is formed in the bulwarks to take the tiller.

Other plans of English merchant pinks include two plain-bowed bessels: the brig *Industry* of 221 tons, whose lines were taken off in 1765 by the Navy, had very full ends and a long parallel body; and an unnamed sloop 50ft 6in long with good deadrise and flaring sides but undated, although the presence of an iron hanging knee suggests the end of the eighteenth century. This has been re-drawn in figure 113.[11]

Fig 24. Pink. *Lines plan, reproduced from plate XIV No 19 in* Architectura Navalis Mercatoria *by Fredrik af Chapman, rigged as a brig. Dimensions in the English index to the plans: 62ft 2in (length between perpendiculars), 18ft 9in (moulded breadth), 9ft 3in (draught of water), 89 tons burthen at 9ft 8in draught. The stern window within the quarter piece shows dark in the sheer elevation. The pink has an ornamented head, but the wales go round to the sternpost.*

24

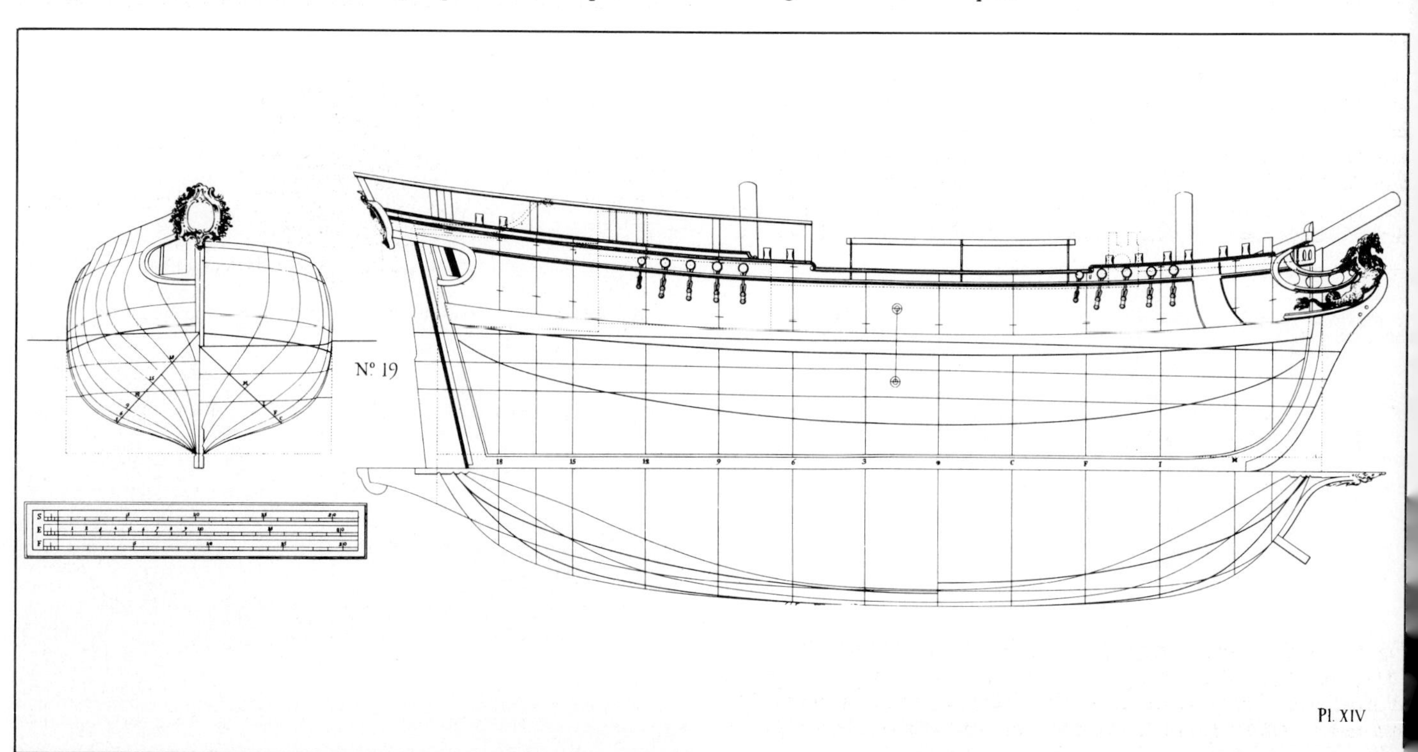

25

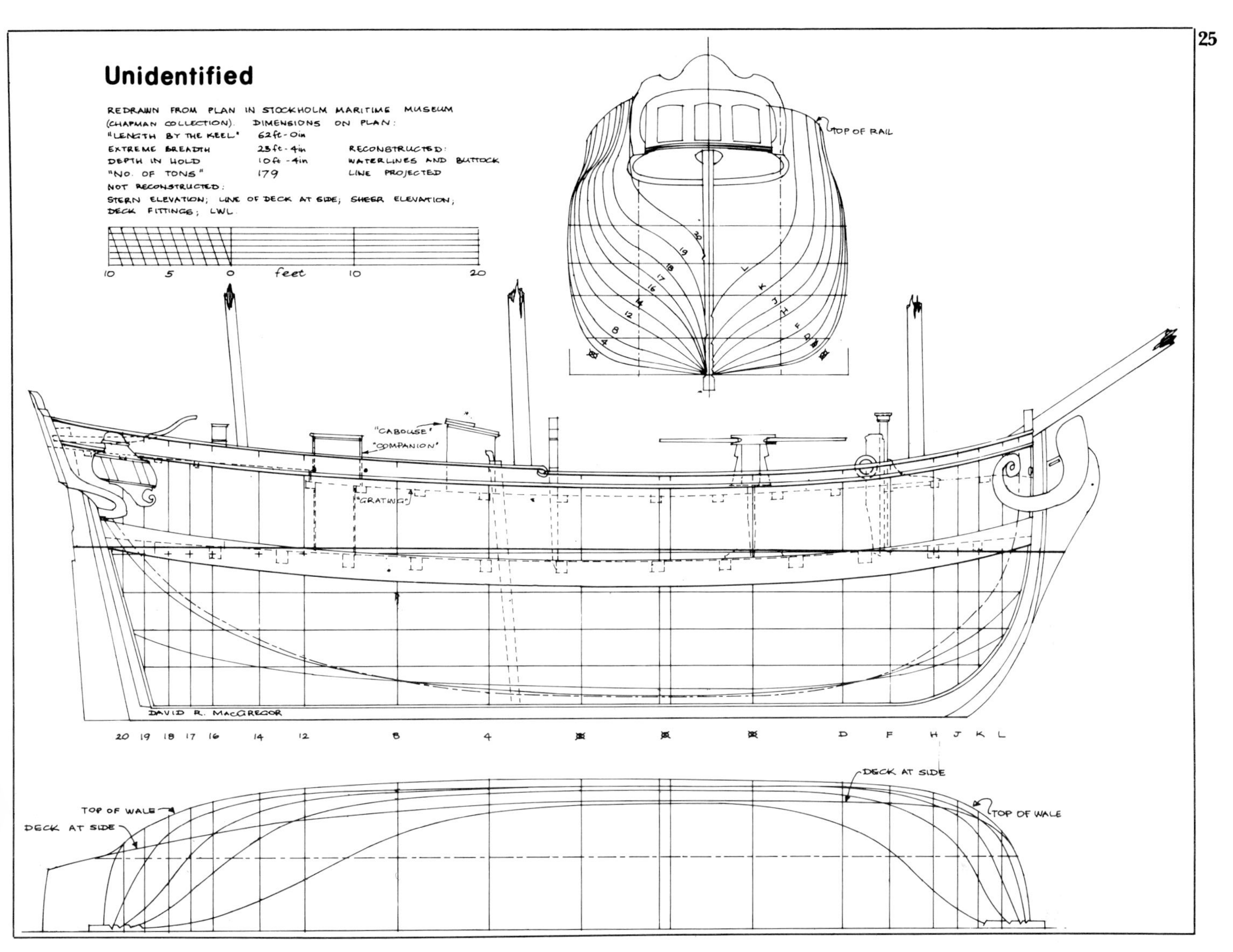

Fig 25. Ship with pink stern. *Lines plan. Redrawn from an unidentified plan in the Chapman Collection at Sjöhistoriska Museum, Stockholm. Dimensions on the plan: 62ft 0in ('length by the keel'), 23ft 4in (extreme breadth), 10ft 4in (depth in hold), 179 tons. Reconstruction: waterlines taken from the body plan and projected on the half-breadth plan; also the buttock line. The deck fittings have not been reconstructed. The 'Cabhouse' is illustrated in figure 27 and is the cooking stove, placed here on deck. No hair rails have been drawn at the head. I am grateful to David Lyon for drawing my attention to this plan.*

27

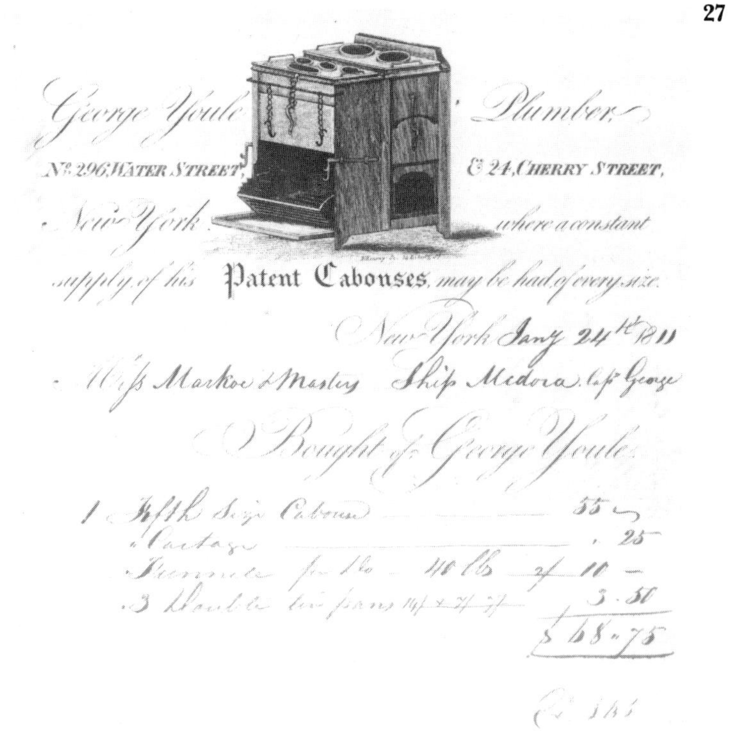
George Youle Plumber
No. 296 Water Street & 24, Cherry Street,
New York where a constant supply of his Patent Cabouses, may be had of every size.

New York Jany 24th 1811
Messrs Markoe & Masters Ship Medora Capt George
Bought of George Youle

1 Fifth Size Cabouse		55 —
Cartage		.25
Funnels for do 40 lbs	2/	10 —
3 Double tin pans 14/ & 7/		3.50
		$ 68.75

Fig 27. George Youle's invoice for supplying a cabouse to the Medora *in 1811; (see figure 25, which has a 'cabhouse' on deck). Smyth's* Sailor's Word-Book *(1867) has an entry for '*Caboose, or Camboose. *The cook-room or kitchen of merchantmen on deck; a diminutive substitute for the galley of a man-of-war ...' The amounts here are in dollars.*

26

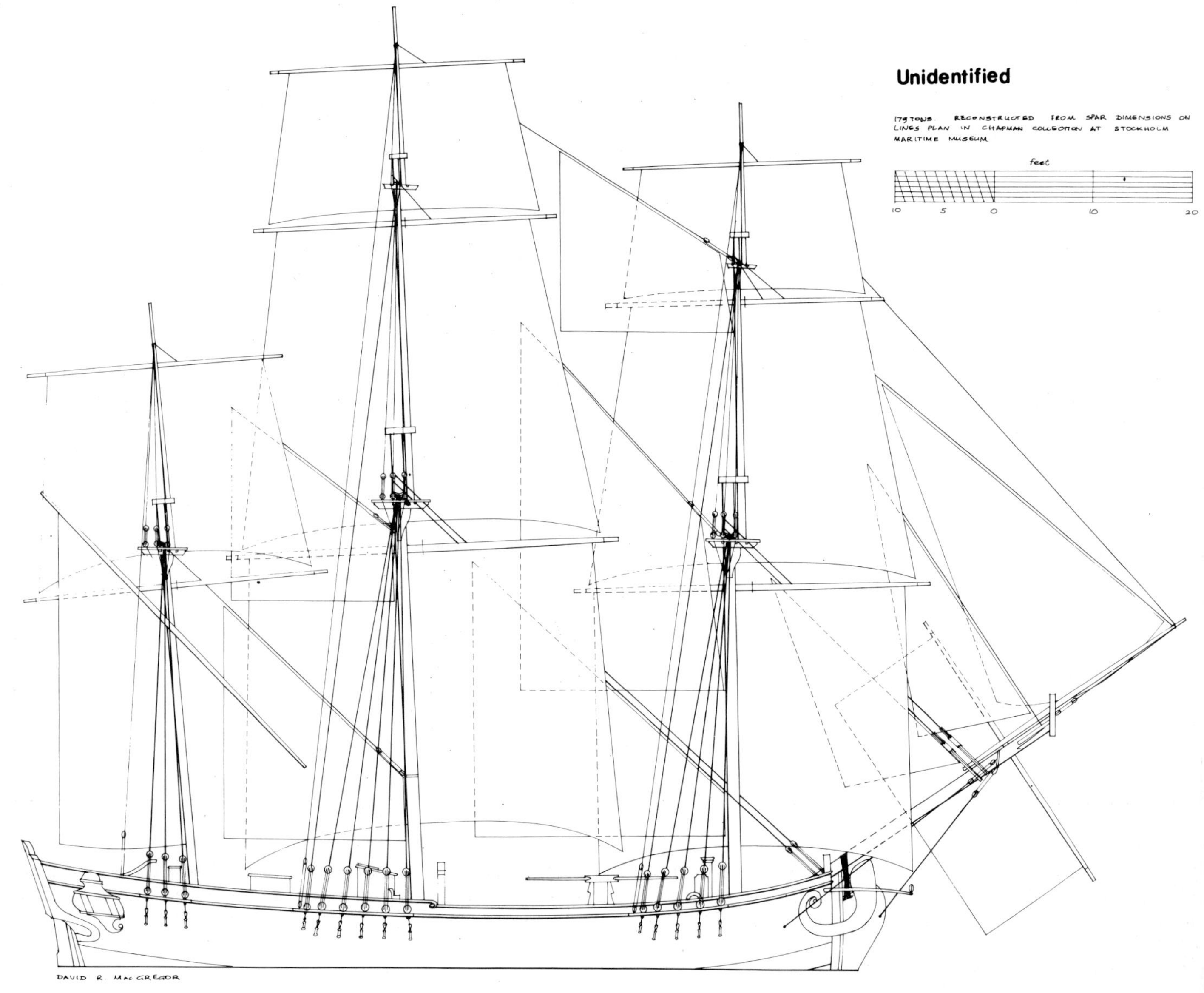

Fig 26. Ship with pink stern. *Sail plan, reconstructed from spar dimensions listed on the lines plan of the ship in figure 25, with only the positions of masts, their rake, and the steeve of the bowsprit shown. No jibboom was listed and no lengths of mast heads or doublings were given so all have been reconstructed. Deadeyes have been drawn on the original, but no chain plates.*

CAT Lines plan figure 28 (Chapman plate XVII); perspectives figures 29 and 30

Its development from the flute was mentioned above. Two of Chapman's plans (plates XV and XVI) show cats with a double tier of stern windows set in a narrow stern; both of these ships have three decks. The run of the planking is so similar to that of the hagboat in the stern that it is hard to see the reason for running the quarter piece forward and then down to the sternpost as in a flute or pink. Perhaps it was a traditional decoration. There are two fine perspective views of cats given by Chapman, and that in plate XVII also has an iron bumpkin projecting some distance from the hull with a block for the main brace to reeve through (figure 28).

In the 1769 and 1780 editions of his Dictionary, Falconer described a cat as follows:

> *Cat*, a ship employed in the coal trade, formed from the Norwegian model. It is distinguished by a narrow stern, projecting quarters, a deep waist, and by having no ornamental figure on the prow.
>
> These vessels are generally built remarkably strong, and

28

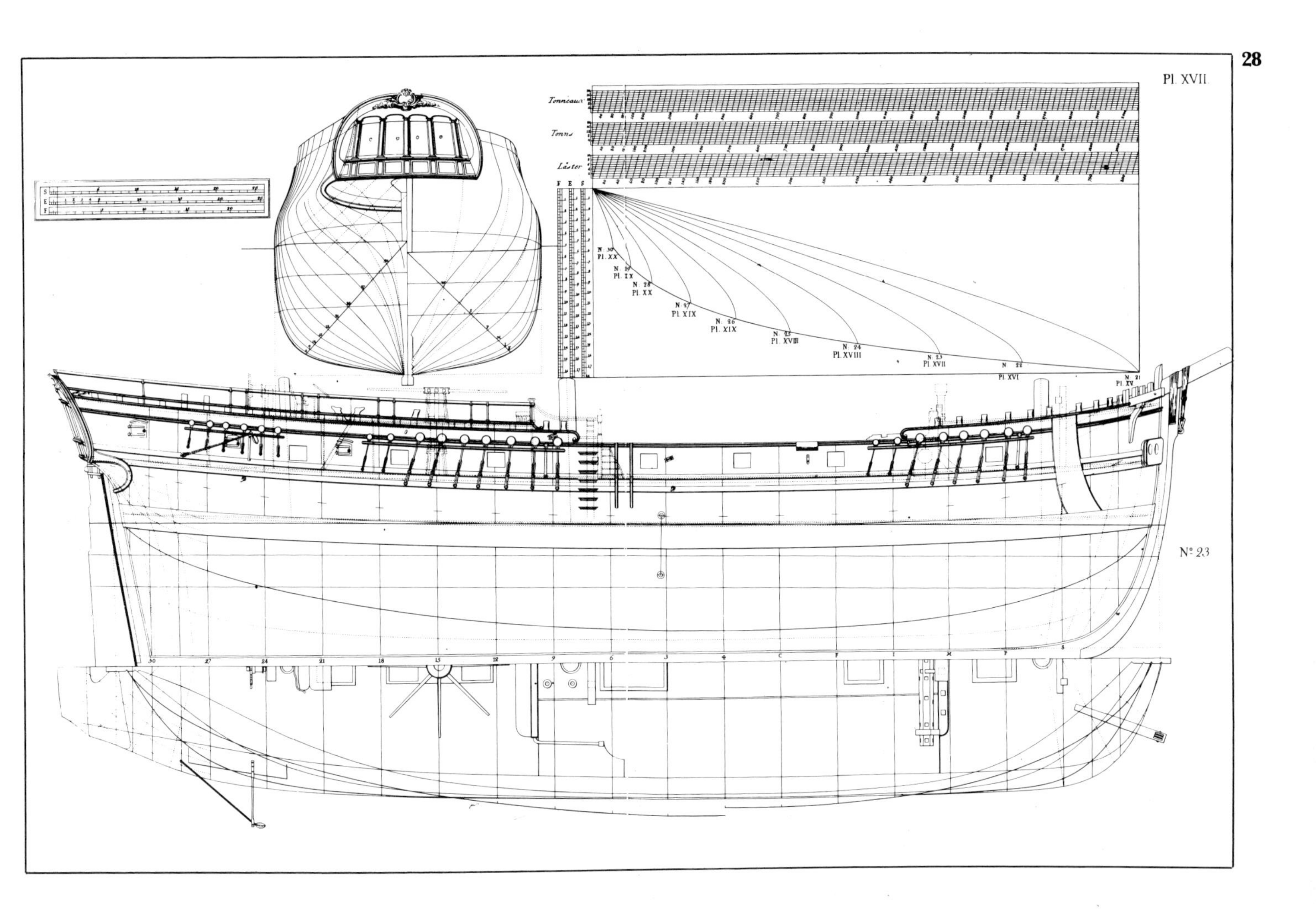

Fig 28. Cat. *Reproduced from plate XVII in* Architectura Navalis Mercatoria *by Fredrik af Chapman (1768). There are some interesting details on hull and decks. Dimensions in the English index to the plans: 130ft 3in (length between perpendiculars), 33ft 1in (moulded breadth), 17ft 6in (draught of water), 711 tons burthen at 17ft 6in draught.*

Fig 29. Bow view of a large cat, hove down so that her keel is out of the water. This illustrates her remarkably bluff bows. It is reproduced from plate XVI in Chapman's work.

29

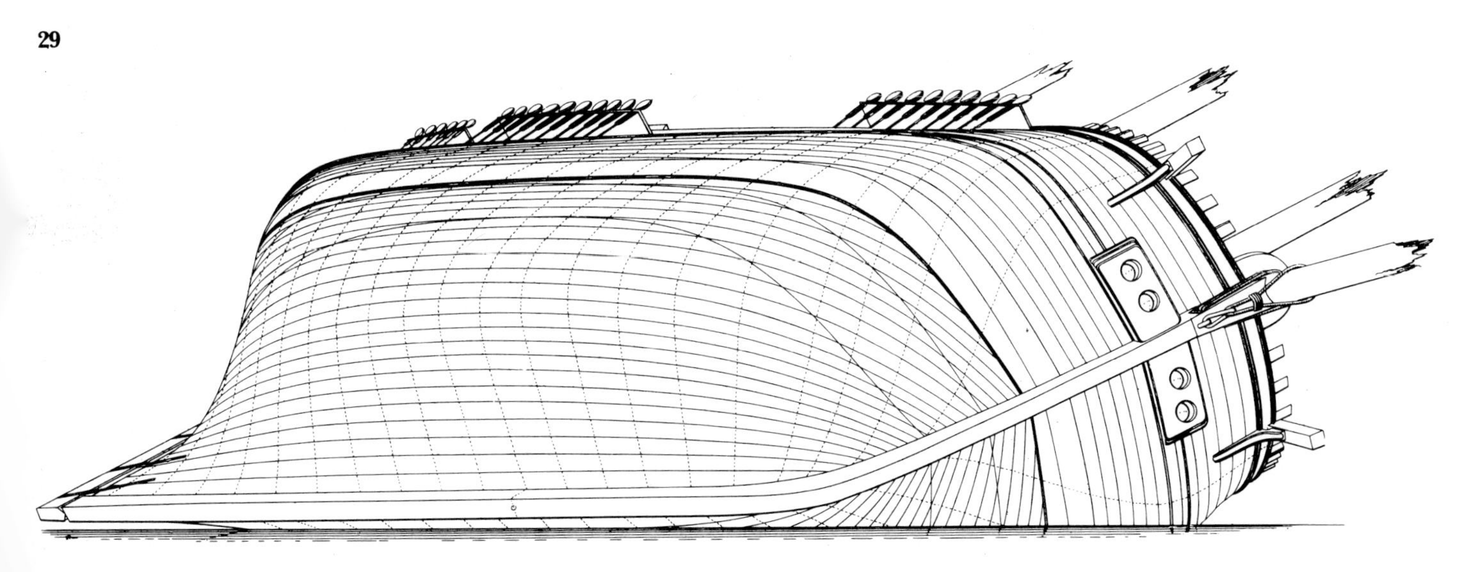

32

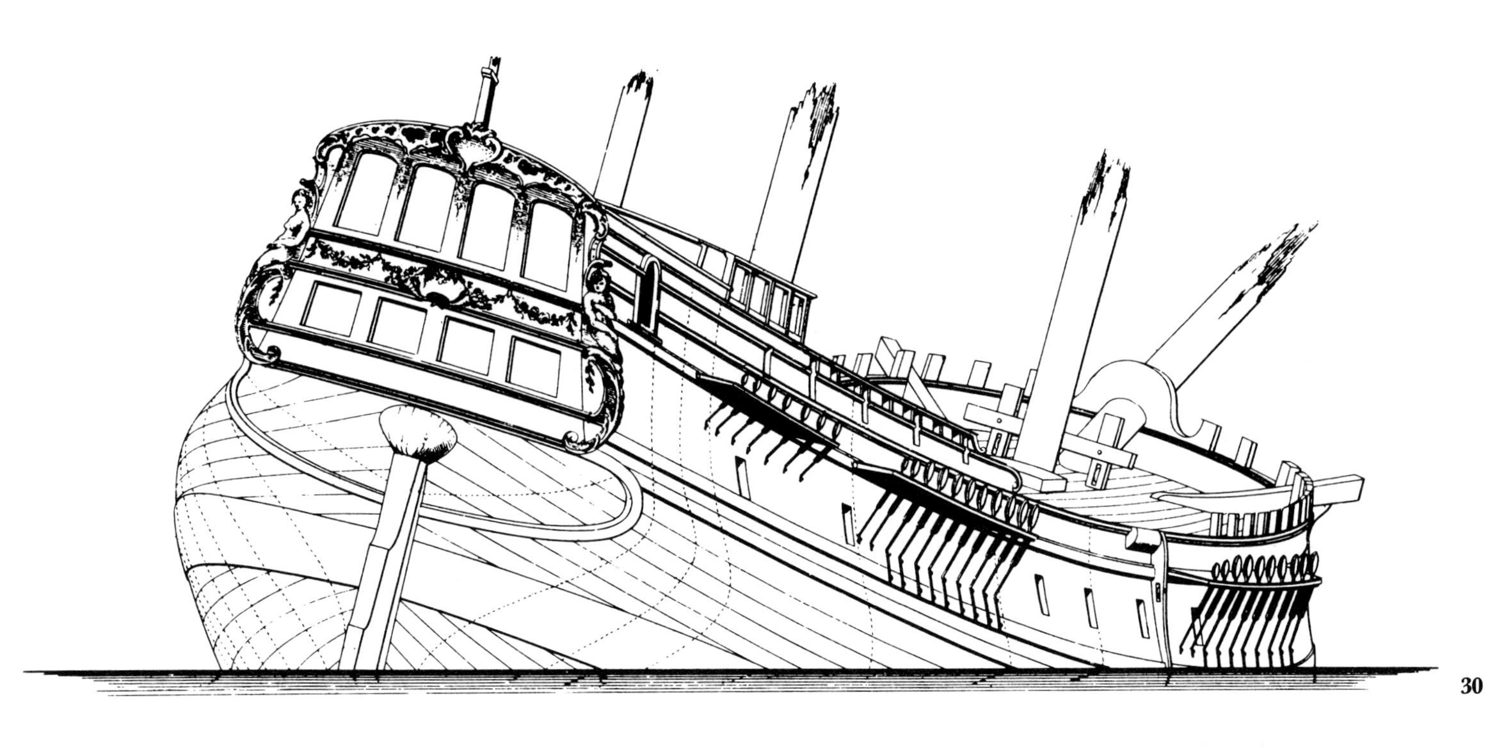

30

Fig 30. Starboard quarter of a ship-rigged cat with a double-tiered stern window from plate XV in Chapman's book.

31

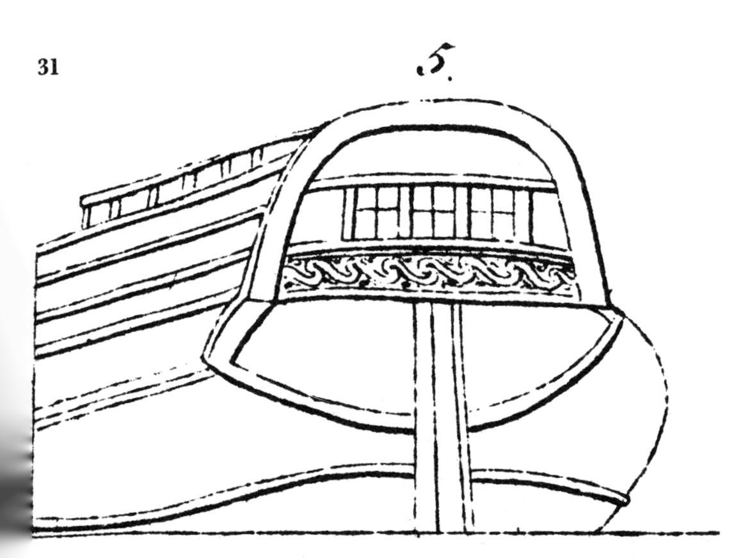

Fig 31. 'The stern and quarter of a cat' from Falconer's Dictionary of the Marine, *plate VIII, No 5.*

Fig 32. Stern view of a ship with a cat's stern, close-hauled on the port tack. This is a detail from a print of ships entering the mouth of the River Tyne, and shows what is probably a collier in ballast. The long pole heads to the masts were prominent in many vessels; the ship's head is out of sight so that it cannot be verified whether she is a true cat. My print has lost its title and date. (MacGregor Collection)

carry from four to six hundred tons; or, in the language of their own mariners, from twenty to thirty keels of coals.[12]

Figure 31 of a cat's stern is taken from Plate VIII of Falconer's Dictionary, which is used to illustrate his entry 'Quarter'. In this entry he writes:

> Hagboats and pinks approach the figure of cats, the former being a little broader in the stern, and the latter a little narrower; the sterns and quarters of cats seem to be derived from those of fly-boats.

Figure 49 represents a cat as reproduced in Steel's *Masting and Rigging* of 1794. The round stern below the lower counter is easy to see and the narrow square stern above. A translation of his entry under *Chat* reads:

> *Cat.* A sort of merchant ship used by the Danes, and especially in Norwegian ports and other northern countries, including the English. The construction of these vessels is generally quite good; they are designed to carry the maximum amount of cargo and withstand heavy seas. They are very bluff-bowed and extremely round in the quarters... These vessels are mostly employed to carry timber or coal and can load from 400 to 600 tons.[13]

A good example of a cat can be seen in a rigged model at the National Maritime Museum dating from about 1750 and with its original rigging, although recently it has been given sails, and the form of the hull obscured by being placed in a sea. This model exhibits many of the features of a cat which Chapman illustrates: plain stem without a head; bluff bows; flat bottom and full body; hull rounded below counter and planking turned into sternpost; narrow square stern above. Chapman actually allots a 'pink' stern to a cat. In addition, there is a fairly short mizen lower mast with lateen yard, and a topmast above, capable of setting a small topsail. There are pole heads to each of the three masts.

Amongst Edward Gwyn's drawings, attributed to about 1780, there are 'A Collier', rigged as a three-masted barque (figure 46), and 'A Coal Brig'. Both have pink sterns and plain stems without a head.

Of ships built or owned at Whitby prior to 1790, which Richard Weatherill lists, a random selection shows several to have pink sterns, others to be cat-built, and some a combination of the two. One, the *Volunteer*, built in 1756 of 302 tons, had a round stern.[14] The plan of a Whitby-built cat, dated about 1770, is discussed below, in the section on 'Shipbuilding at Whitby'.

Fig 34. The most prominent feature in Groenewegen's engraving of a 'Kat' published in 1789, is the cocked up stern which rises up, probably to afford a double tier of stern windows. The port anchor has just broken water and the ship is ready to get underway.

Fig 33. This is what the model of the cat looked like, before sea and sails were added by the Museum staff. The rigging is considered contemporary with the hull, and a date of 1750 has been assigned to it. The yards on the main mast and mizen mast are seen end-on; the wales are taken round to the stern post; the presence of the mizen yard gives an early date, and it is much closer to the deck than that in figure 26. (National Maritime Museum)

33

34

HAGBOAT or HECKBOAT Lines plan figure 35 (Chapman plate X); perspective figure 36

This type of ship bore strong similarities to the *bootschip* at the stern but, in contrast, had a head with the full elaboration found in the frigate. Both types brought the wales over the quarter to the sternpost, but in the hagboat the rudder trunk passed through the counter, which projected as in the frigate. In the *bootschip* the rudder head was outside the ship, as in the flute, and the tiller entered the ship through the lower counter. Above the rudder head was a highly ornamented stern.[15]

In Chapman's plans of the hagboat, the cross seam runs under the quarter to meet the sternpost just above the wale, somewhat after the manner of a flute. Even by his time, 1768, the term may have been confined to Baltic-built ships. Lescallier (1777) does not acknowledge the hagboat, nor does Falconer (1780), although there is a side reference to it in his entry under 'Quarter', which is quoted above (see Cat). The hull-form, excluding the stern, is really that of a frigate built to carry the maximum amount of cargo.

Fig 35. Hagboat. *Lines plan. Reproduced from plate X in* Architectura Navalis Mercatoria *by Fredrik af Chapman (1768). Dimensions in the English index to the plans: 132ft 6in (length between perpendiculars), 34ft 4in (moulded breadth), 18ft 3in (draught of water), 716 tons burthen at 18ft 6in draught. The starboard quarter is drawn in perspective.*

35

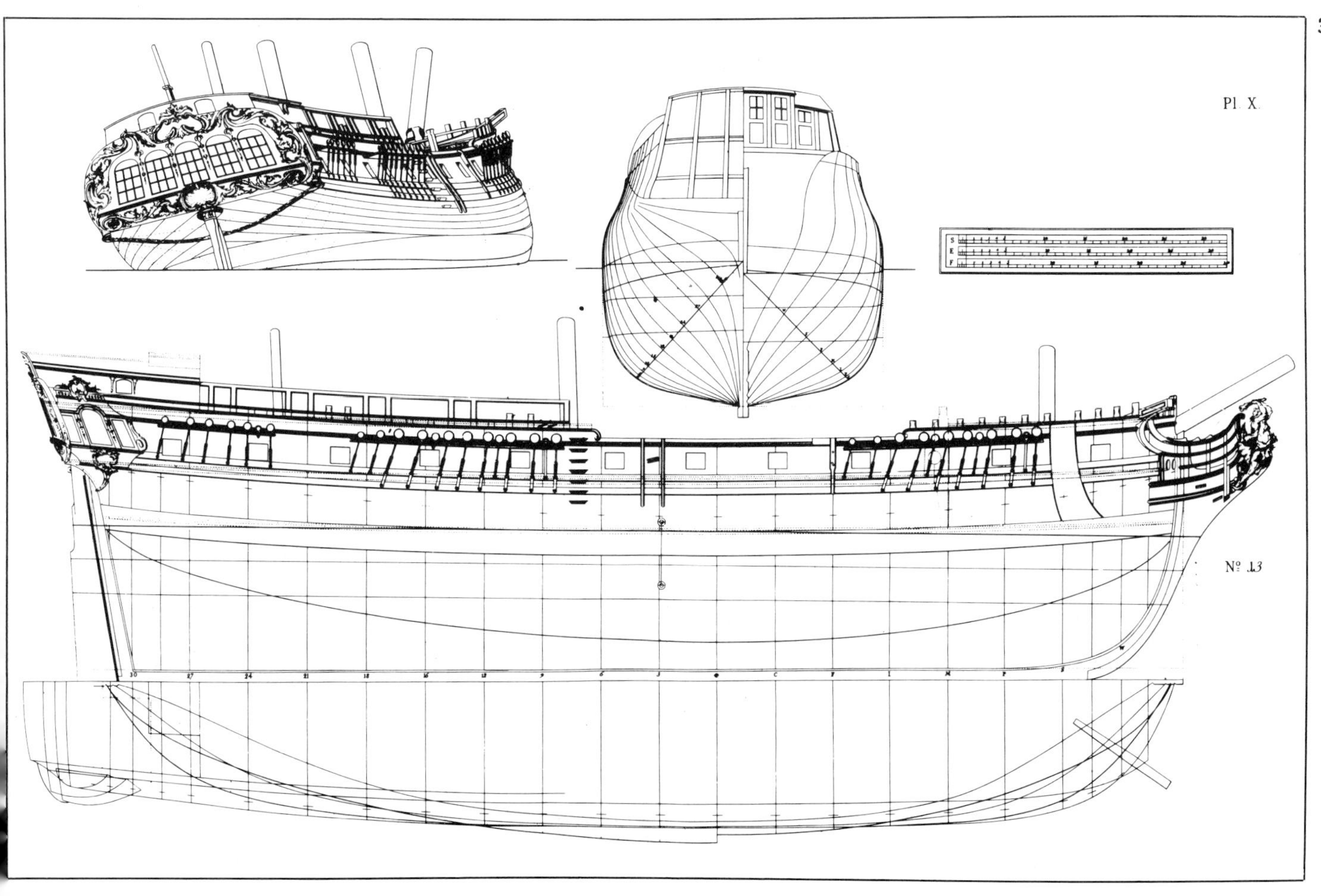

36

Fig 36. Starboard bow view of the hagboat from plate IX in Chapman's work. This is for a ship of 903 tons burthen, and the head is a fairly conventional one for many classes of vessels.

Fig 37. Meeremin. *Built in Amsterdam in 1760 for the Dutch East India Company from a design by I de Vlaming. A three-masted hooker. Reproduced from a contemporary plan. Dimensions: 110ft long, 32ft beam.* (Scheepvaart Museum, Amsterdam)

37

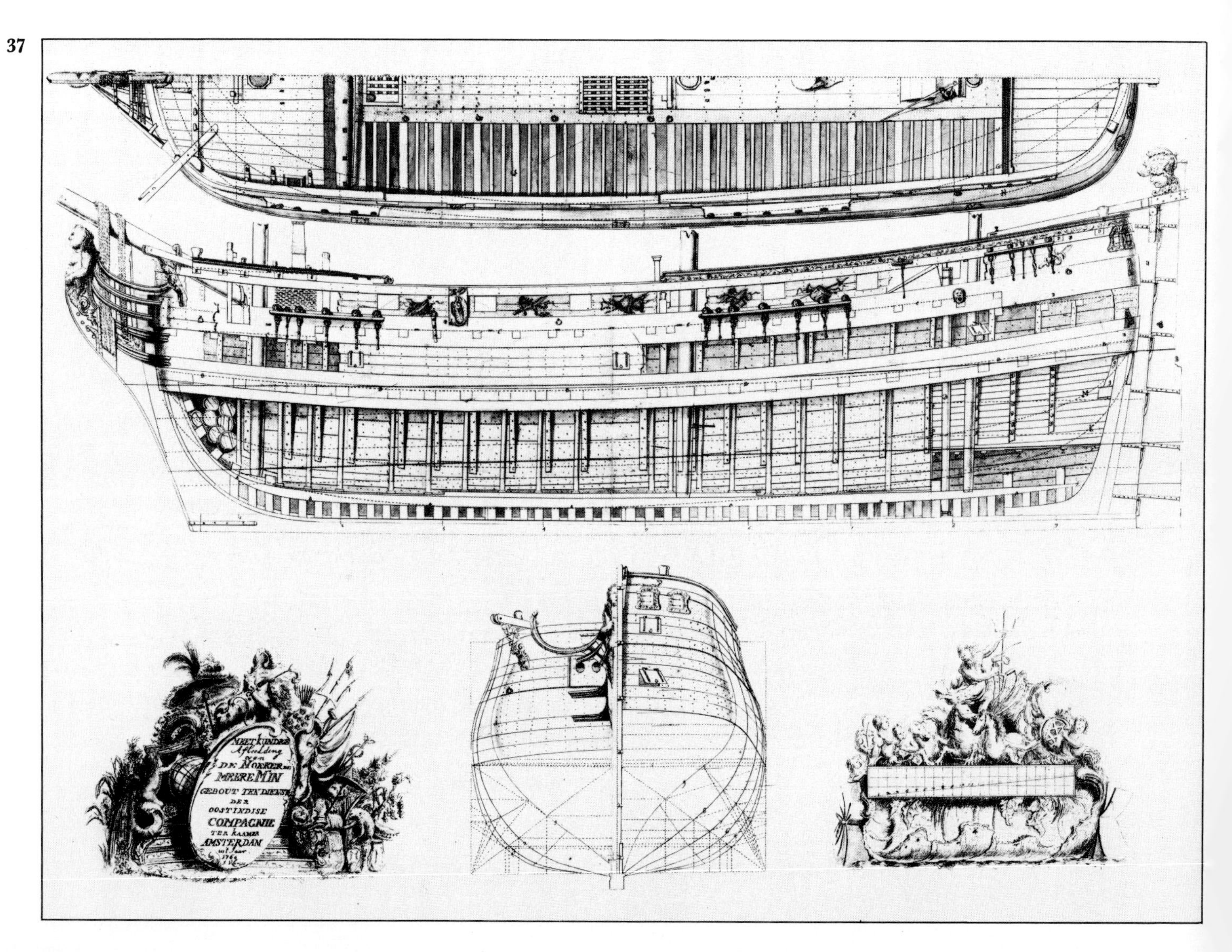

OTHER ROUND-STERNED SHIPS

These were more popular on the Continent than in England. Their form was usually full-bodied with flat floor, plain bows, full buttocks, no projecting counter, and a large outside rudder whose tiller entered the ship above the taffrail.

A lines plan in the Historisch Scheepvaart Museum in Amsterdam represents the *Meeremin*, described as a three-master hooker, built in 1760 for the East India Company. She is a deep two-decked ship, with flat floors, slack rounded bilges, unlike the usual flute style, and an elaborate head and figurehead. However, the stern has the usual massive outside rudder. A windlass barrel stretches the full width of the ship on the main deck at the break of the forecastle (figure 37).[16]

Chapman gives the lines plan of a Dutch hoy with three masts (plate LIV) which makes it very similar to the flute, but the square counter and taffrail are omitted, and the tiller comes in over the raised quarter-deck, the bulwarks being cut down for this purpose. There are also two decks instead of one. The hoy measures 107ft 2in (length between perpendiculars) and 26ft 8in (moulded breadth). There is also the plan of a two-masted hoy, probably with ketch rigging, as the mizen is a long way aft (figure 117).

In *Souvenirs de Marine*, Admiral Pâris gives the lines, deck layout and sail plan of a Dutch galliot (*galjoot*) rigged as a three-masted ship. This plan is reproduced and described more fully in *Merchant Sailing Ships 1815–1850*, figure 28. It is stated on the plan that the sail plan is dated between 1805–15 and that such ships were still to be seen during the first half of the nineteenth century. This galliot is deeper in the hull and finer in the run than Chapman's three-masted hoy, and bears closer affinity to the *Meeremin*. One point of particular interest is the manner of setting the topsail yards on the doubling.[17]

There are no engravings in Groenewegen (1789) of a hoy, but there is one of a three-masted galliot (plate C 10), two of three-masted hookers (plates C 8 and D 1), and one of a brig-rigged hooker (plate B 7). The hookers are more loftily rigged than the galliot, with fidded topgallant masts on fore and main, and sails set on them. The galliot has long flagstaffs fidded on fore and main, although the topmasts have crosstrees and a cap. On the mizen, hooker and galliot set a mizen course on a short gaff and a square topsail. The hull-form of both types is very similar.[18]

Chapman gives the lines plan of a Dutch smack (plate LIV) with a length between perpendiculars of 87ft 2in and a moulded breadth of 22ft 0in. This makes her of comparable size to the largest naval cutters. The floors are flat and she has less tumblehome than the hoy; there is a pair of leeboards, and tremendous sheer.

The hoy, galliot and hooker appear to have developed from the same source and are closely related to the flute. The smaller coastal versions rigged with one or two masts had the same basic hull-formed scaled down to a smaller size. The building of round-sterned ships of these kinds appears to have been unusual in England.

Fig 38. Dutch Smack, *and Dutch* Hoy *with three masts. Reproduced from plate LIV in* Architectura Navalis Mercatoria *by Fredrik af Chapman (1768). Dimensions in the English index to the plans: No 7, Dutch smack, 87ft 2in (length between perpendiculars), 22ft 0in (moulded breadth), 8ft 0in (draught of water); Dutch hoy with three masts, 107ft 2in (length between perpendiculars), 26ft 4in (moulded breadth), 13ft 3in (draught of water). No tonnages are given for either of these two vessels.*

38

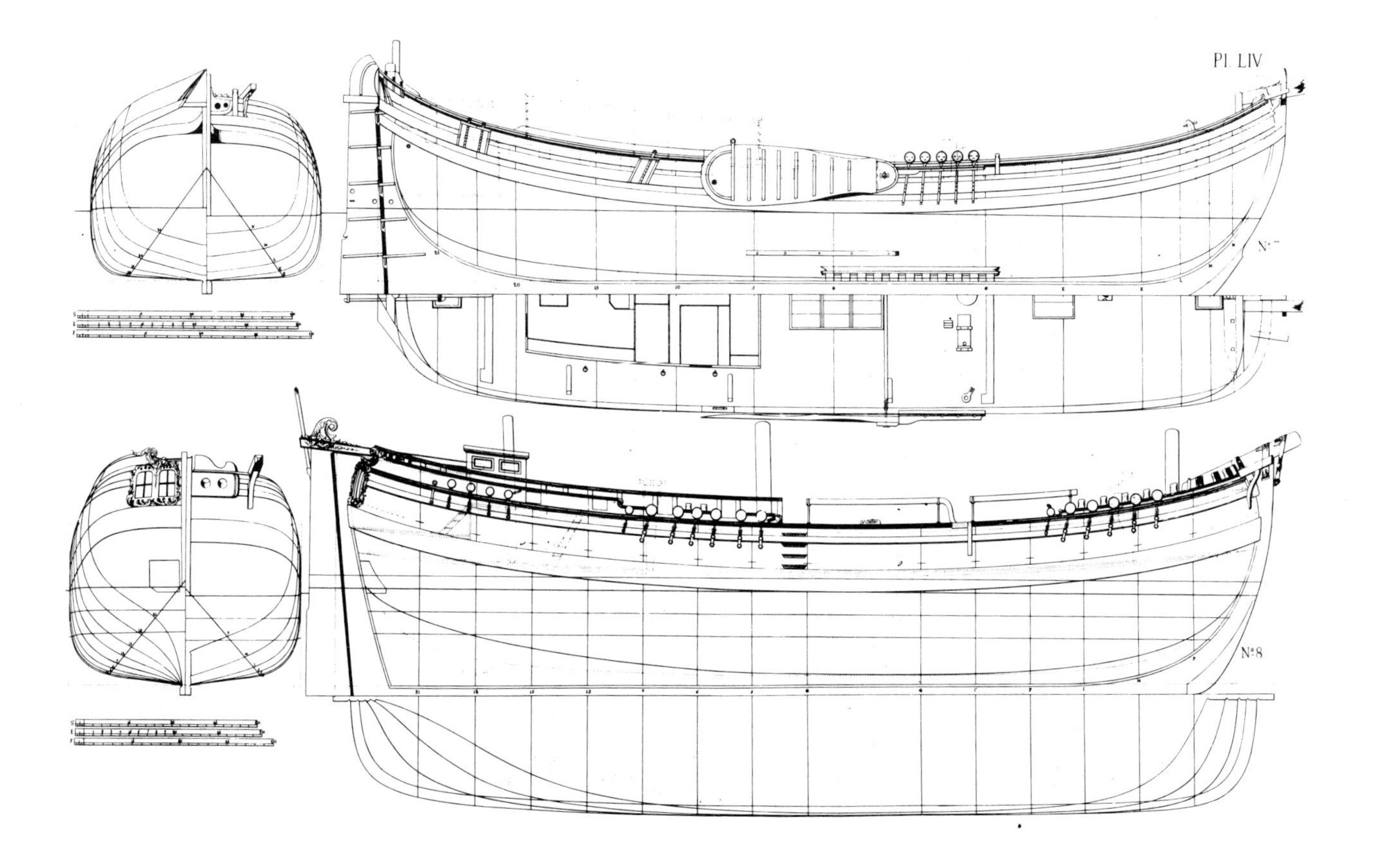

MASTS, SAILS AND RIGGING IN THREE-MASTED VESSELS

Sail plans as they came to be drawn in the second half of the nineteenth century were non-existent in the eighteenth, and the occasional plates in books on shipbuilding and seamanship cannot really be considered as scale plans. Perhaps the twenty-four engravings of different kinds of rig in the last plate of Chapman's work on naval architecture (1768) are an exception since, although the yards are foreshortened, they are actually drawn at half their correct length. Such sail plans are unique and probably the first attempts of their kind. Although Lescallier's *Vocabulaire* of 1777 has drawings that are far superior to what had appeared previously in the matter of detailing the rigging, yet none of the spar or rigging diagrams is to scale. Other eighteenth century books by Forfait, Romme and a second work by Lescallier (1791) still give no sail plans to scale.

However, there is a definite advance in Steel's *Rigging and Seamanship*, which first appeared in 1794, because the four plates illustrating the standing rigging, running rigging, fore-and-aft sails, and square sails are drawn to scale, and the scale is engraved below each one. These four sail plans portray a 20-gun ship which is listed in the tables of spar dimensions as of 429 tons, thus bringing her into the same size as a large West Indiaman. Perhaps we can be thankful that the plans do not concentrate on a 100-gun ship. Checks made of various spars on these four plans indicate that their lengths agree with the dimensions tabulated on page 50 Volume I of Steel's book, with the exception of the yards which have been foreshortened in the engraving to improve the appearance of the ship under sail. Sail diagrams in books usually show the maximum number of sails that can be carried, and so there are royals here on each of the three masts, although a mizen royal was comparatively uncommon except as a flying kite in light favourable winds.[19]

The four sail and rigging plans published by Steel are reproduced here as figures 39, 40, 41 and 42 and although they were said to illustrate a 20-gun ship, they were little different from a merchant vessel. The scale drawn below each plate on the original is repeated here and indicates the intended accuracy of the drawings. The plan of the standing rigging is famous for the drawing of a dolphin striker, which is an early example of this spar.

In Lescallier (1777), royals are drawn only on fore and main masts in the plates, nor are there any English or French equivalents in the text for a mizen royal.[20] At that time the term was commonly 'topgallant royal'. The sail plan given by Chapman of a three-masted full-rigged ship has no royal yards crossed at all and only a topsail yard on the mizen.[21] This was a strictly conservative view, but also a fairly accurate one, of the practical use of the sails. From descriptions in both Steel and Darcy Lever, it seems that royal yards were not often crossed and that when the sails had to be set, they were hoisted from the deck already bent to the yard. As they had no lifts, buntlines, or clewlines to

Fig 39. Mast and Standing Rigging Plan. *More information was always published about warships than merchantmen, but prior to 1815 there were many similarities. Reproduced from* Elements and Practice of Rigging and Seamanship *by David Steel (vol I 1794), plate facing page 208*. This is the famous plate with the dolphin striker.*

43

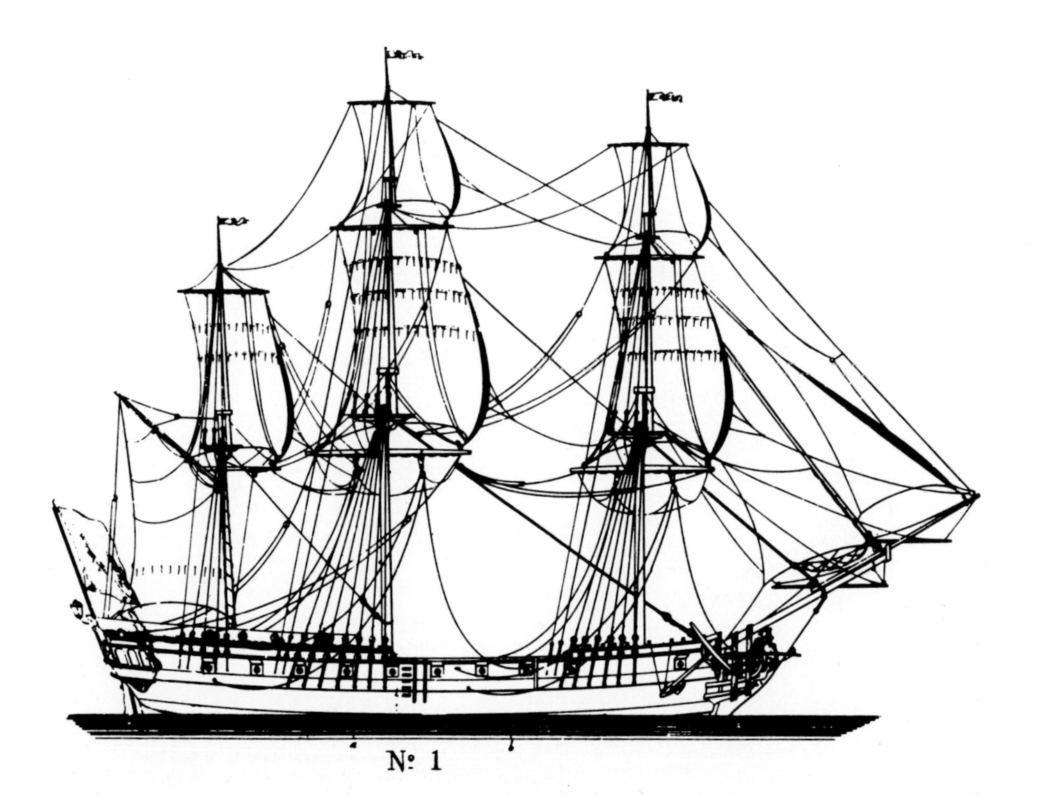

Fig 43. The only sail plan given by Chapman for a three-masted ship is produced from plate LXII in his Architectura Navalis Mercatoria *(1768). The ship is drawn under easy sail without any staysails between the masts, and with no courses or spritsails set.*

39

1 *Gammoning*
2 *Bobstays*
3 *Bowsprit shrouds*
4 *Fore tackle pendents*
5 *Main tackle pendents*
6 *Mizen burton pendents*
7 *Fore shrouds*
8 *Main shrouds*
9 *Mizen shrouds*
10 *Fore preventer stay*
11 *Fore stay*
12 *Main preventer stay*
13 *Main stay*
14 *Mizen stay*
15 *Fore topmast burton pendents*
16 *Main topmast burton pendents*
17 *Fore topmast shrouds*
18 *Main topmast shrouds*
19 *Mizen topmast shrouds*
20 *Fore topmast breast backstay*
21 *Fore topmast standing backstay*
22 *Fore topmast shifting backstay*
23 *Main topmast breast backstay*
24 *Main topmast standing backstay*
25 *Main topmast shifting backstay*
26 *Mizen topmast standing backstay*
27 *Mizen topmast shifting backstay*
28 *Fore topmast preventer stay*
29 *Fore topmast stay*
30 *Main topmast preventer stay*
31 *Main topmast stay*
32 *Mizen topmast stay*
33 *Fore topgallant shrouds*
34 *Main topgallant shrouds*
35 *Mizen topgallant shrouds*
36 *Fore topgallant standing backstays*
37 *Main topgallant standing backstays*
38 *Mizen topgallant standing backstay*
39 *Fore topgallant stay*
40 *Main topgallant stay*
41 *Mizen topgallant stay*
42 *Martingal stay*
43 *Bowsprit horse*
44 *Fore stay tackle*
45 *Main stay tackle*
46 *Main stay tackle pendent*
47 *Fore futtock shrouds*
48 *Main futtock shrouds*
49 *Mizen futtock shrouds*
50 *Stay tackle tricing lines*

The following remarks were added below the table, referring to the standing rigging plan:
'To prevent confusion of appearance in the plate of standing rigging, the shrouds and backstays are represented only on the starboard side; but it must be remembered, that an equal number of them belong to the larboard side. In ships, from twenty guns downwards, the preventer stays are sometimes placed under the stays; and to them the stay sails are bent.'

40

1 *Jib horses*
2 *Jib guy pendents and falls*
3 *Spritsail yard horses and stirrups*
4 *Spritsail topsail yard horses*
5 *Spritsail brace pendents*
6 *Spritsail braces*
7 *Spritsail lifts*
8 *Spritsail haliards*
9 *Spritsail topsail braces.*
10 *Spritsail topsail lifts*
11 *Spritsail topsail haliards*
12 *Fore yard horses and stirrups*
13 *Main yard horses and stirrups*
14 *Cross jack horses*
15 *Fore yard tackle pendents*
16 *Main yard tackle pendents*
17 *Fore yard tackles*
18 *Main yard tackle pendents*
19 *Inner tricing line to the main yard tackle*
20 *Outer tricing line to the main yard tackle*
21 *Fore brace pendents*
22 *Main brace pendents*
23 *Fore lifts*
24 *Main lifts*
25 *Tye of the fore jeers*
26 *Tye of the main jeers*
27 *Fall of the fore jeers*
28 *Fall of the main jeers*
29 *Nave line of the fore truss pendents*
30 *Nave line of the main truss pendents*
31 *Fore topsail yard horses and stirrups*
32 *Fore topsail yard flemish horses*
33 *Main topsail yard horses and stirrup*
34 *Main topsail yard flemish horses*
35 *Mizen topsail horses*
36 *Fore topsail brace pendents*
37 *Main topsail brace pendents*
38 *Mizen topsail brace pendents*
39 *Fore braces*
40 *Main braces*
41 *Fore topsail braces*
42 *Main topsail braces*
43 *Mizen topsail braces*
44 *Fore topsail lifts*
45 *Main topsail lifts*
46 *Mizen topsail lifts*
47 *Fore topsail reef tackle pendents*
48 *Main topsail reef tackle pendents*
49 *Fore topsail tye*
50 *Main topsail tye*
51 *Fore topsail haliards*
52 *Main topsail haliards*
53 *Fore topgallant yard horses*
54 *Main topgallant yard horses*
55 *Mizen topgallant yard horses*
56 *Fore topgallant brace pendents*
57 *Main topgallant brace pendents*
58 *Fore topgallant braces*
59 *Main topgallant braces*
60 *Mizen topgallant braces*
61 *Fore topgallant lifts*
62 *Main topgallant lifts*
63 *Mizen topgallant lifts*
64 *Fore topgallant haliards*
65 *Main topgallant haliards*
66 *Mizen topgallant haliards*
67 *Fore royal haliard*
68 *Main royal haliard*
69 *Pendent haliard*
70 *Cross jack brace pendents*
71 *Cross jack braces*
72 *Cross jack lifts*
73 *Gaff throat haliards*
74 *Gaff peak haliards*
75 *Vang pendents*
76 *Vang falls*
77 *Boom topping lift*
78 *Guy pendent and tackle*

41

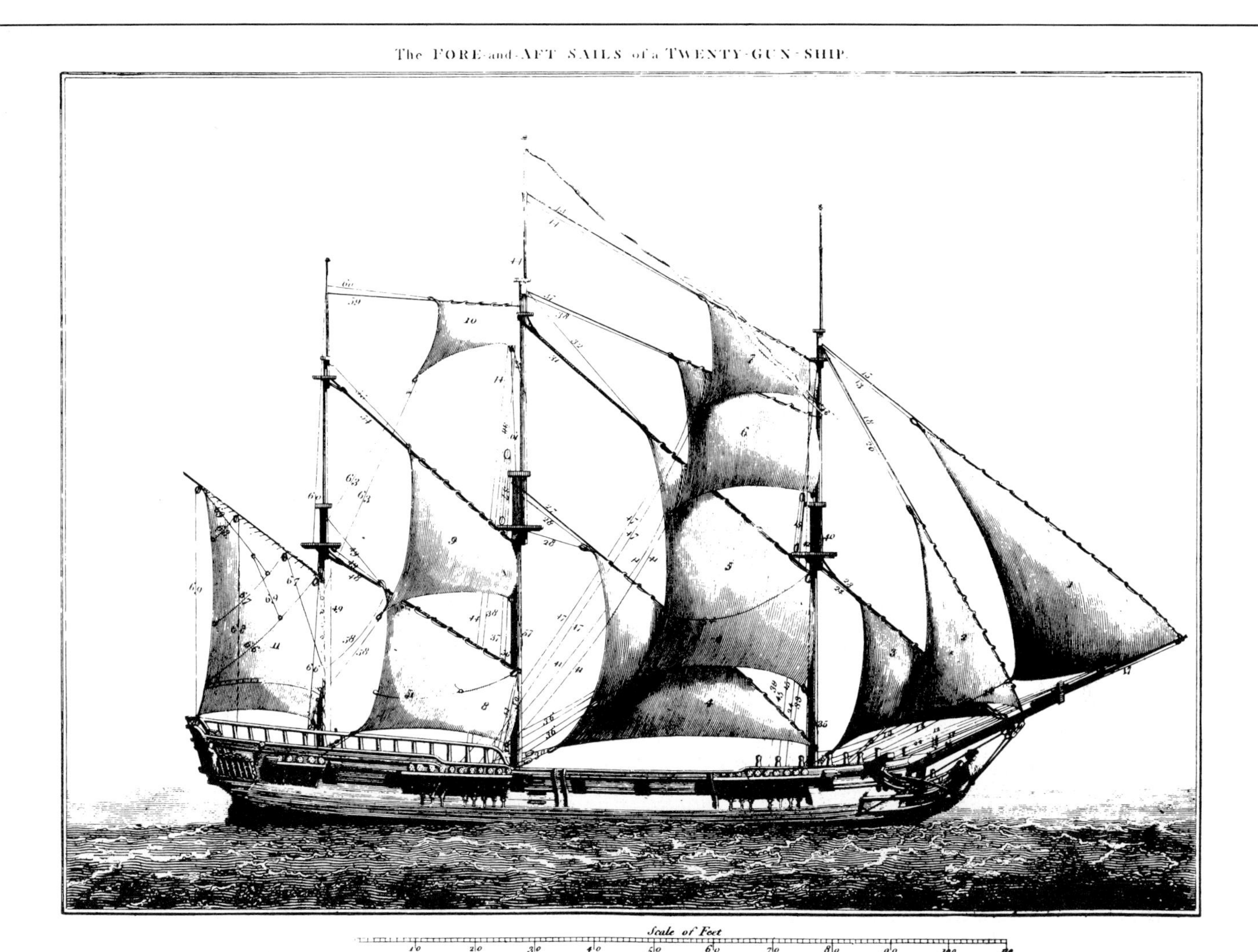

1 *Jib*
2 *Fore topmast staysail*
3 *Fore staysail*
4 *Main staysail*
5 *Main topmast staysail*
6 *Middle staysail*
7 *Main topgallant staysail*
8 *Mizen staysail*
9 *Mizen topmast staysail*
10 *Mizen topgallant staysail*
11 *Mizen*
12 *Jib downhauler*
13 *Jib haliards*
14 *Jib sheets*
15 *Jib stay*
16 *Jib outhauler*
17 *Jib inhauler*
18 *Fore topmast stay*
19 *Fore topmast staysail downhauler*
20 *Fore topmast staysail haliards*
21 *Fore topmast staysail sheets*
22 *Fore topmast staysail outhauler*
23 *Fore preventer stay*
24 *Fore staysail haliards*
25 *Fore staysail downhauler*
26 *Fore staysail sheets*
27 *Main staysail stay*
28 *Main staysail haliards*
29 *Main staysail downhauler*
30 *Main staysail sheets*
31 *Main topmast preventer stay*
32 *Main topmast staysail haliards*
33 *Main topmast staysail downhauler*
34 *Main topmast staysail brails*
35 *Main topmast staysail tacks*
36 *Main topmast staysail sheets*
37 *Middle staysail stay*
38 *Middle staysail haliards*
39 *Middle staysail downhauler*
40 *Middle staysail tacks*
41 *Middle staysail sheets*
42 *Middle staysail tricing line*
43 *Main topgallant staysail stay*
44 *Main topgallant staysail haliards*
45 *Main topgallant staysail downhauler*
46 *Main topgallant staysail tacks*
47 *Main topgallant staysail sheets*
48 *Mizen stay*
49 *Mizen staysail haliards*
50 *Mizen staysail downhauler*
51 *Mizen staysail brails*
52 *Mizen staysail tacks*
53 *Mizen staysail sheets*
54 *Mizen topmast stay*
55 *Mizen topmast staysail haliards*
56 *Mizen topmast staysail downhauler*
57 *Mizen topmast staysail tacks*
58 *Mizen topmast staysail sheets*
59 *Mizen topgallant stay*
60 *Mizen topgallant staysail haliards*
61 *Mizen topgallant staysail downhauler*
62 *Mizen topgallant staysail tacks*
63 *Mizen topgallant staysail sheets*
64 *Tack of the mizen course*
65 *Sheet of the mizen course*
66 *Throat brails* }
67 *Middle brails* } *of the mizen course*
68 *Peek brails* }
69 *Fancy line*

Fig 40. Masts, Yards and Running Rigging Plan. *Reproduced from Steel's* Rigging and Seamanship *(vol I 1794) plate facing page 209*.*

Fig 41. Sail Plan of Fore-and-aft Sails. *Also their rigging. Reproduced from Steel's* Rigging and Seamanship *(vol I 1794) plate facing page 210*.*

42

1 *Fore course*
2 *Main course*
3 *Fore topsail*
4 *Main topsail*
5 *Mizen topsail*
6 *Fore topgallant sail*
7 *Main topgallant sail*
8 *Mizen topgallant sail*
9 *Fore royal*
10 *Main royal*
11 *Mizen royal*
12 *Driver*
13 *Fore studding sails*
14 *Main studding sails*
15 *Fore topmast studding sails*
16 *Main topmast studding sails*
17 *Fore topgallant studding sails*
18 *Main topgallant studding sails*
19 *Spritsail course*
20 *Spritsail topsail*
21 *Foresail sheets*
22 *Foresail tacks*
23 *Foresail leech lines*
24 *Foresail buntlines*
25 *Foresail bowlines*
26 *Foresail bowline bridles*
27 *Main sheets*
28 *Main tack*
29 *Mainsail leech lines*
30 *Mainsail buntlines*
31 *Mainsail bowlines*
32 *Mainsail bowline bridles*
33 *Fore topsail buntlines*
34 *Fore topsail bowlines*
35 *Fore topsail bowline bridles*
36 *Main topsail buntlines*
37 *Main topsail bowlines*
38 *Main topsail bowline bridles*
39 *Mizen topsail buntlines*
40 *Mizen topsail bowline*
41 *Mizen topsail bowline bridles*
42 *Fore topgallant bowlines*
43 *Fore topgallant bowline bridles*
44 *Main topgallant bowlines*
45 *Main topgallant bowline bridles*
46 *Mizen topgallant bowline*
47 *Fore royal haliards*
48 *Main royal haliards*
49 *Mizen royal haliards*
50 *Driver haliards*
51 *Driver sheet*
52 *Driver downhauler*
53 *Fore studding sail inner haliards*
54 *Main studding sail inner haliards*
55 *Fore studding sail boom guy*
56 *Fore studding sail tacks*
57 *Fore studding sail sheets*
58 *Main studding sail tacks*
59 *Fore topmast studding sail downhauler*
60 *Fore topmast studding sail tack*
61 *Main topmast studding sail downhauler*
62 *Main topmast studding sail tack*
63 *Fore topgallant studding sail tack*
64 *Main topgallant studding sail tack*
65 *Spritsail clue line*
66 *Spritsail buntline*
67 *Spritsail sheets*
68 *Spritsail topsail sheets*

44

control them, but only braces, they were said to be set 'flying'. Of the mizen royal, Steel comments in the text, 'This sail is seldom used'.[22]

In his *Treatise on Naval Architecture*, William Hutchinson refers to the shape of square sails in these words:[23]

> The good effects of deep and narrow squaresails, cannot be better recommended as answering this purpose, than by the performance of ships in the coal and timber trades to London, though the designed properties in building and fitting these ships, are burden at a small draft of water, to take and bear the ground well, and to sail with few hands, and little ballast; yet these ships perform so well at sea, that government often makes choice of them for store ships, in the most distant naval expeditions; and in narrow channels among shoals, and in turning to windward, in narrow rivers, there are no ships of equal burden can match them, which I attribute a great deal to their deep narrow squaresails, which may be perceived to trim so flat and fair, upon a wind, that all the canvass stands full, at a proper angle from the direction of the keel...'

Fig 42. Sail Plan of Square Sails and Studding Sails. *The driver was classed for use when running before the wind in the days when a mizen course was set from the mizen gaff. Reproduced from Steel's* Rigging and Seamanship *(vol I 1794) plate facing page 211*.*

Fig 44. Two sail plans separating fore-and-aft sails from square sails. Three jibs from the fore topmast head were none too common at this time. The drawings are from Lescallier's Traité Pratique du Gréement *(vol II, 1791), plate XII. These sail plans are more diagrammatic than David Steel's four sail and rigging plans and include the old-fashioned long mizen yard. The driver is shown either set like a studding sail (lower plan) or as a ringtail (upper plan).*

William Hutchinson gives two engravings of a full rigged ship under a press of sail; in figure 51 she is close-hauled on the starboard tack (his frontispiece) and in figure 67 she is running before a quarterly breeze (plate I). What adds to their merit is that he gives a partial description in the text which is the more valuable as he was a professional seaman who experienced the conditions described. The ship sailing close-hauled appears later in this section, but the ship running free has her flying kites and studding sails described in these words:[24]

> In sailing anything from the wind, to right before it, we easily shifted our driver boom to different parts of the stern, and by the heel ropes at the heaviest end within board, trimmed it as the wind required, so as to make the driver and water-sail stand as fair and as far, or further out from the ship, as could be done by a yard across for a boom, as above-mentioned. We set

45

Fig 45. Garneray's drawings of men furling sails: pulling a topgallant sail up to the yard (upper); and trying to smother a headsail on the jibboom (lower).

top-gallant studding sails, without troublesome and cumbersome booms on the top-sail yards, by having thimbles fixed at the outer end of the top-mast studding-sail yards, we kept the tacks reefed and both ends made fast to the inner yard-arm, so that they could be come at from the topsail yard-arm, to bend the tack and haul it out, which spread the sails and made them stand very well, and shewed with the driver and water-sail as in plate the 1st, where the ship is represented sailing with all sails set, with the wind quartering. But I must own we were obliged to stop the inner yard-arm of the topmast studding sail, with the outer gasket of the topsail yard-arm, when the sail was set abaft the top-sail, to prevent the outer yard-arm from flying forward.

In *The Young Sea Officer's Sheet Anchor*, Darcy Lever agrees that stunsails can be set flying in the way described above but remarks that when set forward of the topsail and topgallant the lee yard arm of the stunsail can press against the square sails and damage them.[25] John Harland in his splendid recent work, *Seamanship*, covers the whole subject of stunsails,[26] but before closing the subject it might be worth adding Darcy Lever's own words on how stunsails should be set in normal conditions:

A Topmast Studding Sail is set abaft the Topsail when to windward, and before it when to leeward; because to windward the outer Yard Arm must incline rather forwards, to make the Sail stand fair; which could not be the case if the Sail were set before the Topsail, for the Pressure of the inner Yard Arm would prevent it, and might injure the Topsail. When a Topmast Studding Sail is set before the Topsail to leeward, the *Deck Sheet* is then hauled forward, and the Yard Sheet let go.[27]

Spar dimensions tabulated on the lines plans of ships bought into the Navy give a further indication of the spars being carried and their proportions. American-built ships taken into the Navy between 1774 and 1778, such as the *Grasshopper* ex *London*, *Cherokee* ex *Codrington*, and *Beaver Prize* ex *Oliver Cromwell* could have set royals on fore and main masts although no such yards are listed.[28] They all set a mizen topgallant. The last two named ships had fidded topgallants on the mizen long enough to set a small royal. The *Grasshopper* did not fit a mizen topgallant mast but her topmast of 25ft 10in had a 'pole head' 11ft long, which was almost identical in length to the pole head given to the ex-Whitby collier *Endeavour* before she began her voyage of exploration. The arrangement of sails to be seen in Steel's ship of 330 tons, figure 126, appears to be the most common arrangement during the period 1775–1815. Conversely, if nothing was carried above topgallants on fore and main, then nothing above a topsail was carried on the mizen.

At the end of the eighteenth century, there were still many full-rigged ships to be seen which fidded no mizen

Fig 46. Entitled 'A Collier', this watercolour drawing by Edward Gwyn is dated about 1780 and shows the hull of a cat with an early form of barque rig. The long boat rests on the spare spars. (National Maritime Museum)

topgallant mast and whose only square sail on the mizen was a topsail. G Groenewegen drew several examples in his plates of ship types, published in 1789 at Rotterdam.[29] French and Danish examples may be cited, at the beginning of the nineteenth century.[30]

Some notable exploration ships, built as colliers on the north-east coast of England, employed this form of rig, and, in the case of the *Endeavour* ex *Earl of Pembroke*, the crossjack yard was only some 20ft above the deck. In the case of the *Bounty* ex *Bethia*, it was some 22ft above the deck. With such a short mizen, the result is a rather unbalanced-looking rig, but the square topsail was being discarded by many such craft so that only fore-and-aft sails remained on the mizen, and as a number of the vessels using this arrangement of sails had a bark's hull-form, the rig became known as a 'bark'. As we have seen, Falconer was already referring to this bark rig in the 1769 edition of his Dictionary.[31] He also tells us that the name is derived from the low latin *barca*. The spelling changed to 'barque' in the nineteenth century.

One of the earliest illustrations of this rig was a watercolour drawing by Edward Gwyn, done in about 1780, which is entitled 'A Collier'. As can be seen from figure 46, she is barque-rigged, with a boomless mizen on a short mast and a flagstaff fidded above; there is neither fore royal nor dolphin striker; the hull is that of a cat, with a plain bow and a pink stern. Another example dated 1795 is the Swedish *Fortuna* of Umea as painted by a contemporary artist. She sets nothing above topgallants and the mizen topmast is fidded only to hoist a flag.[32] Groenewegen has no illustration of any such rig, but Baugean has one of a Swedish vessel with a larger mizen on a boom. The latter was, however, not published until 1817.[33]

The 'barque' of the Mediterranean was a recognized type with a broad hull and projecting beakhead; rigged with three masts, the mizen carrying a topsail, the main being polacre-rigged with three square sails, and the foremast either the same or else having a single huge lateen sail (figures 46 and 47).

In his *Vocabulaire*, Lescallier includes in his definition of a cat the following sentence, which is translated to read:

47

Souvenirs de marine conservés.

FRANCE _ CHÉBEC « MISTICQUE » 1750 A 1786

D'après le modèle 647 du musée de marine à l'échelle de $\frac{1}{24}$

Élévation de l'arrière jusqu'à la coupe Z Z

Trou de la barre

Dimensions principales

Longueur extrême, sans le berthelot	30m 02
" de rablure en rablure à la flottaison	26,20
" de quille	23,70
Largeur au plat-bord	7,70
" à la flottaison, hors bordages	6 85
Saillie de la muraille à 2m 40 du tirant d'eau	1 1,12
Creux sur quille	2,80
Tirant d'eau	2,40
Couples doubles excepté au dessus du pont	0,23 x 0,22
Maille	0,16
Baux ou lattes espacés de 0m 20	0,20 x 0,12
Quille, étrave, étambot	0,19
Quête de l'étambot	0,35
Bouge du pont	0,18
Guibre à jour, son élancement	5 70
Surface du maître couple	13m² 5
Surface de voilure	502m² 0
Rapport	1 à 42
" du plan de dérive du gouvernail	1 à 39
Position du centre vélique sur la flottaison	10m 0
" en avant du milieu id.	6,50

5 Trou du haut. Drisse de foc
1, 2 Clans de l'itague d'antenne
3 à tribord, support du bas de l'antenne
4 à babord, draille du foc
Ces deux manœuvres ont des palans en quatre, crochés au pied du mât

Coupe au maître Vue de l'avant

Coupe suivant YY et fronteau de dunette

Coupes hors bordages

Coupe suivant XX

Mâture

Grand mât 13,5 + 5,5 + 4,8 =	23,80
Diamètre des deux mâts	0,48
Mât de misaine	17,50
Antenne 9m 7 + 14,6	24,30
Grande vergue carrée	16,00
Hunier	14,00
Perroquet	8,9
Vergue carrée	9,8
Perroquet de fougue	7,60
Ourse 7,50 + 6,50	14,00

La voilure carrée était souvent à l'avant, ce qui était préférable. Les formes évasées de l'avant rendaient le navire ardent lorsqu'il inclinait, d'où la nécessité d'incliner le mât de misaine qui se trouve mal appuyé.

Légende

A Panneau
B Trou de bouteille
C Cage à poules
D Support
EE Chambres
FF Couchettes
GG Petits meubles
HH Quatre armoires
I Claire-voie
K Fronteau de dunette
L Courbes
NN Caisson à portes à coulisses
OO Cloisons
O'O' Lisse intérieure
MM Bordage en chêne, plus épais

P Bossoir appliqué sur la traverse P', fortifiée par les courbes P''. QQ Deux pièces courbes à tenon dans les courbes P''', qui tiennent les montants de la traverse P'. Q est endenté dans P''', soutient R et porte la traverse Q' qui complète l'espèce d'étambrai supérieur du mât de misaine, enfin Q arcboute contre une forte courbe de guirlande Q''. S est un bloc fixé au pont et servant d'étambrai.

Toute cette charpente obvie au peu de pied qu'a le mât de misaine qui est très mal tenu par ses haubans à cause de leur peu d'empâture.

T T Rouleaux sur lesquels portent les cables. VV Planche en travers appuyée contre les montants V'V' et formant une gatte pour maintenir l'eau.

A l'avant du grand mât les montants a a qui portent la potence p descendent dans la cale et servent d'encoignures à l'archipompe b b.

L'entourage du grand mât est formé de pièces d d plus épaisses que le bordé qu'elles affleurent par les bouts et dans lesquelles sont encastrées à queue d'aronde les traverses c c dont les bouts en saillie servent à amarrer les cordes comme sur les chébecs latins.

Les haubans sont crochés à des pitons sur la gouttière.

La drisse de basse vergue est à itague double sans dormant, c'est-à-dire qu'il y a un palan à chaque bout, et ces palans sont crochés au pied du mât, la drisse de hunier est semblable. Les cargues fonds sont parallèles aux laizes, il en résulte que celle d'en dehors laisse trop peu de ralingue pour la cargue point, qui est comme maintenant, et il doit y avoir une différence marquée dans la manière de serrer les voiles carrées.

Le modèle du musée qui a été mesuré exactement, avait ses sculptures dorées, d'habitude ces navires étaient peints en noir. Ils ne sortaient pas de la Méditerranée Occidentale.

Les gravures si exactes de Baugean en représentent plusieurs.

Gravé par J. Geisendorfer

N° 90

48

Fig 48. A painting signed 'Antne. Roux à Marseille 1818' depicts a chebec like the Misticque *but with square sails on the foremast instead of a lateen. Only on the mizen is there a fidded topmast; the other masts are poles.* (Parker Gallery)

Fig 47. Misticque. *Lines, sections, deck, sail plan. Reproduced from* Souvenirs de Marine Conservés *by Vice-Admiral Paris, vol 2, plate 90. Dimensions as given on the plan: 30.02m (extreme length), 23.70m (length of keel), 7.70 m (breadth at the gunwale), 2.80m (depth of hold to keel). Date ascribed is 1750–1786.*

'They are usually pole-masted [*mâté à pible*] and carry three masts with square sails, like those of full rigged ships, except that sometimes there are no topgallant sails.' Figure 49 is a reproduction of an engraving illustrating this craft, and the pole masts on fore and main are evident, although on the mizen the topmast appears to be fidded in the normal manner. No indications have yet been found of English cats rigged in this manner, and indeed no examples of pole-masted vessels have been found in England other than the polacres of the north Devon coast. The only pole-masted vessel given by Chapman in his plate of rigs is number 10 entitled, in the English table of contents, 'Kray, used in Finland'; Lescallier confirms that they had pole masts, adding that the Danes and Swedes both used these craft.[34] Describing a cat's rig, the Dutch historian, E W Petrejus, writes:

> The rig was unusual, fore and mainmasts being single poles or, if in two sections, with the topmast lashed to the lower and no tops were used. Courses and topsails were lowered on to the deck to be furled. The mizen, a tall narrow sail, was bent to a small gaff and spread by a boom. However, this odd rig was replaced eventually by the normal ship rig throughout the eighteenth century.[35]

Up to 1750, three-masted ships carried a lateen on the mizen, set from the 'mizen yard', although after about this date the sail carried was restricted to the area abaft the mast. In smaller vessels like snows and ketches, the mizen

49

Fig 49. A three-masted cat with pole masts at fore and main, but a fidded topmast on the mizen. In the previous edition of this book I used an engraving from Lescallier's Vocabulaire *of 1777, but the one reproduced here is from David Steel's* Elements and Practice of Rigging and Seamanship *(vol I 1794), plate facing page 236. Both engravings are the same way round but Steel's has blocks for the running rigging and the lines are firmer.*

yard had been abandoned much earlier, although it had remained in the bilander (as described later), but in three-masters it was retained longest by large warships and East Indiamen. It disappeared from the Navy between 1796 and 1799. By 1775, the mizen yard had been generally replaced in merchant ships by the gaff from which the mizen course was set. Nevertheless the yard to which the square mizen topsail was sheeted still retained its name of crossjack, while the term 'mizen yard' was gradually allowed to drop out of use. Nomenclature in ships has always been inconsistent.

The mizen course still referred to the tall, narrow and boomless gaff sail used for most purposes aboard, but when running before the wind, the mizen course was brailed in, and a driver set. This was a much larger gaff sail set on a boom, and the top half of the head was secured to a yard where it overlapped the mizen gaff. The arrangement is illustrated in figure 50. An older form increased the mizen course by setting a ringtail, which was also called a driver. Sometimes this form of driver was set when the mizen course was furled. By 1808, Darcy Lever was commenting that in the merchant service it was more common to have a gaff all the way from the throat to the peak, to spread the head of the driver, now also called 'spanker'. In Groenewegen's book of engravings, published in 1789, the only vessel still to carry a mizen yard was a Dutch East Indiaman.

As headsails became larger and more important, their lifting power needed a properly stayed bowsprit to counteract the additional pull, and thus the dolphin striker came into being. There are some early examples of its use: Chapman's model of a Swedish schooner yacht has an iron one, said to be original, and the yacht was built in 1776;[36] a painting of the bark *Hoffnung* of Apenrade, built in 1787, has a short version;[37] a painting of the Dutch two-topsail schooner *Mercurius* of 1790 shows it;[38] finally it is confirmed in Steel's first edition of *Rigging and Seamanship*, published in 1794. For it to appear in Steel's plate of the 20-gun sloop, it must have been well established for certainly ten, perhaps twenty, years. Also in 1794, the Admiralty ordered dolphin strikers to be fitted with jaws like gaffs.[39] When dolphin strikers are seen in models of eighteenth century vessels built prior to 1790, there is justifiable doubt as to whether later restorers have not added them. The fitting of dolphin strikers spread rapidly to ships of all classes, especially when flying jibbooms were rigged out. As rigging improved in quality the bowsprit became shorter, but it remained a massive stick for many years in small vessels, particularly in brigs and schooners.

In his description of a ship close-hauled under a press of

sail, also shown in an engraving which appeared as his frontispiece, William Hutchinson does not comment on the plain square sails but on the fore-and-aft sails and flying kites. Under the latter heading come the royals, which in his terminology are called 'topgallant royals'. This is his description:[40]

> I have had the experience of turning to windward with 30 effectual sails, set in a simple easy manner, and had them drawn, when in real practice at sea, and they were as represented in the front plate. – Besides two jibbs, fore-top-mast-stay sail, sprit-sail, and sprit-sail top-sail, all which are known to stand very well upon a wind; we had a fore-stay sail stood very well by our foremast standing well aft, and the fore-tack well to windward, as before recommended; and by having two sheaves in each truck, at our long top-gallant masts' heads, we hoisted the top-gallant royals up to the trucks by the sheaves on one side, and the main and mizen spindle stay-sails by the sheaves on the other side of the trucks, at the main and mizen top-gallant-masts' heads we set a gaff top-sail with a light yard slung by the thirds, hoisted up through a block at the after part of the cap at the mizen-top-mast head, the tack hauled down on the weather side, to the after corner of the mizen top, and the sheet to the gaff end. This sail was easier managed, and stood more to advantage, than when set with a cumbersome heavy gaff, rigged at the mizen-topmast head for that purpose. We set a large driver with a light pole for a boom, with two tail blocks at the small, or outer-end, which we ran out aft on either side, and lashed it to the rail, so that the blocks on the outer end stood right aft, facing the middle of the stern, upon either tack, the driver slung by the third of the yard, like a lug-sail, hoisted within about four feet of the end of the mizen gaff, which was about three feet longer than the mizen required it, on account of this sail; the tack hauled down to the weather quarter piece on either tack, and the sheet to the block amidships, with a bowline hauled to the mizen mast, which made the sail stand fair upon a wind, at an angle of about a point and a half, or 16 degrees from the direction of the keel; we set a fore-top-mast studding-sail for a water-sail, the yard slung by the third, hauled out to the other tail block at the driver boom end, with the straight leech or the sheet clue uppermost, and made fast to the weather corner of the stern rail, and the lower clue had two sheets or lines led into the after-most gun-port or scupper in the waist on each side, so that in tacking when the wind was near a-head, we shifted the fore part of these sails to the weather side, which trimmed them ready for the other tack, by which means they prevented the ship from falling too much off, and had good effect upon her sailing in a light breeze of wind.

In 1775 some merchant ships continued to set a spritsail topsail below the jibboom, but it was rapidly being superseded, although the spritsail itself continued in use until the first or second decade of the nineteenth century. When a spritsail was regularly set, the jibboom or martingale guys were led from cleats on the dolphin striker up through a block on the fore side of the spritsail yard below the bowsprit.

The jib was the principal headsail and hooked on to a traveller on the jibboom; the jib stay was shackled to this traveller before leading out to a sheave in the end of the jibboom and thence back to the bowsprit cap or the bows, where it was set up with a tackle. Once the dolphin striker was in regular use, the jib stay became permanently set up which increased the efficiency of the jib. In 1794, the

Fig 50. Comparison of mizen course with driver or spanker, based on Steel's dimensions for a ship of 300 to 330 tons.

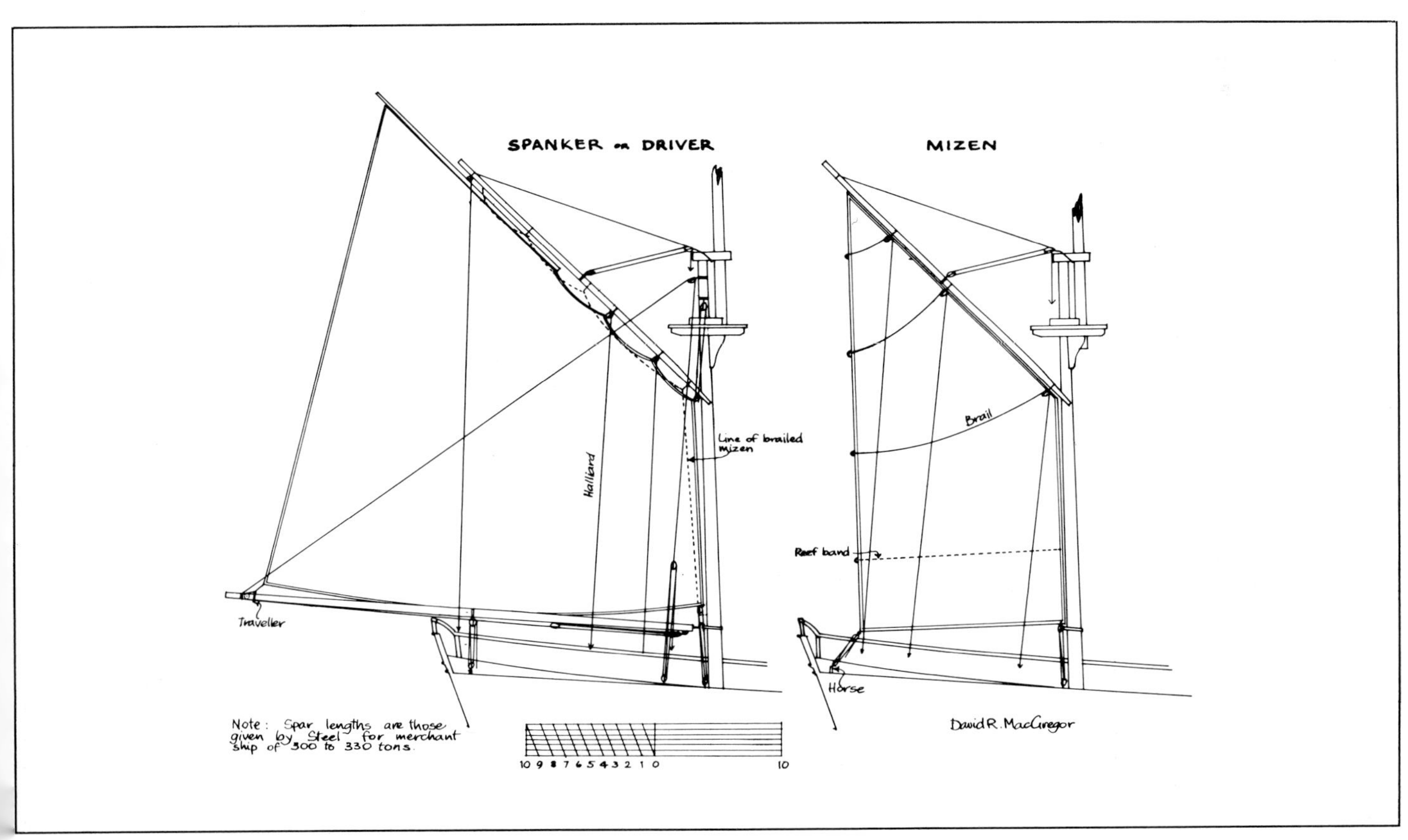

51

52

Fig 51. This was the Frontispiece to William Hutchinson's Treatise on Naval Architecture *(1794) depicting the ship* Hall *of 375 tons, as described in the text in Hutchinson's own words. 30 sails are set, as he claims including several flying kites, but excluding any stunsails.*

Fig 52. Now termed a 'jackass barque', this rig was originally described as a ship 'with a fore-and-aft mainsail', and this engraving was given by Darcy Lever in The Young Sea Officer's Sheet Anchor *(1808), figure 357. The fore-and aft mainsail and mizen are drawn in more detail in his figure 356.*

Fig 53. Model made by J N Hampton of HMS Endeavour *ex* Earl of Pembroke. *When she was taken into the Navy, the poop was continued forward without a break, the iron standards of the poop rail were replaced by wooden uprights, and mountings for swivel guns were fitted.* (Photo by Edward Bowness)

Admiralty ordered that a flying jibboom and flying jib be carried in certain classes of ships, so that it must have been well-tried by this date.[41]

Darcy Lever wrote in 1808:

> Ships in the Baltic and coasting trade, which carry fore and aft mainsails, have the mizen mast as taunt [i.e., as high] as the mainmast and seldom carry any mizen topmast, but a flag staff to hoist the ensign &c. This is sometimes made strong enough to hoist a small topsail with a gaff or yard slung by the third, the clue hauling out to the mizen peak. They carry no cross jack yard, consequently no square topsail; but the mizen is very large in proportion.
>
> Ships rigged in this manner can sail with a hand or two less and answer very well for working through the Narrows, there being no after sail to brace about, but the main topsail and main topgallant sail and *their* braces lead forwards.[42]

The accompanying drawing, here reproduced in figure 52, reveals that she was a type of jackass barque or 'barquetta', because she set no main course. An identical form of rig can be seen in paintings of the Hull whaler *Diana*, built in 1785, and the capture of the English vessel *Arcade* off Dragør in 1807.[43] Ships in the Greenland trade, sailing out of north Norfolk ports such as King's Lynn and Blakeney, reputedly carried a similar rig at the beginning of the nineteenth century. This form of rig was employed spasmodically throughout the century and is discussed in later volumes of *Merchant Sailing Ships*.

THE *EARL OF PEMBROKE* AND SHIPBUILDING AT WHITBY AND ON THE NORTH-EAST COAST

Ships built on the north-east coast of England were always known for their solid and rugged construction, and this endeared them to the Admiralty who were looking for a suitable ship for a voyage to the South Seas, where at the request of the Royal Society, the transit of Venus could be accurately observed on 3 June 1769. As no naval vessel was deemed suitably capacious to stow the provisions required

53

for a long voyage, the Navy Board suggested, in a letter dated 21 March 1768, that a 'cat-built vessel. . .of about 350 tons' would suit, and that she could be purchased in the River Thames.[44]

The Deptford Yard organized the survey of *Ann and Elizabeth*, *Valentine* and *Earl of Pembroke*, and recommended the last, which was promptly purchased by the end of March and renamed *Endeavour*. The value of her hull, masts and yards was put at £2307 5s 6d. She had been built at Whitby in 1764 by Thomas Fishburn for Thomas Milner. The Admiralty proceeded to fit her out immediately, appointed Lieutenant James Cook in command and on 21 July 1768 she left the Deptford Yard for Plymouth. Her passage finally began on 26 August with 94 persons aboard, and she returned in July 1771 after her epic voyage of circumnavigation.[45]

The *Earl of Pembroke's* dimensions were reported when she was surveyed, but they differ slightly from those which later appeared on the plans drawn of her, as listed above:

	When surveyed[46]	**On plans**[47]
Length on lower deck (afterside of rabbet of stem to foreside of rabbet of sternport)	97ft 7in	97ft 8in
Length of keel for tonnage	81ft $0\frac{3}{8}$in	81ft 0in
Breadth extreme	29ft 3in	29ft 2in
Depth in hold	11ft 4in	11ft 4in
Burthen in tons	$368\frac{71}{94}$	$366\frac{49}{94}$

Fig 54. Earl of Pembroke. *Lines plan, deck and longitudinal section. Built at Whitby in 1764 by Thomas Fishburn. Plan redrawn from undated Admiralty draught [cMarch 1768] No 3814B at the National Maritime Museum, Greenwich. Dimensions on plan: 97ft 8in (length on lower deck), 81ft 0in (length of keel for tonnage), 29ft 2in (extreme breadth), 11ft 4in (depth in hold), 366 tons. Reconstruction: entire deck plan (deck fittings only shown in elevation); longitudinal section. Chain plates drawn on sail plan.*

54

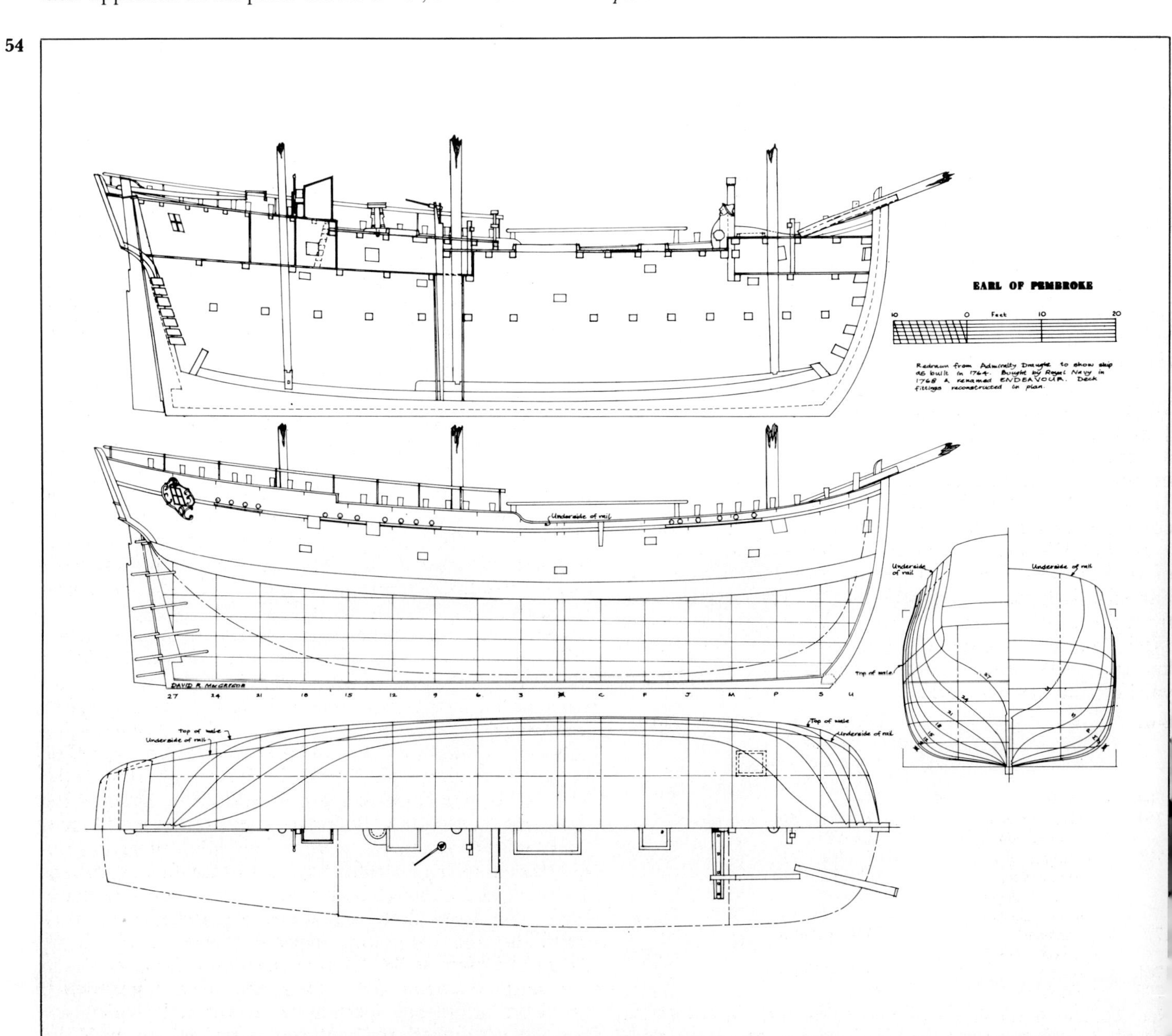

55

Fig 55. Bracket half-model of the collier Liberty and Property. *She was built at Whitby in 1752. This is probably the earliest surviving half-model in England.* (Liverpool County Museums)

Thomas Fishburn (builder of the *Earl of Pembroke*) started as a shipbuilder in about 1748 and nine years later made a dry-dock at Boghall; he was succeeded by his son, Thomas, who took Thomas Brodrick into partnership in 1795. The yard was eventually closed down in 1830, and six years afterwards the site was converted into the town's new railway station. Another shipyard of long standing was run by George and Nathaniel Langborne from 1760 until it closed in 1837; at one time they built some of the big Leith smacks. Two other yards built large numbers of ships: Robert, and later his son John Barry had a yard from about 1775 next to Bagdale beck; south of this was the yard of Henry Barrick. From only five yards turning out ships in 1790 there were thirteen operating by 1802, but none was as prolific as the Fishburn shipyard, which between 1790 and 1815 launched 88 vessels totalling 23,535 tons. In the four years 1790-1793, Whitby yards turned out between 10.1 per cent and 11.6 per cent of the total annual tonnage produced in England and Wales, and in 1792 and 1793, Whitby was the second largest shipbuilding port in Britain (Scotland excluded).[48]

Not much is known about prices of actual ships at Whitby, but they probably followed the national average. John Barry built the *John Barry* in 1814, a ship of 520 tons, at a cost of £14,000 or £26 18s 6d per ton. The following year he built four vessels of between 100 and 250 tons at a cost of £12 to £14 per ton for hull and spars only; to fit them complete for sea would have cost a further £2 per ton.[49]

In 1908 Richard Weatherill had his book on the history of Whitby published. In it he provides numerous lists of named vessels for the years 1717-1900, presumably taken from the Custom House registers when these existed after 1786. Before this date, the builder's name is not often known, but Weatherill ascribes the following vessels to the yard of Thomas Fishburn:

Built	Name	Dimension (lower deck × extreme breadth × depth of hold	Tons
1764	*Union*	?	289
1764	*Earl of Pembroke* (later *Endeavour*)	97ft 7in × 29ft 3in × 11ft 4in	368
1770	*Marquis of Rockingham* (later *Raleigh*, later *Adventure*)	97ft 3in × 28ft 4in × 13ft 0in	340
1777	*Chapman* (afloat 1851)	116ft × 33ft × ?	558
1781	*Esk*	127ft × 33ft × ?	629
1790	*Favourite*	?	312

Note: See later in text for comparison of plans of *Earl of Pembroke* and *Marquis of Rockingham* which show that latter was about 2ft shorter.

Several of these were big ships for their day, and were suited to carry timber from the Baltic or coal from north-east England. The Deptford surveyors described the *Earl of Pembroke* as a 'square stern Bark, single bottom, full built'.[50] William Hutchinson gives his opinion of a similar vessel in these words: 'I examined into the properties of a collier cat, of about five hundred tons burden, that carried her loading of Riga timber, without any ballast in the hold, who had about a ninth part of her cargo upon deck and on the quarters, and was sufficiently stiff, and remarkably easy in her rolling, in great seas...'[51]

James Cook, who had been brought up in Whitby ships, appreciated their qualities to the full, especially their ability to take the ground and sit fairly upright, as well as their strength and their large stowage capacity.[52]

There are several plans of the *Earl of Pembroke* after she was purchased by the Navy and renamed *Endeavour*, but there is only one which seems to show decks and fittings in her collier days. This is plan No 3814B in the Admiralty Draughts at the National Maritime Museum. Although it is undated, red and blue dotted lines clearly indicate the alterations made, and plan No 3814A shows these alterations completed. Our discussion of the ship concerns her time before the Admiralty bought her, and so it is to the former plan that we must have recourse. This plan has been redrawn and is reproduced in figure 54.

In hull-form she has fairly flat floors, with slight deadrise, full bilges, vertical sides and a long box-like body for 30ft of her length, yet the waterlines in the half-breadth plan are not parallel to the centreline as in Hilhouse's ship *Exeter* (figure 65). The entrance is very full, but with some concavity in the lower part, and the run is also concave. The height of the underside of the wale above the bottom of the keel is 12ft, which was her probable draft of water as the *Endeavour*, and she has 10ft 6in topsides above this. There is no head and no gammon knee. The only decoration is a quarter badge. Right in the bows is a port which is perhaps a timber port, although it gives access to a space only 4ft 6in high. The lower deck beams are not decked over, thus providing the maximum stowage space in the hold. Admiralty plan No 3814B has five rectangular openings in the sides averaging 18in long and 10in high, which provided additional loading ports through which the keelmen could pitch the coal from their keels on the River

56

Fig 56. A modern model of the bark Liberty and Property. *The hull is from a contemporary half-model, but the deck fittings, spars and rigging are reconstructed. This ship was built at Whitby in 1752 of 274 tons. The planking is omitted below the wale to show the framing.* (Merseyside County Museums)

Tyne; the ports were of course caulked before the ship put to sea. When she was a collier her draft of water was surely greater than when she was an exploration ship, and it is drawn here as 14ft 9in.

The arrangement of the decks is interesting: the main deck is on four levels and there is a curious overlapping of decks by the main mast; the wheel is fitted at the afterside of the prominent companionway; the long tiller has an iron termination, cranked up to pass over a chimney pipe; the entrance to the forecastle is on the port side only, and is dotted on; the rail to the quarter deck and poop is supported on iron standards; the top of the carrick bitt is carved with a seaman's head, which is a well-known feature of the ship. All this can be deduced from the sheer elevation, but no plan exists of her deck layout as it was when she was purchased, the earliest date being 11 July 1768. Accordingly, a deck plan has been reconstructed here and a separate longitudinal section drawn.

Until the end of the eighteenth century, ships were generally classed by their hull-form, as outlined at the beginning of this chapter, but in 1768 the exact difference between 'cat' and 'bark' must have been becoming obscure, because in that year the Navy Board referred to the newly purchased *Earl of Pembroke* as a 'cat-built bark'.[53]

As the *Endeavour* is described both as a 'bark' and as 'cat-built', either separately or together, it would appear that even by 1768 the term 'bark' was becoming associated with the type of rig she had, placed on a plain full-bodied hull. Gwyn's 'Collier' in figure 46 could be termed a 'cat-bark' if a correct example of this somewhat ill-defined term were required, because she has a cat's stern and a barque's rig. The *Endeavour* certainly did not possess the cat's stern illustrated by Chapman. Lescallier or Falconer. The only slight shred of evidence in mitigation of this fact is that on her plan, the wale narrows in at the counter to give the quarter pieces very little projection, and so avoids any quarter galleries. This results in a narrow stern. That is all. The Admiralty surveyors must have reckoned that 'cat-built' covered any collier from the north-east coast that was of rugged construction with a plain stem and full-bodied hull.

A half-model in the Liverpool Museum which really is of a cat represents the *Liberty and Property*, built in Whitby in 1752 of 380 tons, and dimensions scaled off the model give a lenth of keel and forerake of 92ft and a beam of 25ft (figure 55). There is a plain bow; the wales go right round to the sternpost, which has a rake of about six feet to the underside of the counter; there is a square counter with a narrow stern above it; and below is the oval-shaped cross seam which connects the side of the counter and the sternpost. Like the *Earl of Pembroke*, the *Liberty and Property* has a full, bluff entrance and she is even fuller in the run; she also has flatter floors and less curvature in the sides, but there is the same sudden tumblehome above. The *Earl of Pembroke* is a broader ship by some five feet. The *Liberty and Property* has a short forecastle, long poop and a high sheer aft, but there are neither mast positions nor any deck fittings. But what is of interest are the five small rectangular openings along her side through which coal could be loaded, thus corroborating the ports on the *Earl of Pembroke*'s plan. Of particular importance is the fact that this model of the *Liberty and Property* is probably the oldest half-model of a merchant vessel that has survived in England. It is of the bracket or 'hawk's nest' type, being planked down to the bottom of the wale, below which there are frames and two ribbands. The *Liberty and Property* was assigned the rig of brig in *Lloyds Register* of 1776, but her next appearance in this Register was not until 1800 and then only in the Shipowners' Red edition, where she is a 'ship' with a draft of 15ft. She had large repairs in 1798 and her tonnage is now 249. She remained all her life in the coal and Baltic trades, and was finally wrecked in 1856 on Gothland Island in the Baltic at the age of 104 years.

It is interesting that two of Thomas Fishburn's ships, the *Earl of Pembroke* and the *Marquis of Rockingham*, should both have been purchased by the Royal Navy, and a comparison of their plans indicates many similarities. When tracings of the plans are laid over each other so that the keel rabbet and stem coincide, then the main and mizen masts also coincide, but the foremast in the *Marquis of Rockingham* is some two feet abaft that in *Earl of Pembroke*. Both ships have the same unusual bearding line at the heel of the sternpost; the run of the wale coincides; the profile is generally similar, although *Earl of Pembroke* is higher at the stern; and there is the same rider keelson between fore and main masts in each. Although the dimensions give almost identical lengths on the lower deck, the plans show *Earl of Pembroke* to be 2ft longer.

The *Marquis of Rockingham* was built for an owner in Hull and bought by the Navy in 1771 for £2103. Her lines were taken off at Woolwich in November. At first she was renamed *Raleigh* and Admiralty plan No 4096 in box 66 bears this name, but a month later her name was changed to *Adventure*, and the following year she was fitted out to accompany the *Resolution* under the command of Cook, now promoted to Commander R N.[54]

This *Resolution* was another Whitby-built collier launched under the name of *Marquis of Granby* in 1769, purchased by the Royal Navy two years later and renamed *Drake*. Almost immediately, her name was altered to *Resolution*, and her lines were taken off in November the same year. Dimensions on the plan give 110ft 8in (lower deck) × 30ft 5½in (extreme) × 13ft 1½in, and 461 tons. Yellow ink lines on plan No 3254 show the additions made by the Navy which include a cut-water, head and trail boards (indicating that she must have had a plain stem like the *Earl of Pembroke*); raising of bulwarks the entire length; adding poop and cabin with ornate stern; insertion of extra gunports in waist; raising height of channels and chainplates; and generally converting the holds. She was full-bodied like other colliers, but the quarter did not narrow in as on the *Earl of Pembroke*.

There is a slight problem here concerning the lengths of masts and yards with which these colliers were fitted when they were carrying coal, because the Navy was in the habit of reducing the lengths of spars in ships bound for the 'Southern Ocean', and it may be that the spar lengths inscribed on the plans are the cut-down versions, not the original. Most students of naval architecture seem more interested in the appearance of these colliers *after* they were

58

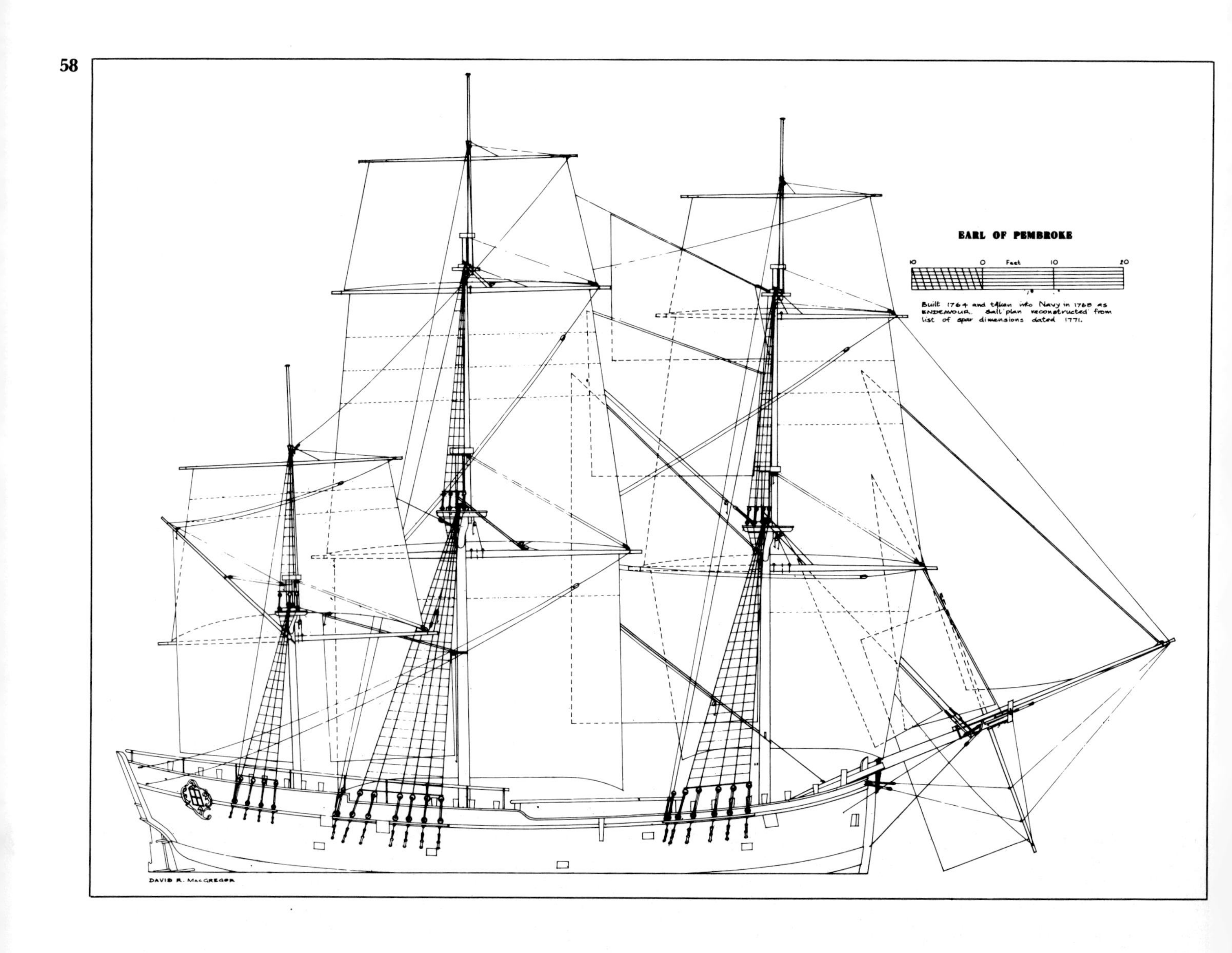
EARL OF PEMBROKE
10 0 Feet 10 20
Built 1764 and taken into Navy in 1768 as ENDEAVOUR. Sail plan reconstructed from list of spar dimensions dated 1771.
DAVID R. MacGREGOR

57

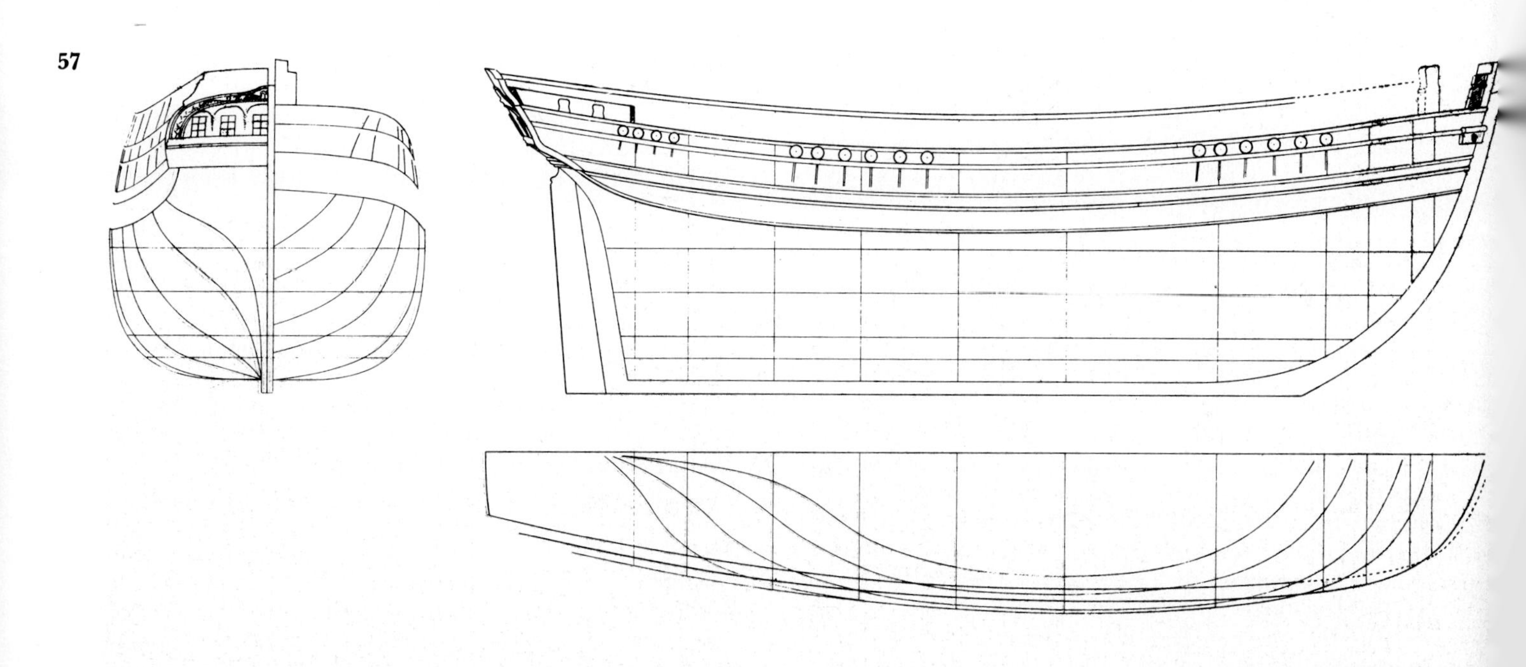

Fig 58. Earl of Pembroke. *Sail plan reconstructed from the sheer elevation and from a list of spars dated October 1771 after the ship had returned from her first voyage of exploration under the name of* HMS Endeavour. *No stunsail booms are listed. The sprit topsail has been omitted, although a yard was listed.*

Fig 57. Two Sisters. *Lines plan drawn by W Salisbury from a take-off he made of a planked half-model in Liverpool Museum. The vessel was built at South Shields in 1783. Dimensions measured on plan, assuming a scale of ¼in to 1ft: 65ft 0in keel, 18ft 6in fore rake, 29ft 6in maximum breadth, 19ft 9in depth from rail at the level of the channels to the keel rabbet. Her great beam, bluff entrance and hollow run are features of this sort of hull; she has three masts, but the small deadeyes on the mizen indicate only a lower mast and topmast.*

Fig 59. The Minerva *is pictured here making sail, possibly off some foreign port. In the centre view she has got only her topsails and fore course set, but is already hoisting topmast stunsails and a driver from the mizen gaff. On the right she is under full sail with a main royal set and drawing, and the driver boomed out abaft the mizen course. Identification has not been established beyond the name written on the back of the framed photograph when I bought it, and a note added that her master was Captain Thos Worsfield and she was afloat in 1759. The picture closely resembles the style of Luny's painting in figure 75. The ship seen here is too small for the East Indiaman of the same name built in 1787 of 798 tons.*

fitted for naval use, whereas we are concerned with what they were like *before*.

There was a paramount need to reconstruct a sail plan of the *Earl of Pembroke*, but unfortunately the earliest list of spars is dated October 1771 when she had already made one voyage of circumnavigation as the *Endeavour*. Nevertheless, for the reasons already stated, these spar lengths have been adopted for the sail plan because it was considered that the Navy would have reduced, not enlarged her sail area. The result is an impressive amount of canvas with long fore and main lower masts, and a very square appearance aloft. No stunsails are drawn although they were probably carried. The foot of the foresail has been narrowed to bring the tack down to the cathead without fitting a bumpkin, and only one spritsail has been rigged, although the *Endeavour* carried a spritsail topsail as well. The mizen is very short compared with the other masts, but stepping the heel of the lower mast on a block supported on the keelson - a practice adopted in the *Raleigh* which came from the same yard - has the effect of raising the height of the crossjack yard. Because of the short lower mast, the mizen course is small, whereas the topsail is a large sail because of the long crossjack yard, which is equal in length to the main topsail yard. In fact, the crossjack yard overlaps the main shrouds, and difficulty was experienced on the drawing here in adequately showing the run of the braces. This sail plan appears as figure 58.

Some points about the rigging are worth recording: the braces from yards on the foremast lead to blocks on the stays, and thence down the stay and so to the deck near the foot of the foremast; the mizen topsail braces lead to the

59

peak of the mizen gaff or yard; the topmast and topgallant stays are set up to the mast with tackles; the long brace pendants are taken from a watercolour by Francis Swaine, reproduced in *Coals from Newcastle* by Roger Finch; owing to the large size of the main topmast staysail, no main staysail is drawn. Although men-of-war set royals at this date, few colliers are thought likely to have done so, even though Edward Gwyn drew them on his collier (figure 46), and so there are long pole heads to each of the three masts. But these long mastheads did enable ships to display flags clearly without the need to lower the topgallant yards.

The question of the short mizen lower mast is a vexed one, but a few examples, such as Swaine's watercolour, do confirm the small mizen topsail. It is a curious fact that of the spars which the Navy bought with the *Earl of Pembroke*, no mizen lower mast is listed and one may conjecture whether the ship carried a longer mizen as a collier than as an exploration vessel. Incidentally, this list of spars was for valuation only and no dimensions are given.[55] An indication that the *Endeavour's* mizen lower mast was unduly short may be had from the following table, which is compiled from spar dimensions to be found on Admiralty draughts of various colliers bought into the Navy:

Considering that *Endeavour* and *Raleigh* were from the same shipyard, it is possible that the former would have been built with a longer mizen lower mast at least equal in height to the *Raleigh's*, especially as the latter was the smaller ship of the two. This would give an approximate height above deck of 36ft to the mizen cap, making the topsail a taller sail.

CONTEMPORARY APPRAISAL OF SHIP DESIGN

Most authors of text books on naval architecture attempted to state the desiderata for design of a ship, whether for war or for commerce, but perhaps Fredrik af Chapman sums it up as well as anyone. To use his own words,[56]

A Merchant Ship ought:
1. To be able to carry a great lading in proportion to its size.
2. To sail well by the wind, in order to beat easily off a coast where it may be embayed, and also to come about well in a hollow sea.
3. To work with a crew small in number in proportion to its cargo.
4. To be able to sail with a small quantity of ballast.

date built	date spars listed	name when listed	mizen lower mast	approximate height of mizen lower mast above deck	mizen top mast	mizen top pole
1764	1771	*Endeavour*	50ft 5in	29ft 9in	24ft 10in	11ft 2in
1769	1771	*Resolution*	63ft 4in	35ft 0in	28ft 6in	not stated
1770	1771	*Raleigh*	58ft 0in	39ft 0in	24ft 2in	13ft 6in
1784	1787	*Bounty*	48ft 2in	32ft 0in	24ft 3½in	3ft 1in

60

Fig 61. An engraving by Groenwegen of a snow going about on to the port tack; the helm has been put down, the jib and staysail sheets eased off, and the yards on the foremast braced up until they are now aback as the vessel starts to swing round, although the sails on the mainmast are still full of wind. From his book of engravings Hollandsche Schepen *(1789).*

To procure these advantages to a ship, it appears:
1. That to take a great lading with respect to its size, it ought to have great breadth and depth, in proportion to its length, and to be full in the bottom. Such a ship would also work with a small number of hands in proportion to its cargo. But it would neither sail well nor beat to wind-ward.
2. That to give the property of sailing and beating to windward, to the end that it might beat off a lee shore, as well as come about well in a hollow sea, the ship must necessarily have a considerable moment of stability in proportion to the plane of resistance, that it may be able to carry a press of sail, notwithstanding a strong wind; with this view it is necessary to give to the ship in question, great breadth in proportion to its length; to fill it much towards the load water-line, curtailing it in the bottom. Such a ship would require a numerous crew because of the largeness of the sails, and the weight of its anchors.
3. That if it be required to navigate a ship with few men, in proportion to the lading, it should have a small surface of sails, and anchors of small weight. For this purpose it should have little breadth in proportion to its length.

It would also be enabled to carry a great lading, in proportion to its equipment of men, by giving it great fulness in its bottom; but such a ship would sail badly close to the wind, and would come about with difficulty in a hollow sea.
4. That to enable a ship to sail with a small quantity of ballast, it is necessary to fill the body between wind and water, when it has the ballast in; it should be large and little elevated above the water. A ship of this kind would carry a sufficient lading in proportion to its size, but it would ply badly when laden, especially if it were a large ship; without giving it a considerable quantity of sail, which would render it necessary to have a great number of men.

By this it is again proved, that we can conclude nothing concerning the length, breadth, and depth of ships, since different qualities require conditions diametrically opposite to each other. We may succeed in uniting two of these advantages by a certain form and by certain proportions given to ships, but it is impossible to combine all four in an eminent degree. It is not possible to gain on one side without losing on another.

Wherefore, for a merchant ship, it is necessary to combine these qualitites, so that it may have the most possible of each. That is to say, that the expression representing the velocity and quantity of lading divided by the number of the crew and quantity of ballast, may be a *maximum*.

Again, however, as certain commercial speculations require one quality in preference to another; the nature of this commerce; the latitudes in which it is necessary to navigate; the ports for anchorage; all these must be considered in determining which of these qualities ought to prevail, without altering in any respect the size of the ship.

Fig 60. A painting by Robert Dodd of the ship Lady Juliana *riding out a gale in a convoy off Newfoundland in 1782. She has only a partly brailed-in mizen course set, and has struck her fore and main topgallant masts, and hauled her jibboom inboard. Other ships in the convoy have lost all or some of their spars. Although the painting's title allots her a tonnage of 379, the most likely candidate in* Lloyd's Register *is the* Lady Juliana *of 250 tons which was built at Whitby in 1769 and voyaged to Halifax. She was armed with 8-pounder and 2 4-pounder guns and was owned in London; she was re-named in 1782 and again in 1784.* (Parker Gallery)

62

Fig 62. Groenwegen's deck view of a full rigged ship heeled over, showing the deck fittings. All the yards have been sent down and the topmasts housed. This engraving was published in 1789 in his book on Dutch vessels.

Every author had his own personal views on how ships should be designed but their works were weighed down with general instructions in mathematics. Mungo Murray's *Treatise on Ship-Building and Navigation* is a case in point. First published in 1754, it appeared in 1765 as a second edition of 344 pages in which the art of shipbuilding occupies a fairly small part compared with geometry, logarithms, trigonometry, land surveying, use of charts, latitude and longitude. Murray does give some plans, instructions for whole moulding, methods of forming the ship's body and how to form the timbers. There are also some tables of offsets including the pink *Bonetta* of 398 tons. He uses her as an example on how to draw the lines from these offsets and includes a plan (plate IX) of her body plan, bow and stern profiles, and the superimposed plan of each end. At the end of the Supplement are rules for masts and yards.

Murray also includes a translation of Duhamel du Monceau's *Elements of Naval Architecture* which he has 'carefully abridged', and this includes the following comments on ship design. Presumably the first person is Duhamel speaking:[57]

General Remarks on Ship Building.

All the rules we have hitherto laid down, collected from the principal dimensions of ships built by the most eminent masters, should only be so far regarded as they may assist the artist in forming the body in such a manner as to produce effects answerable to the service for which the vessel is designed.

In order to qualify a builder for such an undertaking, it is necessary he should understand the nature of fluids, and of such bodies as will float in the water; when he has made himself acquainted with these, I would recommend him to M. *Bouguer's* treatise on ship-building.

The principal Qualities belonging to Ships.

1st. To be able to carry a good sail, not only because, in forming the body, the water lines are all supposed to be described when a ship is upright in the water, but likewise for doubling a cape, or getting off a lee shore, which will be impossible to be done when a ship lies over in the water, this will likewise render her lower tier, if not all her guns useless.

2nd. A ship should steer well, and feel the least motion of the helm.

3rd. A ship should carry her lower tier of guns four feet and a half, or five feet out of the water, otherwise a great ship, that cannot open her ports upon a wind, but in smooth water, may be taken by a small one, that can make use of her guns, or she must bare away before the wind, to have the use of her guns; on which account it will be proper to raise the ports higher before than in midships, because the fore part of the ship is often pressed into the water by carrying sail.

4th A ship should be duly poised, so as not to dive or pitch hard, but go smooth and easy through the water, rising to the sea when it runs high, and the ship under her courses, or lying to under a mainsail, otherwise she will be in danger of carrying away her masts.

5th A ship should sail well before the wind, large, but chiefly close hawled, keep a good wind, not fall off to the leeward.

Now the great difficulty consists in uniting so many different qualities in one ship, which seems indeed to be impossible; the whole art therefore consists in forming the body in such a manner, that none of these qualities shall be entirely destroyed, and in giving the preference to that which is most required in the particular service for which the vessel is built; in order to which, it will be necessary to know, at least nearly, what form will give a vessel one of these qualities, considered abstractly from the rest.

To make a Ship carry a good Sail.

A flat floor timber, and somewhat long, or the lower futtock pretty round, a streight upper futtock, the top timber to throw

63

Fig 63. An armed French ship close-hauled on the starboard tack under full sail with the exception of her spritsail. A lateen sail is set from the ensign staff and sheeted out to a long bumpkin. Probably engraved by Jean Baugean.

the breadth out aloft; at any rate to carry her main breadth as high as the lower deck: Now, if the rigging be well adapted to such a body, and the upper works lightened as much as possible, so that they all concur to lower the center of gravity, there will be no room to doubt of her carrying a good sail.

To make a Ship steer well, and quickly answer the Helm.

If the fashion pieces be well formed, and the tuck carried pretty high; the midship frame carried pretty forward; a considerable difference of the draught of water abaft more than afore; a great rake forward, and none abaft; a snug quarter-deck and forecastle, all these will make a ship steer well; but to make her feel the least motion of her helm, it will be necessary to regard her masts. There is one thing not to be forgot, that a ship which goes well will certainly steer well.

To make a Ship carry her Guns well out of the Water.

It is plain, that a long floor timber, and not of a great rising; a very full midship frame, and low tuck with light upper works, will make a ship carry her guns high.

To make a Ship go smoothly through the Water without pitching hard.

A long keel, a long floor, not to rise too high afore and abaft, the area or space contained in the fore body, duly proportioned to that of the after body, according to the respective weights they are to carry; all these are necessary to make a ship go smoothly through the water.

To make Ship keep a good Wind.

A good length by the keel, not too broad, but pretty deep in the hold, which will occasion her to have a short floor timber, and great rising.

As such a ship will meet with great resistance in the water, going over the broad-side, and little when going a-head, she will not fall much to the leeward.

Now, some builders imagine that it is not possible to make a ship carry her guns well, carry a good sail, and to be a prime sailer, because it would require a very full bottom to gain the first two qualities, whereas a sharp ship will best answer for the latter; but when it is considered that a full ship will carry a great deal more sail than a sharp one, a good artist may so form the body as to have all these three good qualities, and likewise steer well, for which purpose I would recommend somewhat in length more than has been formerly practised.

After what has been said upon this head, I believe it will not be thought impossible to unite all these different qualities in one ship, so that all of them may be discerned in some degree of eminence; but when it happens otherwise, the fault must be owing to the builder, who has not applied himself to study the fundamental rules and principles of his art.

Excepting some antient builders, who were happily born with a natural genius, and our moderns, who being instructed in the principles of the mathematics, have truly laboured very hard to make a progress in the art of shipbuilding, one may, without violating the truth, affirm that the greatest part satisfy themselves with copying such ships as they esteem good sailers, and it is these servile merchanick methods, which, to the great reproach of the art, are but too common, that have produced all these pretended rules of proportion, all these methods of describing the mid-ship frame, and forming the rest of the timbers, which every builder endeavours if possible to conceal, and keep wholly in his own family.

How low and mean is this? it is as if a great architect should endeavour to conceal the proportions of the different orders of architecture; whereas they are published every where, and so well known that many can raise a very beautiful porch or triumphal arch; but tho' the methods of describing the midship frame, and forming the rest of the timbers, be known to most apprentices, yet we have but few good master builders: This requires more than those mechanick rules; they should at least have such a knowledge of the mathematicks, physicks, mechanicks, of the nature of solids and fluids, as to be able to discover what figure would procure some good quality, without hazarding or putting a bad one in its place.

Let us suppose one to have a collection of draughts of a vast

> number of ships, and whose good and bad qualities have been remarked with all possible exactness, such a valuable treasure would be of great service to a person who could calculate precisely by the draughts where the fault lay, and how it might be rectified. For instance, suppose a ship sails well, but carries her guns too low, a builder who is not acquainted with these principles would raise her deck, in consequence of which she would not sail well; whereas, one that could exactly calculate how much the resistance of the fluid is diminished upon the prow, would take great care to add no more to any of the other parts than he could find by an exact calculation might be done without augmenting the resistance in the fluids.
>
> M. *Bouguer* has published several useful problems for making these calculations, to which we refer the reader, and only explain what regards the height of the gun deck, and the resistance of the fluid, in one example of a 70 gun ship.

Further extracts could be given of what other authors and authorities had to say on the subject, but not much more light would be cast on the subject. Usually their remarks were confined to the hull-form, not to the masting and rigging, but some comments by af Chapman, as translated by James Inman, give an interesting sidelight on his preferences in a mast and rigging plan:[58]

> It is not sufficient to study merely to regulate the height of the masts, and the length of the yards, by the size of the ships; but also to use those which have such a proportion among themselves, that all the rigging may make a handsome appearance.
>
> That the ships may be well rigged, it is necessary in the first place, that the fore-stay and main topmast-stay should be in a straight line, in like manner, the main-stay and the mizen topmast-stay: the fore-stay may end on the bowsprit, between one-third and two-fifths of its length from the small end; secondly, that the top-sails should be of similar figures, or at least, that their sides should be of the same cut; thirdly, that when the ship is seen, at one or the other of the extremities, the shrouds and the breast back-stays should appear parallel: this depends partly on the breadth of the channels, which ought to be regulated in a manner conducive to this end. To effect this, the length of the head of the main-mast, from the underside of the trestle-trees, which is $\frac{5}{36}$ of the length of the said mast, being = T, the cap of the fore-mast should be lower than that of the main-mast by a quantity = $2,22 \times T\frac{1}{3}$ for frigates, and = $2 \times T\frac{1}{4}$ for barks. The cap of the mizen-mast should be on a level with the main-top.

Although the style of rig, the type of cargo, and the quality of the master all exerted an effect on the vessel, a superficial examination suggests great similarities in hull-forms for merchant ships in the eighteenth century. But a closer study reveals some wider variations.

Fig 64. Sail plan of a ship which provides an illustration of some of the points on masting and rigging of which Chapman wrote, as quoted in the text. (Revd James Inman's translation, A Treatise on Ship-Building, *by Fredrik af Chapman, 1820, plate 7; it is the only sail plan).*

64

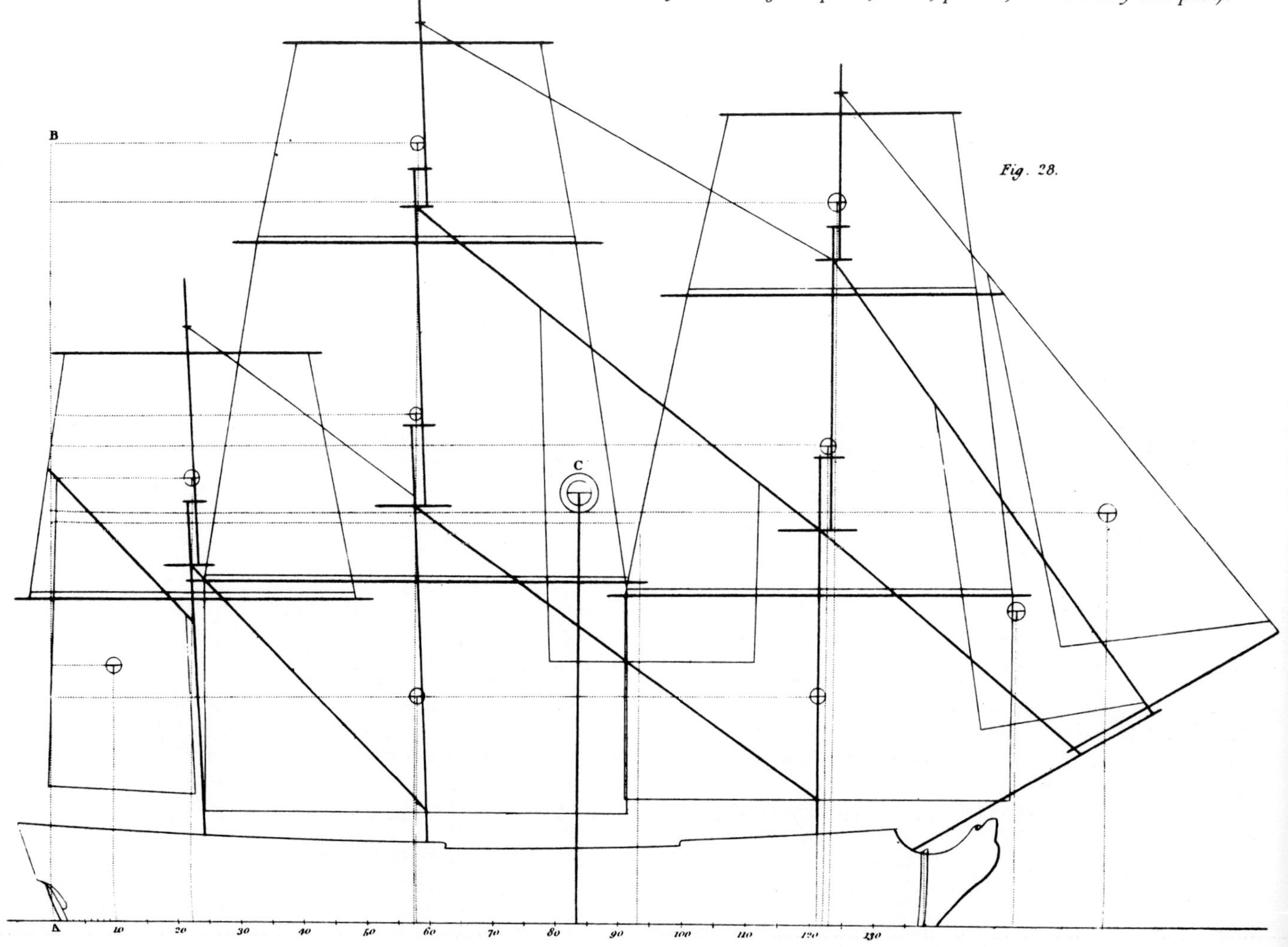

DESIGN AND CONSTRUCTION OF THREE-MASTED VESSELS

The trade to the West Indies was one of the principal sources of revenue, and West Indiamen were built by all European nations. In England, London, Bristol and Liverpool were the principal ports for this trade, and at Bristol the yard of J M Hilhouse (1748–1822) built many suitable ships. One of the earliest plans (folio 112) is of the *Exeter*, built in 1776, four years after the yard opened. The plan is redrawn in figure 65. Measurements inscribed on the plan give 95ft 0in length on the lower deck, 26ft 0in breadth moulded, 11ft 2in depth in hold under the beams, and 4ft 10in height between decks. Height inside the poop scales 6ft 9in and her tonnage was 267. Like all the surviving Hilhouse plans, this one shows a vessel with a parallel middle body, there being about 15ft of dead flats here. The entrance is convex but not too full, and by no means so bluff as some other Hilhouse ships such as the *Pilgrim* (folio 111) or the *William Miles* (1808). It is similar to that of Steel's merchantman of 330 tons and to many other ships. The run is long and concave, especially in the lower half. It should be noted that the lowest waterline is very close to the rabbet and so can give a false impression on the half-breadth plan of the hull shape. The floors are very flat with hardly any deadrise and altogether it is a very full-bodied cross-section, obviously designed to carry the maximum amount of cargo at a good speed. One feature of particular interest is the plain stem and gammon knee without a head. A conventional head has been dotted on the original plan, but it is not drawn here.

There is no deck plan of the *Exeter*, but the sheer elevation has the windlass drawn forward of the foremast, a pair of gallows between the masts on which to sling the spare spars and longboat if the ship was in action, a capstan beneath them, and the wheel abaft the mizen. No spar dimensions have been found, but she would have had a sail plan somewhat similar to Steel's merchantman, though without a dolphin striker.

There are four other lines plans in the Hilhouse Collection for ships of this period, as set out on page 70. (These plans were examined when in the possession of Charles Hill & Sons.)

Fig 65. Exeter. *Lines plan. Built in 1776 at Bristol by J M Hilhouse. Redrawn by Paul A Roberts from a tracing of the builder's plan made by the Author. Dimensions on plan: 95ft 0in (length on lower deck), 76ft 0in (straight rabbet of keel), 26ft 0in (moulded breadth), 11ft 2in (depth in hold under the beams), 4ft 10in (height between decks). The tonnage was 267. No reconstruction, but some of the radii for the arcs forming the body plan have been omitted, and so has a head that was dotted on, under the gammon knee. The half midship section of the* Pilgrim *(1779) is added, as she was of similar hull-form.*

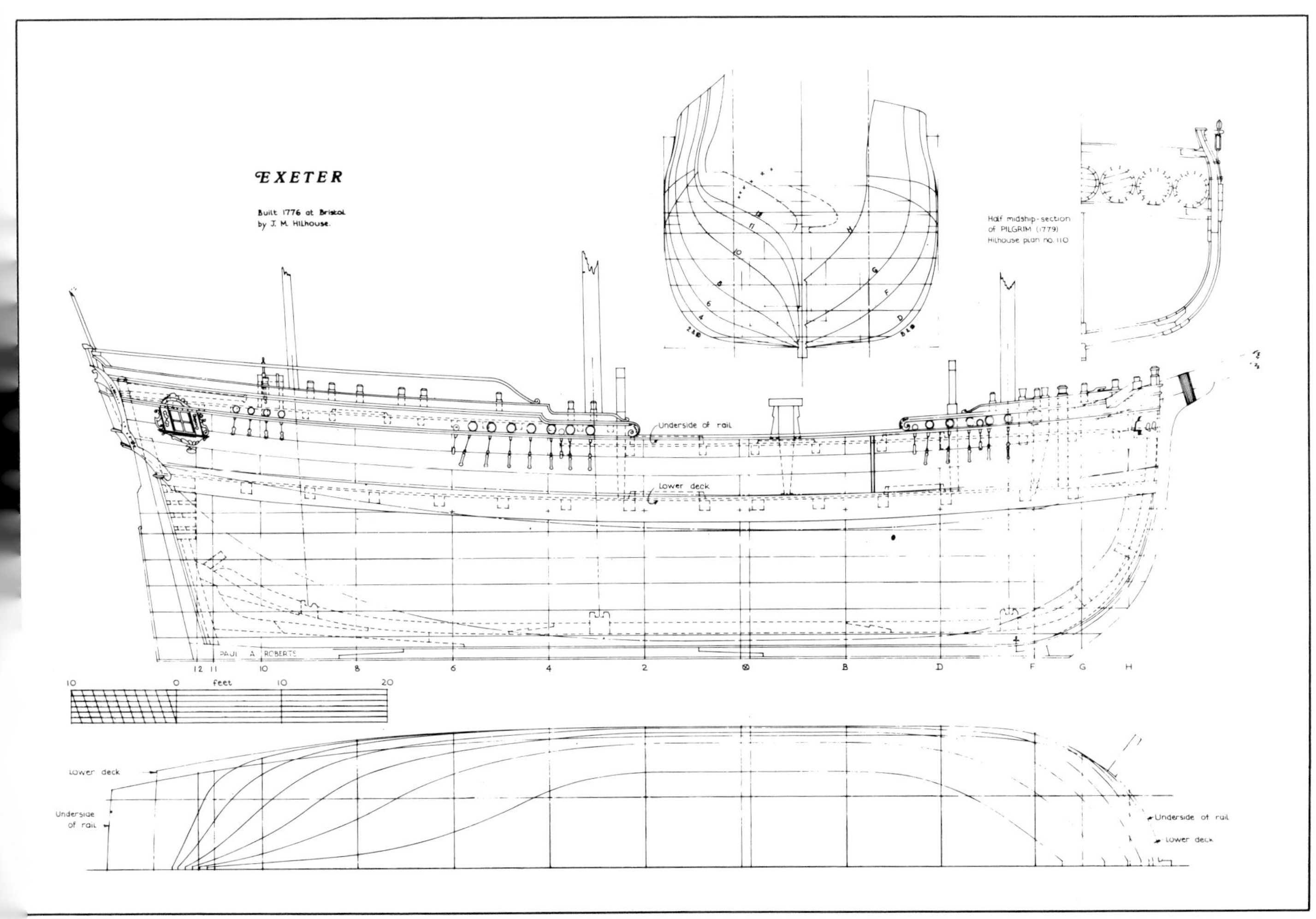

66

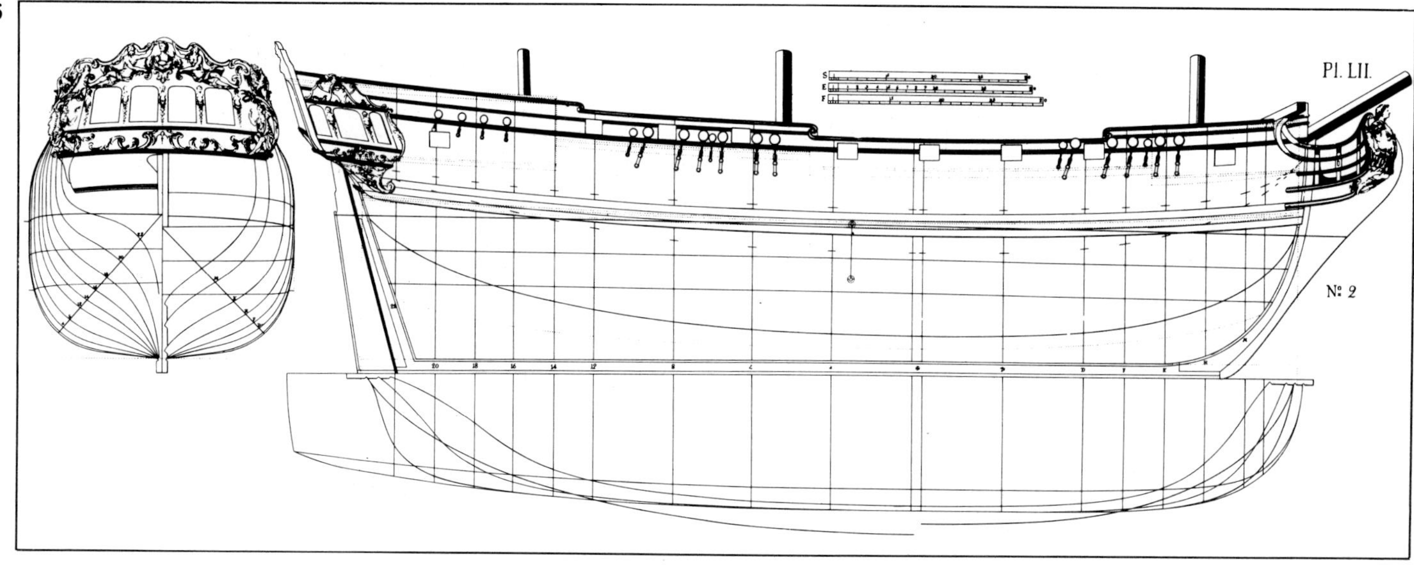

Fig 66. English West India Trader [*Chapman's title*]. *Lines plan, reproduced from plate L11 in* Architectura Navalis Mercatoria *(1768) by Fredrik af Chapman. Dimensions in the English index to the plans: 129ft 9in (length between perpendiculars), 33ft 4in (moulded breadth), 19ft 4in (draught of water). No tonnage is given.*

Folio

107 'Old Ship *Pilgrim*' signed and dated 'R Hilhouse Feby 19 1802'; it is a clean plan and probably a copy of an older plan of the ship of this name built in 1779 of 280 tons with four 3-pounders. In 1787 she was sheathed with copper and fastened with iron bolts. She was a slaver because described as a 'Guinea man' and in 1798 carried a letter of marque.[59] The mid-section is similar to that of the *Exeter* (folio 112) but there is less rake to the sternpost; she has a head; the entrance is fuller and turns rather suddenly into the middle body.

110 Unnamed and undated; only note states '26 Bm', meaning 26ft beam. The entrance is very bluff indeed but the waterlines and part body plan of a finer entrance are drawn; otherwise the design is very similar to that of the *Exeter*. The stern half of the body plan is seperate from the bow half and stowing of barrels on the lower deck is depicted on the half cross-section.

111 '1787 *Pilgrim* 27 Bm 1789 *Marquis* [of] *Worcester*' and signed and dated 'James M Hilhouse 1790'. Dimensions of 105ft 8in (register length) × 27ft 6in (max. beam) × 12ft 0in (lower hold); 307 tons. There is a change in design from the *Exeter* here: the entrance is very full, the middle body has straight parallel sides, and the run is short and hollow: the mid-section has a little more deadrise, hollow garboards and slacker bilges.

105 '*Jamaica* Sherry 30 Bm'. This ship was built in 1790, Captain W Sherry, of 458 tons with three decks and designed with 30ft beam. The hull-form is very similar to folio 111, but the figurehead is elaborate on a long projecting head; she has eleven gunports, and carried a letter of marque in 1791.

Although all the Hilhouse plans show full-bodied ships there is a strong feeling that they were designed from practical experience of the qualities required of a ship in the trade. The *William Miles* (figure 129), built by Hilhouse in 1808, was really a lengthened version of the *Jamaica* and is described in the next chapter.

The West Indiaman whose lines are given by Chapman in his book of plates on Naval Architecture had fairly similar dimensions to the Hilhouse ships, and the general form was somewhat similar, but the waterlines curved throughout their length without any parallel middle body (see figure 66). Chapman's ship had elaborate carved work on the stern and the quarter galleries, and the nine gunports followed the main deck which stepped up and down to four different levels. Other plans of English West Indiamen exist to show that Chapman's example was fairly typical of the merchant ship then being built for this trade or any other. A plan at the National Maritime Museum gives details of the *Hydra* of 447 tons, built at Deptford in 1778 by Adams & Barnard.

Liverpool was likewise closely connected with the West Indies trade and also with the slave trade. During the period when the carriage of slaves was lawful in Great Britain, ships were generally designed with a fair turn of speed but without neglecting the need to carry a large cargo out to West Africa. Their speed enabled them to make the 'middle passage' – as the run from Africa to the West Indies was termed – as short as possiblc, thereby delivering the negroes in a healthy condition, but cargo considerations often filled out a ship's hull-form.

The largest British slaver was said to be the *Parr*, built at Liverpool in 1797 of 566 tons with a loaded draft of 17ft.

Fig 67. Hall. *A remarkable composite drawing of sheer elevation, sails and lines plan, reproduced from* A Treatise on Naval Architecture *by William Hutchinson (1794). The* Hall *was built at Liverpool in 1785. Customs House dimensions: 103ft 0in (length), but plan scales 113ft; 29ft 7in (breadth); 5ft 0in (depth of hold below lower deck); 5ft 7in (height between decks); 375 tons. Dimensions printed on the drawing: 90ft keel [probably straight rabbet], 30ft beam, 18ft hold [perhaps from deck at side to keel rabbet].*

67

PLATE 1st
Billinge Sc. Liverpool.

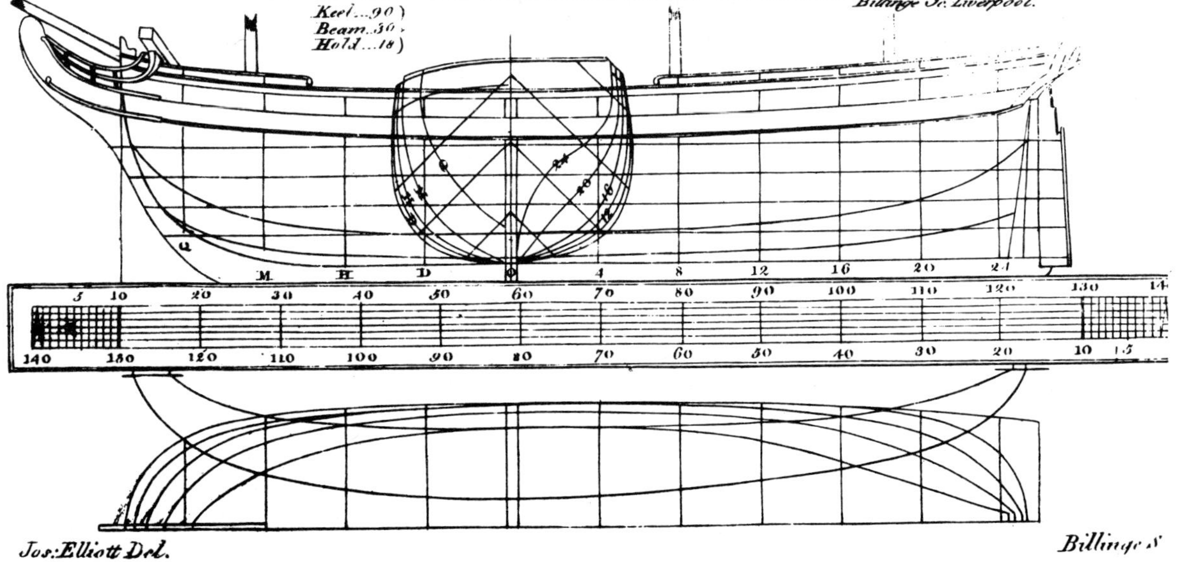
Keel...90
Beam..36
Hold...18
Jos: Elliott Del.
Billinge S

71

According to *Lloyd's Register*, she was heavily armed with twenty 18-pounders and twelve 18-pounder carronades, which was a formidable battery. A ship of this size carried a crew of 50 to 70 men, but with a low proportion of able seamen. In a table which lists ships clearing out from Liverpool between 1793 and 1807 for the coast of Africa, 1800 was the year with the highest average tonnage per ship, namely 281.[60]

The plan of a Liverpool-built West Indiaman and occasional slaver was reproduced in 1794 by William Hutchinson. She was named the *Hall*, her lines appear in plate I of his book and she is referred to extensively in the text. Hutchinson fancied himself as an adviser on the best forms of ships and the following is his story of how they were translated into the design of the *Hall*:[61]

> After the peace 1783, a nephew of mine, William Ward, was going to have a ship built for the Jamaica trade; I gave him a manuscript that I had wrote for the best form, and proportional dimensions, in length, breadth and depth of merchant ships in general, he shewed it to his owners, who approved so much of it as to say, that they wondered that I not published it before. They gave it to an ingenious drafter of ships, Mr Joseph Elliot, who served his time at the King's yard, Deptford, who approved of the plan, and drew a sheet draft, that the ship *Hall*, of 362 tons, carpenters' measure, was built by, which answering so well, that I got Mr Elliot to draw a draft in miniature from the sheet draft, and got a plate engraved, (as represented at the bottom of plate the first) in order to illustrate and help our ideas to fix the best rule for the shape and rake of the stem and stern-post, that makes so essential a part for the best form of ships, which I hope will be perceived by professional men that are concerned in shipping, by this small draft of the ship *Hall*, which will be detailed hereafter, the rule I took for this important purpose.
>
> The curve for the water-line of the harpen forward, and the load-mark aft, was formed by a sweep of half a circle toward the main frame, the three fourths of the main breadth; and from there with a regular convex curve to the midship or main frame: And that the shape and rake of the stem be justly so as to admit the rabbit for the huddens of the bows, from the keel upward, to be exactly in the same form as the water-line from the stem.

I have interpreted the description of her design in his last paragraph above to mean that the loadline in the entrance and run was formed by an arc of a circle, taking the radius as three-quarters of the main breadth, and the rabbet of the stem from keel to load line was an identical curve. The 'harpen' or harpin refers to the forward end of the wale by the bows; 'rabbit' is now spelt rabbet; the 'huddens' is presumably a corruption of hood ends, or the ends of the planking which fit into the stem rabbet.

Joseph Elliot who drew the plan was draughtsman to John Fisher who built the *Hall* at Liverpool in 1785; the Custom House register gives her dimensions of 103ft 0in length, 29ft 7in breadth above the main wales, 5ft 0in depth of hold below the lower deck, 5ft 7in depth between upper and lower decks, and 375 tons. William Ward was her first master and Hutchinson himself eventually got command in 1792. When fully loaded she drew 14ft 9in forward and 16ft 0in aft.

Some further dimensions are given below, prefaced by Hutchinson's opening comments:[62]

> As this ship *Hall*, answers her designed purpose so well as to give satisfaction both to the owners and crew, it may be well to repeat my proposed rules in figures, that they may be the easier and readier understood by inspection.

	Feet	Inches
Extreme length or tread, of the keel from the forefoot to the keel at the after part of the stern-post that stands upright	90	0
The keel to be made and laid upon concave blocks with a curve downward at the rate of 2 inches for every 30 feet, that the curve or sheer of their bottom may be equalled to that of their top.	0	6
The bottom of the keel to be made straight, but put upon blocks laid with a concave curve, an inch for every 30 feet, to make it lie with a convex curve exactly under the main frame for an allowance for the tendency of all ships to hog.	0	6
Extreme breadth at the main frame, one third of the length of the keel.	30	0
Depth of the hollow at ditto from the ceiling to the main deck, 6 tenths of the extreme breadth.	18	0
The main frame to be between the two lower midship floor-timbers, 7 twelfths from the after part of the sternpost.	52	6
The main transom to be three fourths of the main breadth.	22	6
Height of main transom from the upper part of the keel at the main frame to the upper part of the main deck.	19	0

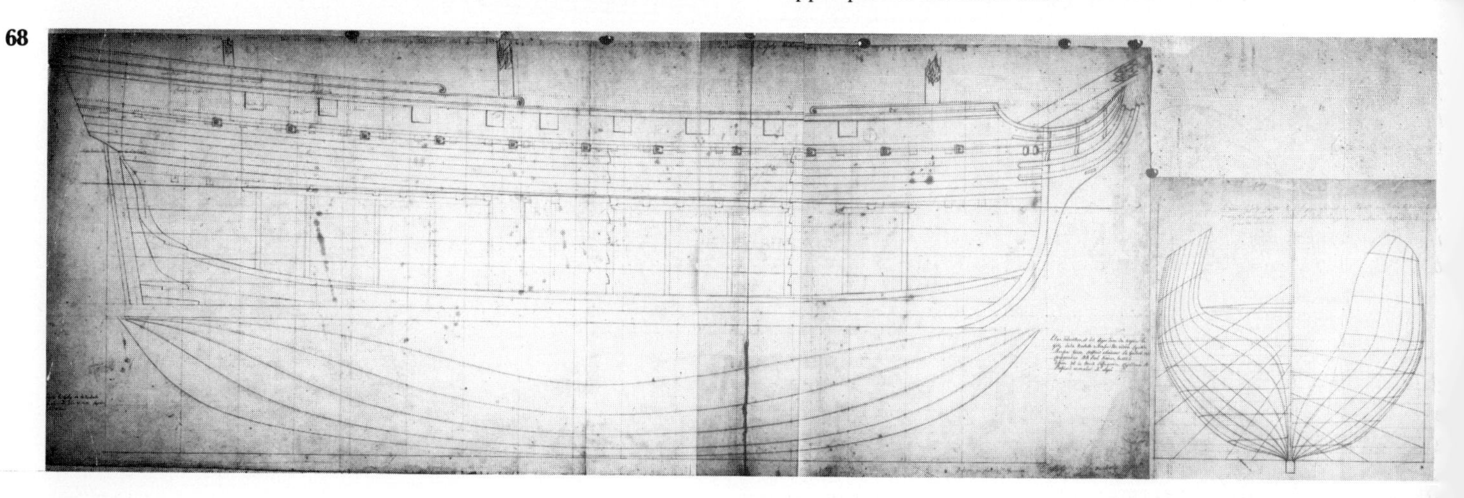

68

69

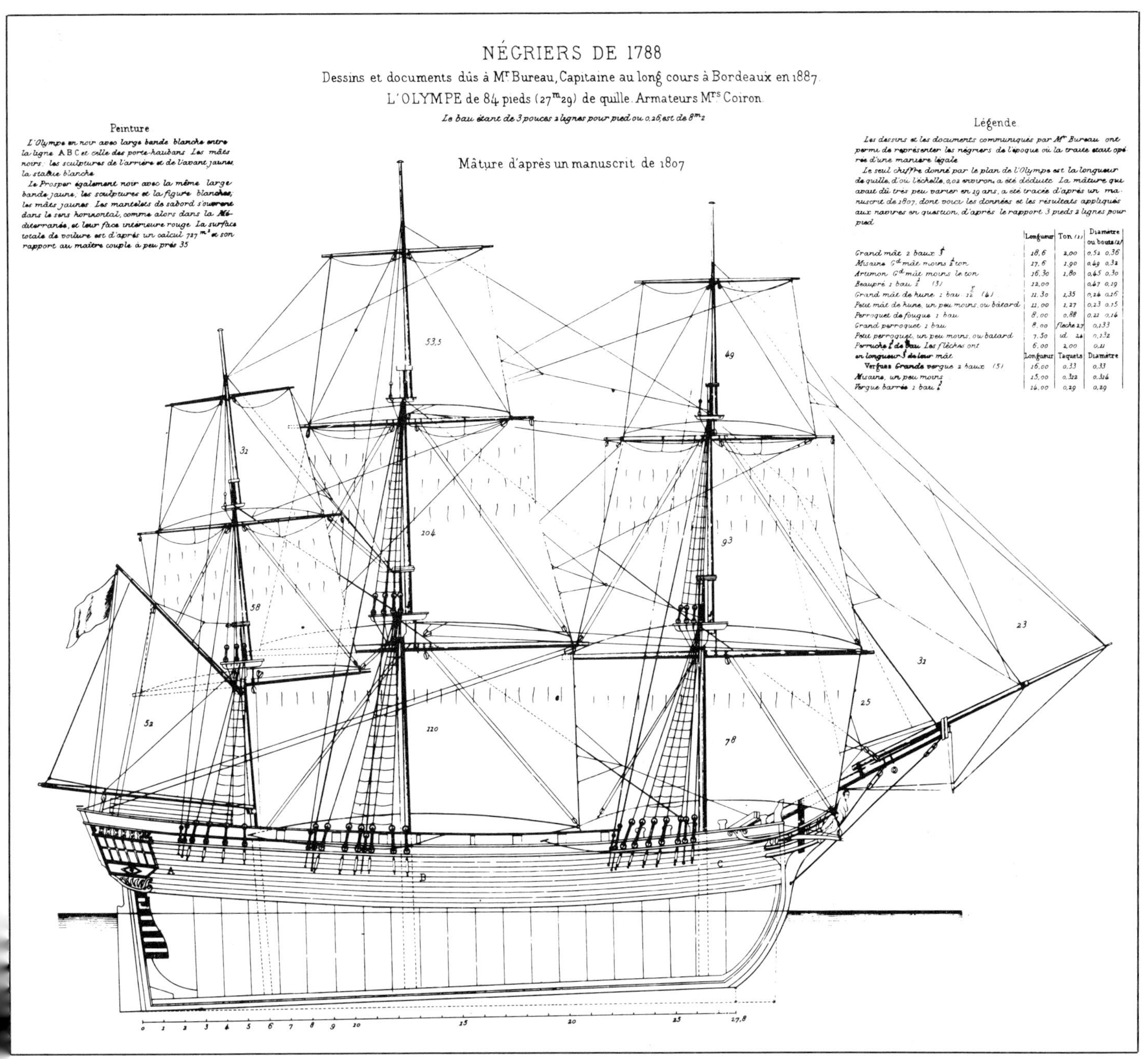

Fig 68. Joly. *Lines plan. Three-masted slaver built in 1776 at La Rochelle. Photograph of an original from the Guibert Collection of plans at the Mariners' Museum, Newport News, Virginia.* (MacGregor Collection)

Fig 69. Sail plan of L'Olympe, *a French slaver built in 1788. The plan is reproduced from* Souvenirs de Marine *by Admiral Pâris, figure 212, but doubts on the authenticity of the rigging are discussed in the text.*

The *Hall*'s lines plan reproduced in figure 67 is a copy of that in plate I of Hutchinson's book. We should describe her as a ship with a full entrance and run, with rounded floors and bilges, but without much tumblehome. The rockered keel is not drawn on the lines plan but does appear in a sheer elevation on plate XII, which also depicts the fitting of a jury rudder. No centres are given for the arcs of circles to construct either the sections in the body plan or the entrance and stem profile. Hutchinson added several novel features, such as a rockered keel fore and aft, which rose at the rate of 2in in every 30ft; also a spar deck built over the waist to avoid shipping water and give her a flush deck.[63]

In the frontispiece of his book and in plate I, he portrays the *Hall* under full sail, close-hauled and running free, and his descriptions of these plates appear earlier in the chapter under the section 'Masts, Sails and Rigging in Three-masted Vessels'. His plates are reproduced here in figures 51 and 67.

In the Guibert Collection of plans in the Mariner's Museum at Newport News are the plans of the three-masted slaver *Joly* of La Rochelle, built in 1776, and of a brig designed for Mr Vincent and dated 1773. Both have concave floors which quickly round up to give excessive deadrise; the brig has no tumblehome, but the *Joly* has some. The latter has a shoulder worked into the fore body just above the load line. Her plan is reproduced in figure 68, and her fine entrance and long fine run can be clearly seen, but the brig has fuller lines. In each case there are small hinged ports in the 'tween decks to give some slight ventilation to the slave deck: in the brig there are but four each side; in the *Joly* there are eleven.

Although no spar dimensions of the *Joly* are listed on the lines plan, there is a reconstructed sail plan of the French slaver *L'Olympe* of 1788 which is reproduced in *Souvenirs de Marine* and is given here in figure 69. Accompanying text on the plan states that the spars and rigging were traced from a manuscript dated 1807 and that there would have been little change during the nineteen years since she was built. Nevertheless, the presence of a dolphin striker would have been unusual in 1788, although not impossible. It is also surprising to note the very deep topgallants; it would have

Fig 71. HMS Buffalo. *Lines plan, traced from the Admiralty draught in the National Maritime Museum, Greenwich, but diagonals and buttock lines have been omitted. Dimensions on the plan: 109ft 2in (length on lower deck), 31ft 0in (extreme breadth), 13ft 2½in (depth in [lower] hold), 462⅔ tons. No spar dimensions are listed. (Further details of career and measurements are given in the text.)*

Fig 70. Sail plan of a Danish West Indiaman constructed by Henrik Gerner in 1778. He was the chief shipbuilder for the Danish Navy. The plan shows the square sails are set on the starboard side, but the yards are lowered on the port side, which brings the lower yards almost down to the bulwarks. No staysails are drawn and the only fore-and-aft sail is set on the mizen yard. (Maritime Museum, Kronborg)

70

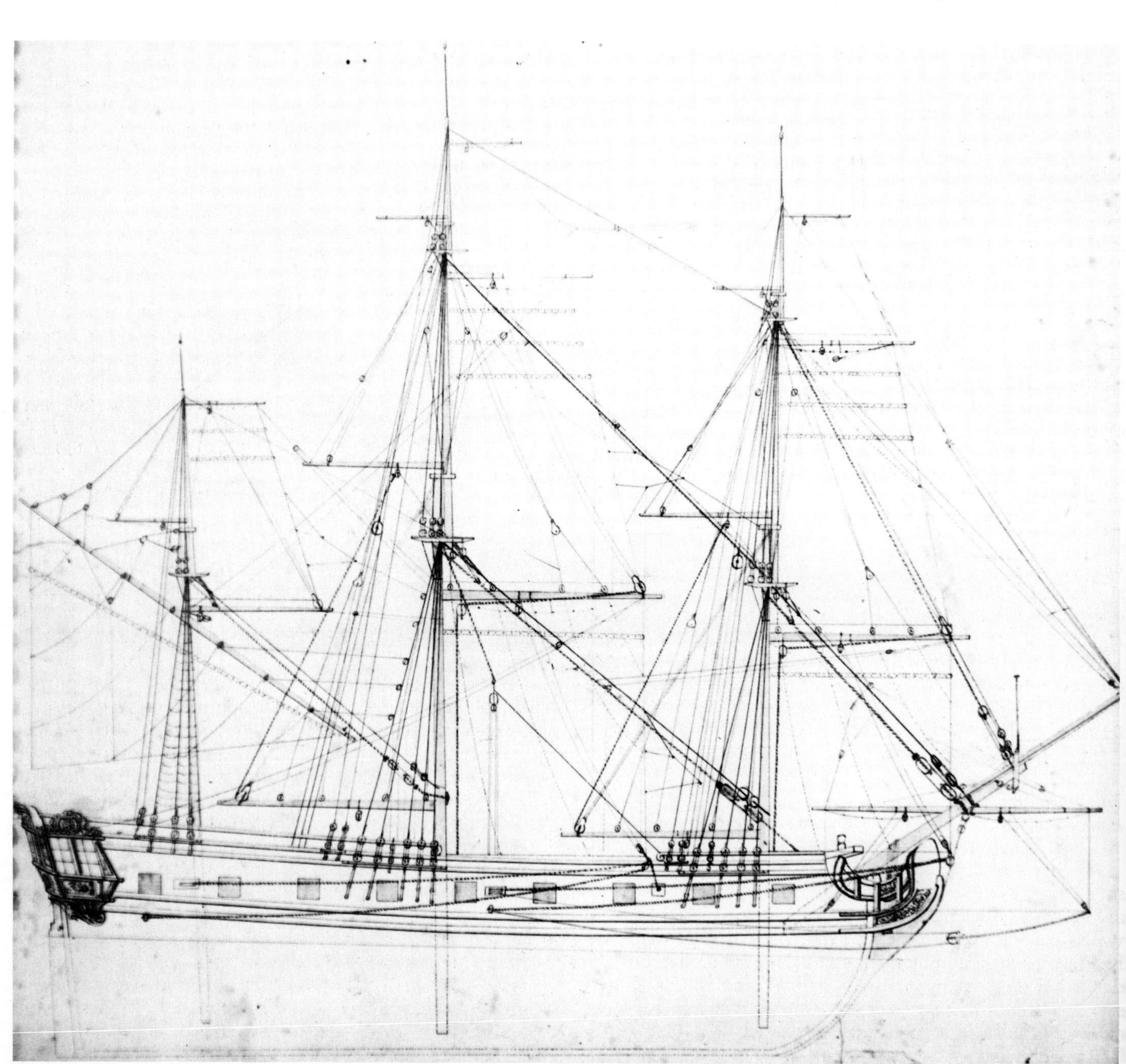

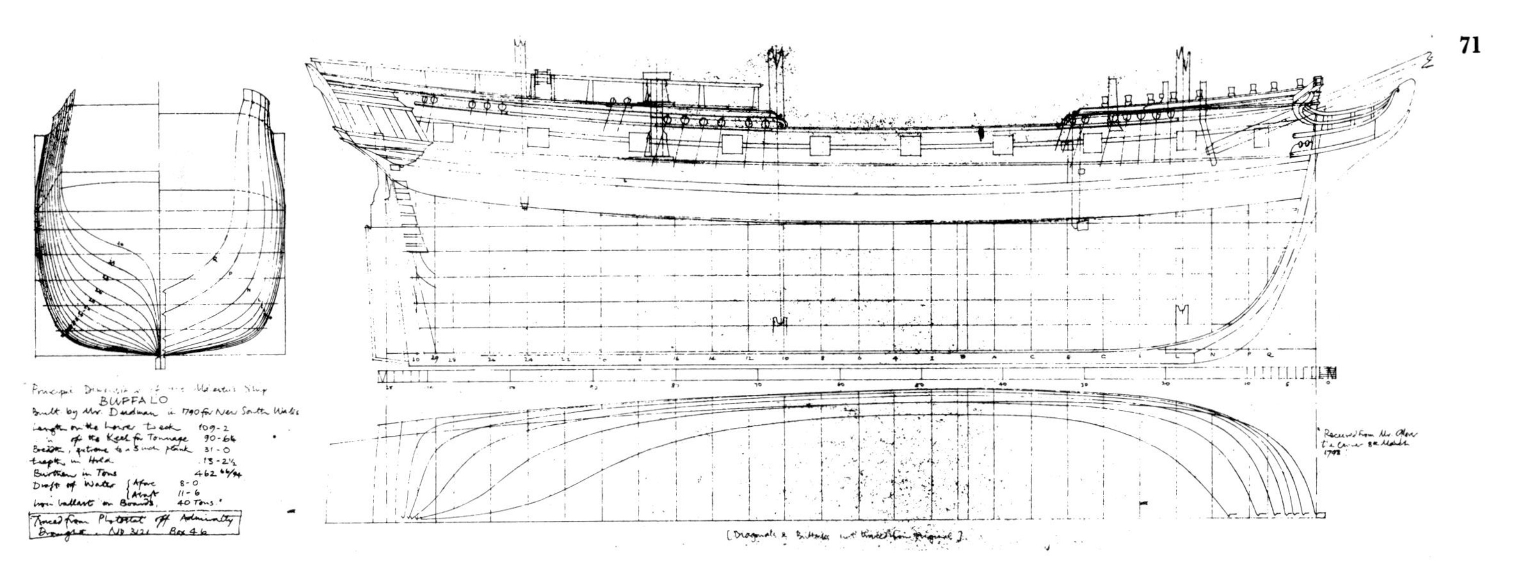

71

been normal to have shallower sails and lowered the corresponding position of the topgallant stays and rigging on the mast, thereby giving adequate space to set royals flying, although the American ships *Codrington* and *London* were so rigged (as described later). Other points worthy of attention are the absence of staysails on the main and mizen stays; the mizen spanker gaff and boom rather than a short mizen gaff; and the manner of setting up the stays. The latter two points in particular suggest that when Captain Bureau sent this plan to Admiral Pâris in 1887 he tended to reconstruct it according to mid-nineteenth century rigging principles.

The sail plan of a Danish West Indiaman designed by Henrik Gerner in 1778 (figure 70), exhibits more of the eighteenth century rigging techniques. The presence of the mizen yard is of interest, as is the manner of taking the lead of the fore and main lower yard lifts to the hounds of the topmast. There are remarkably few lower shrouds, there being only four on the foremast, five on the main and three on the mizen.

For examples of large ships other than East Indiaman one can find plans amongst the Admiralty draughts of vessels hired or bought by the Royal Navy for use as storeships.[64] Many ships were taken up for this purpose during the War of American Independence, such as the *Britannia* of 536 tons which had a length on the lower deck of 114ft 1in and a beam of 32ft 8in, and whose lines were taken off at Deptford in 1781. Here is a list of some typical ships:

Britannia	536 tons	40 men	20 guns	hired 1781; fitted out for £4065
Prosperity	687 tons		3 decks	hired 1782
Clinton	687 tons		32 guns	captured 1780–81 from French
Bountiful	777 tons		3 decks	hired 1782

Of these, *Britannia* has fine lines, but the *Clinton* is even sharper and could have been a privateer. Most store ships are fairly full-bodied with little deadrise, and many have wall sides without much tumblehome. Nearly all have a head, and at the stern there are quarter galleries. The three-decked ships usually have the upper deck flush with the side, without a bulwark except on the quarter-deck. In one case, the bulwarks were carried as far forward as the foremast but were then stopped short to allow the anchors to be worked. The catheads were often long and were taken some distance inboard. The spar dimensions have been recorded on the majority of plans.

Instances of other big ships are met with, such as the three-decked ship *Henrietta* built on the Thames in 1779 of 769 tons with a draft of 20ft.

Dudman & Co had a yard at Deptford with two double docks and five building slips. An Admiralty draught of a ship produced by this yard is entitled *Buffalo* 'built by Mr Dudman in 1790 for New South Wales'. Charnock lists her as a storeship bought into the Navy in 1797; his dimensions agree with those on the draught.[65] Colledge lists her as *Buffalo ex Freemantle* purchased on the stocks for a storeship and built by Dudman in March 1797.[66] Written on the Admiralty draught at the forward end of the half-breadth plan are the words: 'Received from Mr Glover the owner 8th March 1798'. From this conflicting evidence, it may be that she was built as the *Freemantle* in 1790 for Mr Glover, traded to New South Wales and was subsequently bought into the Navy in 1797 for use as a storeship, when she was renamed *Buffalo*. She appears to have been hulked in 1814 and was sold out of the service three years later.

The lines plane in figure 71 shows her to be similar in design to a small East Indiaman, rather like the *Coromandel*, which was built on the Thames thirty years later. The *Buffalo* ex *Freemantle* had a full entrance and run, rounded floors, slack bilges and some tumblehome. She had two decks with a poop and forecastle. No windlass is drawn on the plan but there is a capstan on the poop. Dimensions on the plan are as follows: 109ft 2in length on lower deck, 90ft 6¼in keel for tonnage, 31ft 0in 'breadth extreme to a 3in plank', 13ft 2½in depth in lower hold, 462 66/94 tons burthen; draft of water, 8ft 0in 'afore' and 11ft 8in 'abaft'; 40 tons iron ballast on board. Height between decks scales about 7ft, thus making the total depth in hold about 20ft. There are no spar dimensions on the plan.

The story of the Blackwall Yard is recounted in Chapter 4 but it was by no means only warships and East Indiamen that were launched here, because seven ships for the West Indies trade were built in the years 1785–89, three of them of 371 tons each. Three more West Indiamen were built in the 1790s as well as two South Sea whalers – the *Constance* of 284 tons in 1792 at £9 per ton and the *Walker* of 341 tons in 1799 at £11 per ton. A collier named *Crowley* and a sloop of

72

Fig 72. The whaler Bedford *homeward bound. The most likely ship of this name was built at King's Lynn in 1750 of 255 tons, being lengthened in 1758.* Lloyd's Register, *however, always lists her as a snow or brig, except between 1796–1801 when she is described as a 'ship'. The hull is that of a cat, and in the quarter view, she even has stunsails set on the mizen topsail.* (King's Lynn Central Library)

Fig 73. Isabella. *Lines plan. The* Isabella *was built at Hull in 1786 of 374 tons. The plan is reproduced from* Mercantile Marine Architecture *by Thomas Richardson (1833) plate V. Dimensions scaled off the plan: 107ft 6in (register length along deck), 29ft 0in (maximum breadth), 18ft 0in (depth of hold approx).* See *the text for further comments on the plan.*

73

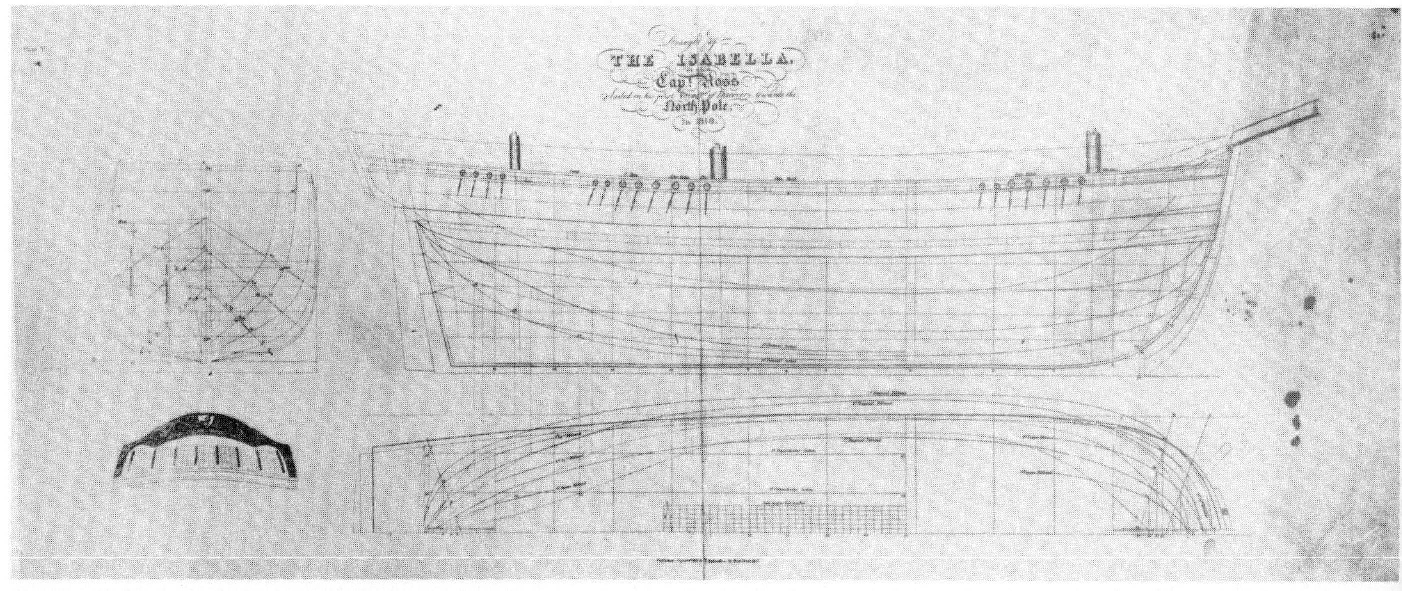

74

87 tons were also built in the years 1775-1793. In Chapter 3, the first section suggests that one of the West Indiamen, the *Three Sisters* of 1788, could be represented in a published plan. A complete list of ships built in the yard is given in Appendix 1 together with their costs.[67]

Whalers were small ships varying between 200 and 300 tons, and they were not usually of any special design, although they had to be strongly built and would be further strengthened and sheathed for protection against the ice. Lines of the whaler *Isabella* which was built at Hull in 1786 of 374 tons, were published by Richardson. His plan in figure 73 shows her to have a very similar hull-form to Hilhouse's *Exeter* (figure 65) both in the shape of the entrance and run and the lack of a head, although the *Isabella* had slightly more deadrise and less tumblehome. Dimensions scaled off the plan give a register length along the deck of 107ft 6in, maximum breadth 29ft 0in, and depth of hold 18ft 0in (approx).[68] On the plan the buttock lines are termed 'perpendicular sections'; the diagonals, termed 'ribbands', are drawn with a sold line, and the waterlines with a dotted line. The names of some deck fittings are written along the top edge of the sheer strake, and the height of the bulwarks on the sheer elevation is given by a dotted line.

Fig 74. The incredibly bluff bows of a 'Danish Greenlandman' which F L T Francia drew while she was being broken-up below Gravesend. W B Cooke, the engraver, published it in 1814. He was E W Cooke's father. There seems a look of hopelessness about the figure at the stem, as if the massive quality of the wooden hull had defeated him. (MacGregor Collection)

Although the *Isabella* has the ordinary English type of stern, many of the Dutch whalers were flutes or *bootschips*, with an outside rudder and a wide, elaborate square stern above, large tumblehome and a plain bow. These were the successors to the flutes of the seventeenth and early eighteenth centuries with their exaggerated tumblehome and narrower, higher sterns. The Dutch ships had a heavy spar passing right across the deck of the poop, close to the taffrail and projecting some distance each side, from which were slung tackles to hoist up one end of a whale boat. The other end of the boat was hoisted by a tackle slung between the main and mizen masts; the ship's side was protected from rubbing by stout vertical wooden fenders. A whaler from Hamburg, such as the *Johanna Magdalena*, had the hull of a *bootschip*, according to a drawing done in 1803; the Danish whaler beyond her has a modified round stern with a square counter.[69]

For the study of ships built in North America, the collection of Admiralty draughts at the National Maritime Museum presents an unrivalled source. American-built

75

Fig 75. The New Amelia *getting underway off Dover in 1777, probably when she first came under British ownership in London. She had been built in 1767 in Maryland with a tonnage of 270 and drew 15ft; her armament consisted of 8 4-pounder and 6 3-pounder guns, and she was employed in the West Indies trade. In the right-hand view, the driver hoisted to the peak of the mizen gaff is like a topmast stunsail; royals have been set on the long pole heads of the fore and main topgallant masts; and the mizen topsail yard has been lowered and the mainsail clewed up to avoid blanketing the other sails. The artist is Thomas Luny and this picture is similar in style to that in figure 59.* (Richard Green Gallery)

ships were purchased for use by the Royal Navy or were captured during the War of American Independence and taken into the Navy, and many had their lines taken off and plans produced. On the majority of plans, the spar dimensions are tabulated, which enables apt comparisons to be made or reconstructed sail plans drawn.

In 1774, the Admiralty purchased the *Codrington* for survey work in America and renamed her *Cherokee*. She had been built at Newbury, Massachusetts, in 1773, and measurements on her plan give a length on the lower deck of 75ft 3in and breadth extreme of 23ft 7in; the depth scaled off the plan gives 17ft 0in from underside of deck at side to rabbet of keel. Howard I Chapelle has redrawn the lines plan and reconstructed the sail plan in his book *The Search for Speed under Sail*.[70]

He describes her as a '"full-built" American merchant vessel' but, compared with some of the English ships examined in this chapter, she has moderately fine lines. She is certainly deep for her length, with rounded floors and sides, but not full in the ends, and the run is reasonably fine. The bulwarks are very low and there is an open rail from the stern for the full length of the raised quarter-deck which terminates just forward of the mainmast; the break is only 1ft 1in high.

She has a large sail plan for her size, including a fidded topgallant on the mizen. The most prominent feature of her rig is the great depth of the topgallant sails but this was not unique as it was repeated in the *Grasshopper* ex *London* whose sail plan has been reconstructed by M A Edson Jnr in Chapelle's book.[71] The spar dimensions listed on the original plan refer to the 'long pole head gallant' on fore and main masts,[72] but the actual length of the pole head is not stated, and has had to be calculated. It was intended that both these ships should be fast sailers, as well as good cargo carriers,like most American ships of this date, and therefore they were over-sparred. *Cherokee* ex *Codrington* carried two spritsails, the *Grasshopper* but one. The four-sided staysails between the masts on the latter are probably more typical of eighteenth century ships than the three-sided sails on the *Cherokee*.

The *Grasshopper* had been built in New York in 1770 as the *London* and was owned there, but must have been re-registered in England as she had been hired as a transport for a year when she was surveyed and purchased for use as an armed ship in the Royal Navy. It was then that she was renamed. Her lines were taken off at Deptford in May 1777 and a lines plan prepared. Howard Chapelle redrew this to show what the ship looked like when purchased.[73]

The *Grasshopper* has sharper ends than the *Cherokee*, with hollows in the waterlines by the stem and a hollow run; the floors and sides are again very rounded; the sternpost has a

76

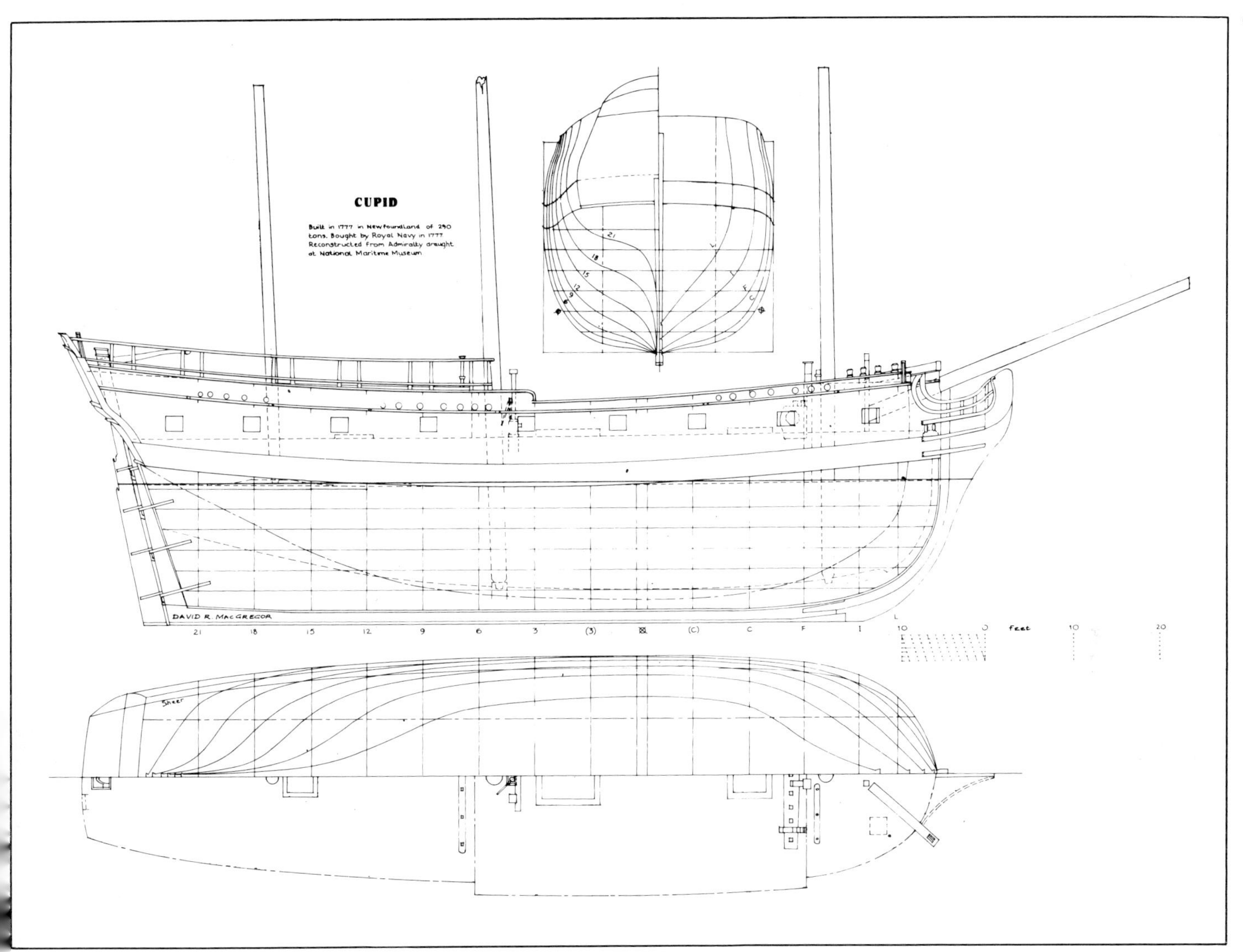

Fig 76. Cupid. *Lines plan. The* Cupid *was built in Newfoundland 1777 and bought by the Royal Navy in the same year. The plan has been redrawn from Admiralty draughts at the National Maritime Museum, Greenwich. Reconstruction: elevation of stern; omission of alterations proposed by Royal Navy; addition of deck fittings from a second plan. Dimensions on plan: 92ft 1in (length on lower deck), 74ft 9¾in (keel for tonnage), 27ft 0in (extreme breadth), 12ft 2in (depth in hold) and 290 tons. Note that the mizen mast steps on the lower deck. Chain plates are drawn on the sail plan.*

big rake; and there are quarter galleries. The ship is not so deep in proportion to her length, the measurements on the Admiralty plan giving 92ft 6in length on the lower deck, 26ft 9in breadth extreme, 10ft 10in depth in hold, and 282 tons. She was said to have been a good sailer and was constructed of oak and cedar. As in *Cherokee*, the fore deck rounds down in the eyes of the ship to give easy access to the hawse pipes. The sail plan has already been discussed.

Another example of a North American ship of this date is the *Cupid*, which was built in Newfoundland in 1777, placed in the Leghorn trade by a London owner, purchased in the same year by the Admiralty for use as an armed ship, and fitted out at Deptford at a cost of £2970 8s 6d. She foundered the following year. Her plan dated August 1777 gives dimensions of 92ft 1in length on lower deck, 27ft 0in breadth extreme, 12ft 2in depth in hold, and 290 tons. The lines plan is redrawn in figure 76 and the deck plan is added, but the alterations made in Deptford Dockyard have been omitted.

Compared with those of the *Grasshopper*, the measurements of length and breadth are almost identical, but she is 1ft 4in deeper in the hold. This appearance of greater depth is accentuated by the high solid bulwarks in the waist, which are 4ft high at their lowest point. There is a good sheer at the rail, but the two decks are almost straight with practically no sheer whatsoever, which was unusual by this date. The height in the 'tween decks is 5ft at the stern and 5ft 6in in the bows. There is a short forecastle up to the foremast, and the poop extends to the mainmast; nine gunports are pierced in her side; there is no decoration at bow or stern; there is a windlass on the main deck; and she has tiller steering. In hull-form, she has a short, sharp entrance, and a longer, more hollow run; the quarter beam buttock is straight where it crosses the load line; the floors are slightly concave, but the bilges and side round up to give a deep mid-section. Above lower deck level, her stem rabbet is plumb vertical. *Lloyd's Register* of 1778 gives her armament as four 9-pounders, four 6-pounders and ten 4-pounders.

One point of interest is that her mizen mast is stepped on

the lower deck, not on the keelson. Her lower masts and topmasts are as long as or longer than those of *Grasshopper*, but her topgallant masts are much shorter, and no long pole heads are indicated, which has been taken as meaning that there was just a short head above the topgallant rigging. *Grasshopper*'s yards, mizen gaff, bowsprit and jibboom are all from 1ft to 2ft longer than those of the *Cupid*. Here is a comparison of their mast lengths, together with those of Steel's ship:

	***Cupid* 290 tons** (fig 77)	***Grasshopper* 282 tons**	**Steel's ship of 330 tons** (fig 126)
Main lower mast	65ft 6in	65ft 2in	66ft 0in
Main topmast	38ft 8in	36ft 9in	38ft 0in
Main topgallant mast	25ft 0in	37ft 0in	32ft 0in[b]
Fore lower mast	58ft 6in	57ft 5in	61ft 0in
Fore topmast	38ft 2in	33ft 10in	37ft 0in
Fore topgallant mast	23ft 3in	33ft 5in	30ft 0in[b]
Mizen lower mast	44ft 11in[a]	56ft 0in	58ft 0in
Mizen topmast	30ft 0in	25ft 10in	28ft 0in
Mizen topmast pole	–	11ft 0in	–
Mizen topgallant mast	–	–	15ft 0in

a mast steps on lower deck and is therefore shorter b length of topgallant mast includes royal mast

The spar dimensions from the Admiralty draught have been utilized to reconstruct the sail plan in figure 77, from which it will be noticed that the *Cupid* is much squarer aloft than Steel's ship and confirms the large sail areas commonly given to ships built in North America. The staysails are typical of ships at this date. There is a dearth of books on rigging prior to the 1790s, which adds to the problems of reconstruction work; but unrestored paintings and models provide vital evidence.

The fine-lined and sharp-built privateers and blockade runners of the American War of Independence form an interesting comparison with the somewhat fuller lined American-built merchantmen which we have examined above. The latter class were of markedly sharper form than the West Indiamen being built in Europe. The relationship occurred again during the Naval War of 1812. Ships of the 1775–83 period were the precursors of the clippers and medium clippers of seventy-five years later.

Fig 77. Cupid. *Sail plan, entirely reconstructed from the sheer elevation on the lines plan and from spar dimensions on an Admiralty draught dated 27 August 1777. Rigging, sails and spar details are from contemporary text books and paintings.*

77

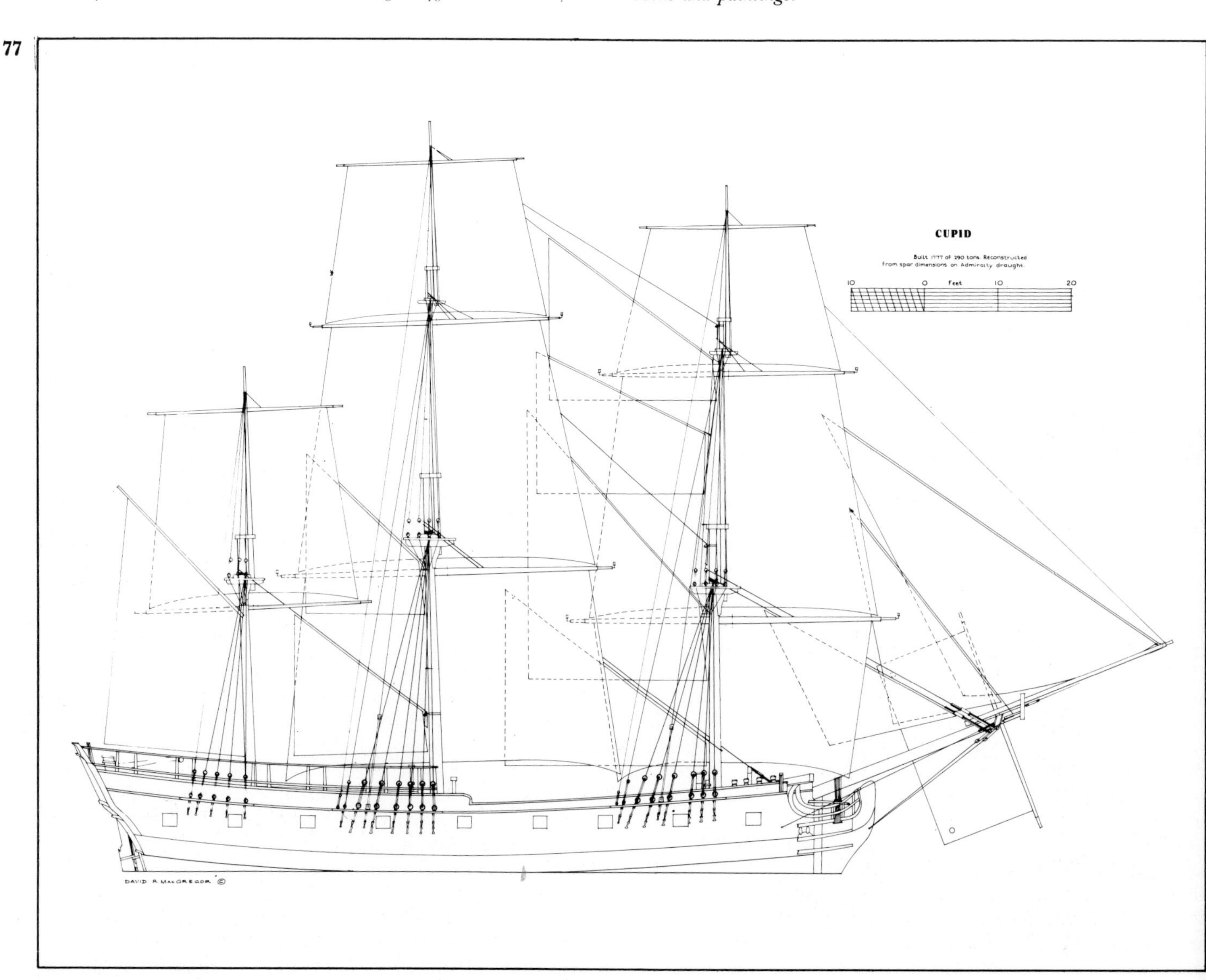

79

Fig 79. Pierre Ozanne's engraving of a brig or brigantine close-hauled. Published in 1762, it portrays a fairly small craft that carried nothing above topsails, and had a short bowsprit with no jibboom and no spritsail yard.

Fig 78. Falconer's representation in 1769, and again in 1780, of 'a brig or brigantine', from plate XII No 6 in his Marine Dictionary.

78

TWO-MASTED SQUARE-RIGGED VESSELS

Some idea of the number of rigs in the eighteenth century which were recognized by *Lloyd's Register* can be obtained from the abbreviations in the edition of 1781, which are here listed alphabetically: 'Billander', brig, cryer, cutter, dogger, galliot, hoy, ketch, 'maphrodite', pink, polacre, schooner, ship, skoot, sloop, smack, snow. These continued until 1789, and six names were removed but none added in the 1790 Register. Those axed were: 'billander', cryer, ketch (re-inserted in 1793), 'maphrodite', pink, skoot. This is fairly good evidence that wuch rigs were by then rare, but no count has been attempted to determine the frequency with which they had appeared in earlier issues.

By the end of the first quarter of the eighteenth century, the brigantine was established as a two-masted vessel carrying a square-rigged foremast and a schooner's mainmast, with or without a small square topsail. Falconer's engraving of 1769 shows in figure 78 what a brigantine of half-a-century earlier may have resembled. Simultaneously the snow was fully square-rigged on both masts, with the addition of a boomless gaff trysail which hoisted on its own trysail mast. This mast was stepped on the deck and terminated at the after end of the main top, and the sail was hooped to this mast. Snows were commonly the largest type of two-masted rig. A third variation was the bilander, with a fully square-rigged foremast and carrying a

80

Fig 80. Chapman's sail plan of a 'snow' from plate LXII No 2 in Architectura Navalis Mercatoria. *This is the rig which is still implied by the term today, with the trysail mast, boomless gaff sail and square mainsail.*

Nº 2

82

Fig 81. Chapman's sail plan of a 'brigg' from plate LXII No 4 in his book has less square canvas on the main than on the fore; the absence of a square mainsail and its replacement by a fore-and-aft mainsail set on a boom was the correct distinction between it and the snow.

81

Fig 82. A small brig running before a following wind; the fore topmast staysail has no wind in it. The spare spars are laid on top of the gallows with a ship's boat beneath. G Groenwegen published this engraving in 1789 as plate C1 in Verzameling van Vier tachtig Stuks Hollandsche Schepen.

square topsail on the main as large as the fore topsail but often no topgallant. Instead of a gaff mainsail she set a sort of lug sail, in which the yard extended some way forward of the mast.

By the middle of the century the word 'brigantine' was becoming abbreviated to 'brig' so that by 1769, when Falconer's dictionary was first published, the entry appeared as '*Brig* or brigantine'. A more accurate drawing of a brig than that offered by Falconer appeared the year before in Chapman's *Architectura Navalis Mercatoria.* This drawing depicts quite a different type and one which was beginning to approach the style of the snow. In Chapman's brig there is no square mainsail and the gaff mainsail is set on a boom, the luff being hooped to the mast. The main lower mast is apprcciably longer than the fore and there are topgallants on each mast. The main topsail is still not as deep as the fore topsail and has only two rows of reef points instead of three on the fore. The rig of the snow, however, has remained unchanged.[74]

A practical example of differences in spar dimensions between a snow and a brig in 1777 can be had in the *Duchess of Manchester*, which in that year had her lines taken off at Deptford. Her design is described later in this section. The plan states that she was bought by the Admiralty as a snow and lists the spar dimensions 'as bought with her', but dimensions in an adjoining table are listed as 'proposed if made a Brig'.[75] The two sets of dimensions have been drawn out in figures 82 and 83, and the chief differences between the two are summarized here.

In the 'Brig' measurements, the main lower mast was 8ft longer, but the main topmast and topgallant masts were 5ft and 2$\frac{1}{2}$ft shorter; the fore lower mast was 4ft longer, but the other parts about the same; the bowsprit was shortened 5$\frac{1}{2}$ft, but the jibboom was unchanged. As to the yards, those on the foremast were a foot or two different; but on the main, the lower yard was now called a 'spread yard' and

SPAR DIMENSIONS LISTED ON PLAN OF *DUCHESS OF MANCHESTER*[76]

	As bought with her				Proposed if made a Brig			
	Masts		Yards		Masts		Yards	
Main lower mast	53ft 6in	15$\frac{5}{8}$in	38ft 9in	9$\frac{3}{4}$in	61ft 4in	16in		
Main topmast	31ft 0in	9$\frac{3}{4}$in	28ft 10in	7in	25ft 10in	9$\frac{1}{2}$in	26ft 5in	7in
Main topgallant mast	15ft 6in	5$\frac{1}{2}$in	18ft 9in	3$\frac{3}{4}$in	12ft 11in	5$\frac{1}{4}$in	13ft 3in	3$\frac{3}{4}$in
Fore lower mast	47ft 6in	15$\frac{1}{4}$in	34ft 3in	9$\frac{1}{2}$in	57ft 8in	13$\frac{3}{4}$in	33ft 7in	9$\frac{1}{2}$in
Fore topmast	29ft 0in	9$\frac{3}{4}$in	27ft 6in	6$\frac{1}{2}$in	30ft 8in	9$\frac{7}{8}$in	29ft 5in	7in
Fore topgallant mast	14ft 6in	5in	16ft 0in	3$\frac{1}{2}$in	15ft 4in	5$\frac{1}{4}$in	16ft 10in	3$\frac{3}{4}$in
Bowsprit	33ft 10in	15$\frac{1}{4}$in	27ft 6in	6$\frac{1}{2}$in	28ft 8in	15$\frac{1}{4}$in	29ft 5in	7in
Trysail boom	35ft 8in	8in						
Gaff	20ft 0in	6in			20ft 0in	6in		
Jibboom	22ft 6in	6in			22ft 6in	6in		
Main boom					38ft 4in	9in		
Spread yard							33ft 7in	9$\frac{1}{2}$in

First dimension is length; second dimension is diameter

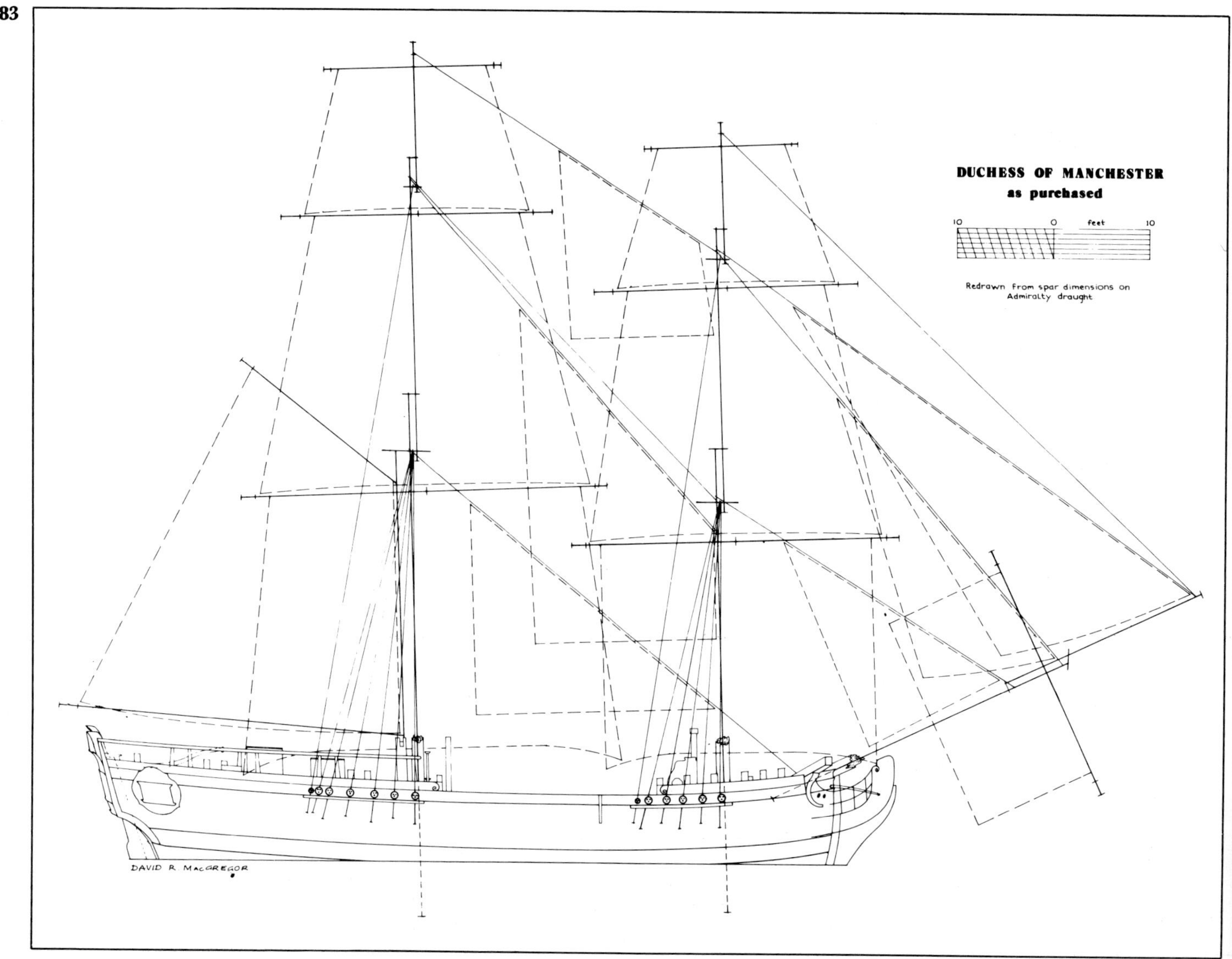
DUCHESS OF MANCHESTER
as purchased
10
0
feet
10
Redrawn from spar dimensions on
Admiralty draught
DAVID R. MacGREGOR

84

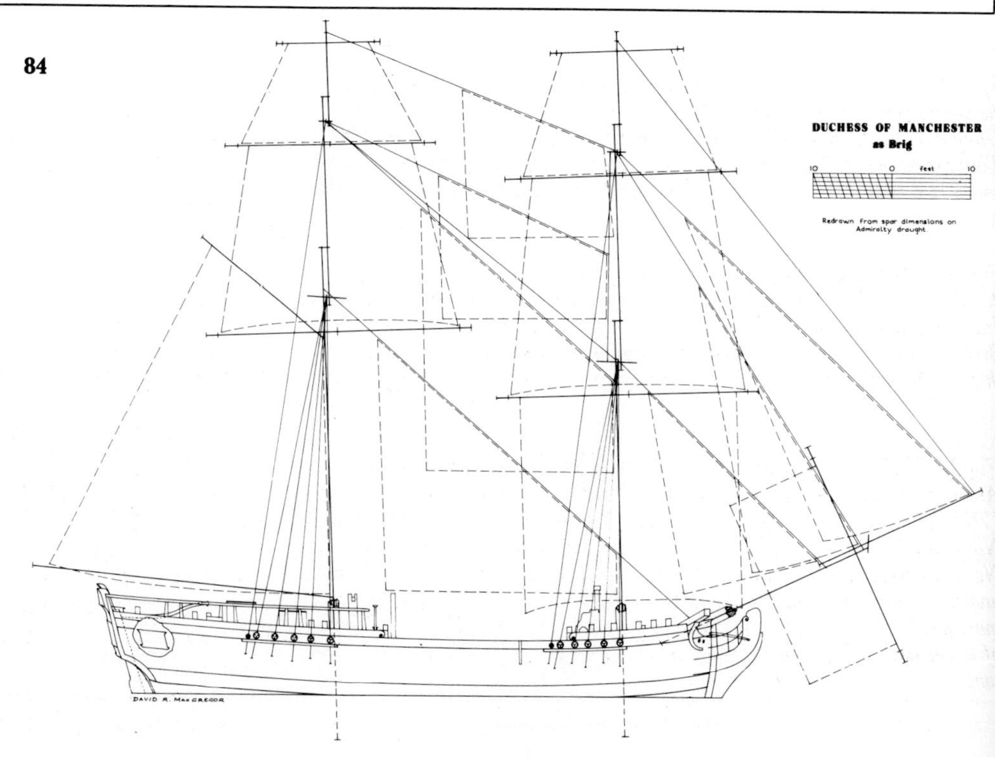
DUCHESS OF MANCHESTER
as Brig
10
0
feet
10
Redrawn from spar dimensions on
Admiralty draught
DAVID R. MacGREGOR

85

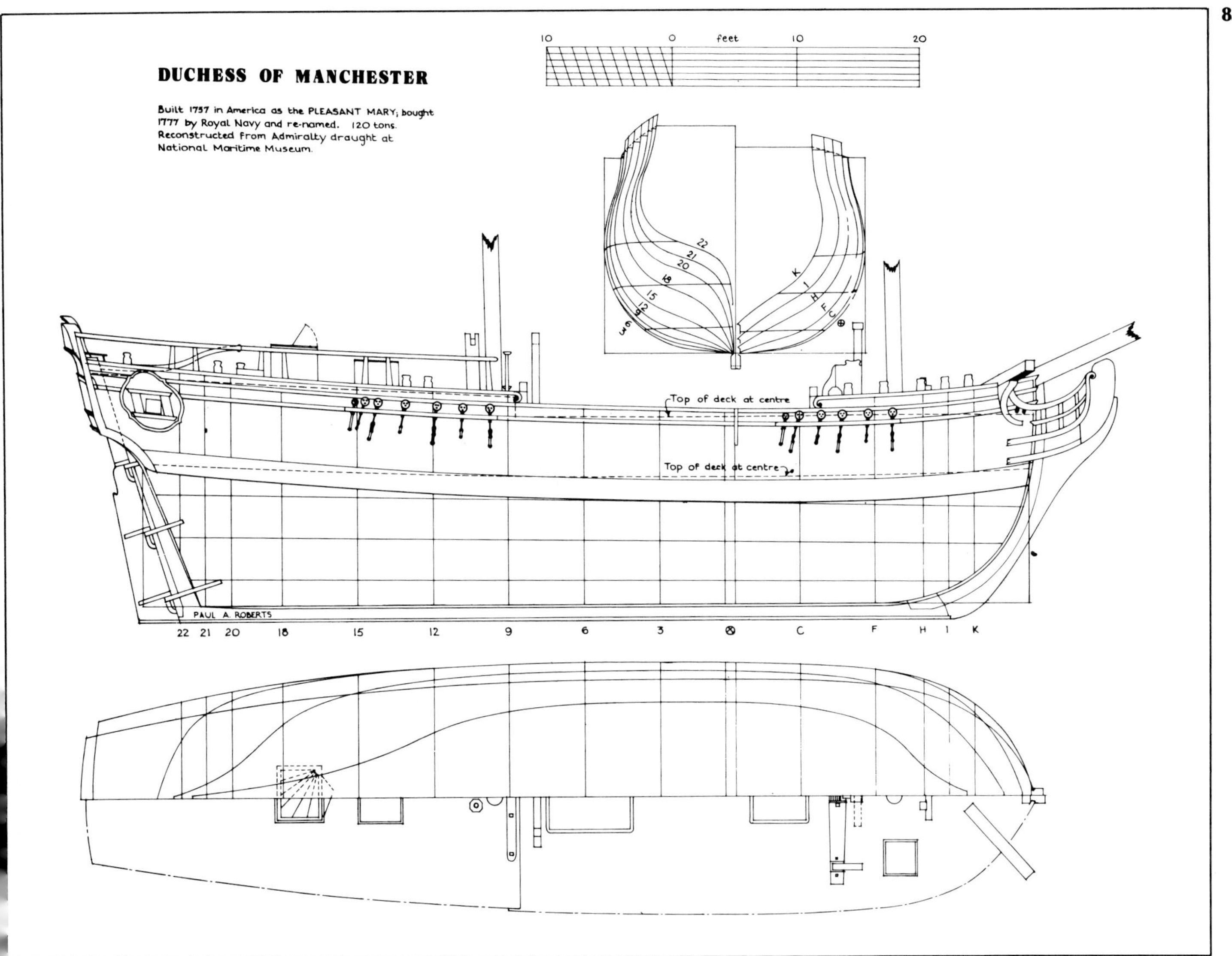

Fig 83. Duchess of Manchester. *Sail plan, entirely reconstructed from the sheer elevation, and from the table of spar dimensions on an Admiralty draught dated 21 May 1777, from a column headed 'As Bought with Her'. This gives the rig of a snow with a main boom. Spars have been drawn to the centre line only, but standing rigging has been added.*

Fig 84. Duchess of Manchester. *Sail plan, entirely reconstructed from the sheer elevation and from the table of spar dimensions on an Admiralty draught dated 21 May 1777, from the column headed 'Proposed if Made a Brig'. This brig is similar to that in figure 81. The mainmast has been shifted 4ft further aft. A main middle staysail has been drawn on this plan.*

Fig 85. Duchess of Manchester. *Lines plan. She was probably built in America in 1757 as the snow* Pleasant Mary *of 120 tons and re-built in 1767. Her name changed in 1776, and she was purchased by the Royal Navy in 1777. The plan has been redrawn from Admiralty draughts at the National Maritime Museum, Greenwich. Reconstruction: deck layout from another draught combined with lines plan; deck beams, keelson etc omitted; mast positions show her as bought. Dimensions on the plan: 71ft 0in (length of lower deck), 21ft 6in (extreme breadth), 8ft $3\frac{1}{2}$in (depth in hold), 137 tons.*

was 5ft shorter, and the topsail and topgallant yards were $2\frac{1}{2}$ft and 5ft shorter respectively. The gaff was unchanged, but the 'trysail boom' on the snow had become the 'main boom' on the brig and was 3ft longer.

From a comparison of the spar dimensions it is evident that the rigs of snow and brig were still substantially different here, and furthermore that the one termed 'brig' was really a brigantine. The differences were undoubtedly becoming less as the century drew to a close until, soon after 1800, the only difference between a snow and a brig was the presence or absence of a trysail mast and a square mainsail. At the same time, a noticeable difference between brig and brigantine began to emerge.

The only vessel with the name *Duchess of Manchester* to be listed in *Lloyd's Register* for 1776 – the name was spelled '*Dutchess of Manchester*' – was an American-built snow which was owned by Joseph Casey, her master. She was of 120 tons, had a draft of 12ft, and changed her name from *Pleasant Mary* in the same year. She had been built in 1757 and re-built ten years later. If this is really the same as the vessel whose lines appear in figure 85, then it provides a rare opportunity to study an American snow.

The *Duchess of Manchester* was surveyed in 1777 and

86

Fig 87. Chapman's sail plan of a bilander appeared on plate LXII figure 5 of his large work.

87

Fig 86. The American-built brig Beckford *was of 140 tons and drew 11ft, but* Lloyd's Register *has the date and place of building as 'New England' in 1774. The main middle staysail is drawn rather low down and overlaps the main topmast staysail; the sail on the ensign staff is a feature; judging by the size of the crew, the royals were very small sails. The painting is signed and dated 'Egidio Filati in Ancona 1784', and is an early example of a ship portrait of such a small vessel.* (Paul Mason Gallery)

Fig 88. Although I used Lescallier's own engraving in the previous edition of my book, the one reproduced here comes from David Steel's Masting and Rigging *(1794 vol I) from a plate between pages 220 and 221. It is the opposite hand to Lescallier's, because of the re-engraving process, but appears to be basically similar. The tack of the fore course is taken to the bumpkin and no headsails are set.*

88

purchased by the Royal Navy for surveying the coast of Great Britain. The measurements on her plan (Admiralty draught 6671) give 71ft 0in length on lower deck, 21ft 6in extreme breadth, 8ft 3½in depth in hold, and 137 tons. The hull-form is full at the load line but below this there is a short sharp entrance and a longer hollow run; the floors have little deadrise, but the bilges round up to the maximum beam with a single sweep, and there is marked tumblehome. The mid-section is much more in the style of a man-of-war, or like the merchantmen whose offsets are given by Mungo Murray in 1754 and which William Salisbury plotted and drew out in the *Mariner's Mirror.*[77] It is interesting that this form of hull persisted in merchant ship design at this date, whereas the mid-section was increasingly being formed by several arcs of circles, rather than by a single sweep.

There is very little sheer to the *Duchess of Manchester*, which has a windlass, a raised quarter-deck abaft the mainmast, tiller steering, and a laid lower deck. The dotted line of the mainmast indicates the new position 4ft further aft, if the proposal to re-rig her as a brigantine was adopted. Abaft the existing mainmast are the pumps, and before it, first the railing at the break of the raised quarter-deck, and then the main topsail sheet bitts extended upwards to form a gallows. There is a similar gallows above the windlass. Although one is not shown on the plan, it was common practice to fit a rough-tree rail at each side of the waist, supported on iron standards. The plan of the transport *Zephyr*, dated 1783, has this rail with standards 6ft 9in apart and stepped on the sheer strake which is widened for this purpose. Contemporary paintings clarify this point.

There seems some confusion over the identification of this *Zephyr*, but she cannot be the fourteen-gun sloop built in 1779, in spite of fairly similar dimensions, because the plans of the two show such marked differences in construction, position and height of beams, and many details, including the complete absence of any gunports or gun positions in the one labelled 'transport'. The fourteen-gun sloop was bought on the stocks, retained the name of *Zephyr*, until renamed *Navy Transport* in 1782 and then *Dispatch* the following year.

The other was named *Zephyr* when her lines were taken off in 1783, and she has a full-bodied hull, with small deadrise to her floors, a square stern, a large hatchway 22ft long and 10ft wide with shifting beams, and a single deck except for a lower deck to form a small forecastle and a longer poop. There is a windlass and a capstan. Tonnage is 189 with dimensions of 76ft 5in × 24ft 2in × 13ft 1in.[78] This is very much the sort of hull-form given by Chapman (1768) for the barks and cats which he denotes as having the rig of snow, brigantine or sloop. Some of the barks, such as figure 9 plate XXVIII of 93ft 3in rigged as a snow, and figure 7 plate XXIX of 72ft 5in rigged as a brigantine, have a head and an elaborate figurehead.

With regard to the bilander, it is difficult to determine how long this rig lasted. John Lyman has written that the 'bilander rig died out on deep-water vessels soon after 1750'[79] and William Salisbury observed that 'Chapman... does not mention the bilander in any [hull] form, probably because the rig was quite obsolete'[80] in 1768, although the rig is depicted amongst the craft on plate LXII of Chapman. Lescallier (1777) gives an engraving of one on a galliot's hull (figure 88) and comments that they were used by the English and the Dutch, but there was nothing distinctive about their hull, only the rigging.[81] Falconer (1769 and 1780 editions of his dictionary) remarked that 'few vessels are now rigged in this method'. Mungo Murray compares the spars of a bilander and a snow in his book on shipbuilding, which first appeared in 1754 and was reprinted in 1765.[82] In Murray's bilander, there is no main topgallant mast or yard, and as only one yard is listed for the main lower mast, there is a doubt if this is the crossjack yard to spread the foot of the topsail or the main yard for the bilander's fore-and-aft mainsail. William Salisbury commented in the *Mariner's Mirror* that the yard below the main topsail was generally called the 'main yard' although he adds that 'it would have been more logical to have called it the crossjack'.[83]

When Salisbury wrote this in 1964, he obviously had not seen the plan in the Chapman Collection in Stockholm which is entitled 'A Billander for the Holland Trade'. The drawing contains no name or date, but has the dimensions of the vessel and her spar measurements; there are a body plan, sheer elevation and outline deck plan below, with a note which reads 'Built by Mr Henry Bird in London'. This

Fig 91. A painting by Francis Swaine (d 1783) of a bilander in two positions. In neither has she any headsails or staysails set. A painting by Brooking of a bilander on the port tack in stormy weather also has only one square sail on the main topmast but, unlike Swaine's painting, has the main yard shifted to the lee side of the mast so that the sail sets better. Swaine's painting is entitled: 'An early Trinity House tender off Castle Cornet, Guernsey'. (Courtesy N R Omell)

Fig 89. Bilander. *Lines plan. The plan is undated and unnamed, but states: 'Built by Henry Bird in London' and '... for the Holland trade'. This has been redrawn from a plan in the Chapman Collection at the Sjöhistoriska Museum, Stockholm. Dimensions on the plan: 62ft 0in (length of keel), 22ft 0in (extreme breadth), 10ft 3in (depth of hold), 3ft 9in (height between decks), tonnage 159½. Reconstruction: waterlines taken from body plan and projected on half-breadth plan: also buttock line; inboard extent of bowsprit. I am grateful to David Lyon for drawing my attention to this plan.*

Fig 90. Bilander. *Sail plan, reconstructed from spar dimensions listed on the lines plan of the vessel in figure 89, with only the positions and rake of the masts and bowsprit drawn. Deadeyes were also drawn, but no chain plates. The table of spars listed in the text indicates the data given. No running rigging has been drawn, except for the mainsail.*

89

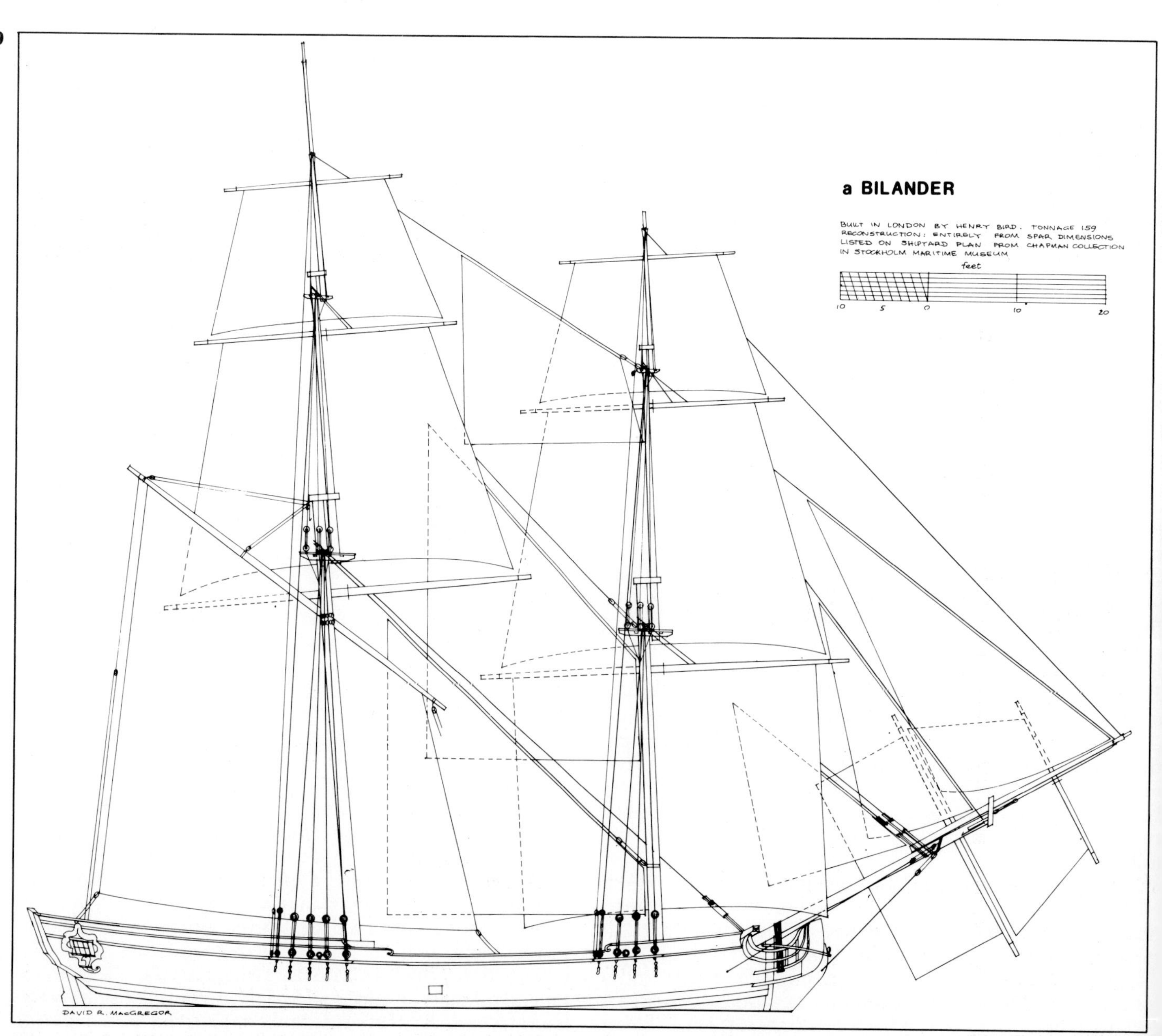

91

90

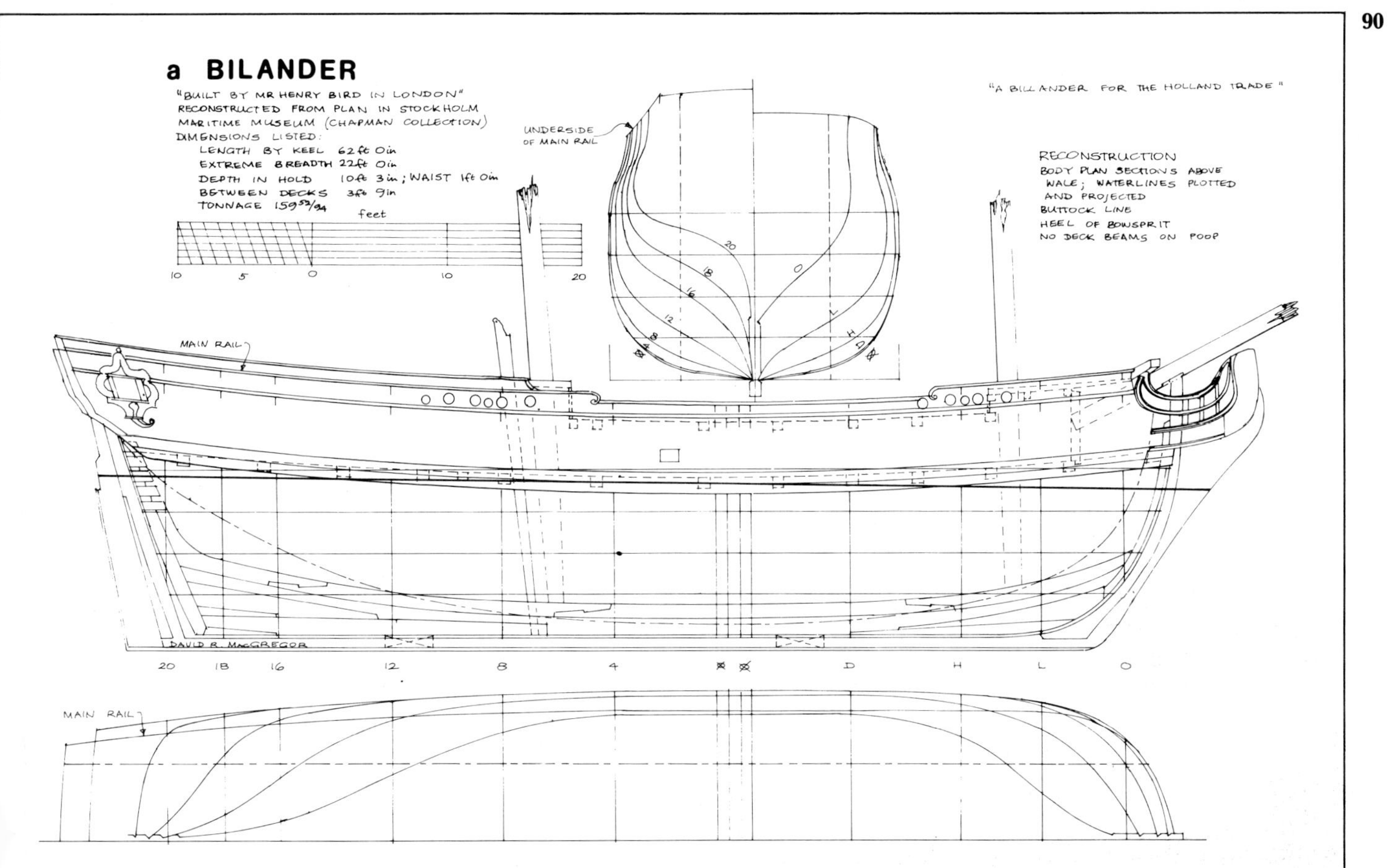
a BILANDER
"BUILT BY MR HENRY BIRD IN LONDON"
RECONSTRUCTED FROM PLAN IN STOCKHOLM MARITIME MUSEUM (CHAPMAN COLLECTION)
DIMENSIONS LISTED:
LENGTH BY KEEL 62ft 0in
EXTREME BREADTH 22ft 0in
DEPTH IN HOLD 10ft 3in; WAIST 1ft 0in
BETWEEN DECKS 3ft 9in
TONNAGE 159 52/94
feet
10 5 0 10 20
UNDERSIDE OF MAIN RAIL
"A BILLANDER FOR THE HOLLAND TRADE"
RECONSTRUCTION
BODY PLAN SECTIONS ABOVE WALE; WATERLINES PLOTTED AND PROJECTED
BUTTOCK LINE
HEEL OF BOWSPRIT
NO DECK BEAMS ON POOP
MAIN RAIL
DAVID R. MACGREGOR
20 18 16 12 8 4 D H L O
MAIN RAIL

92

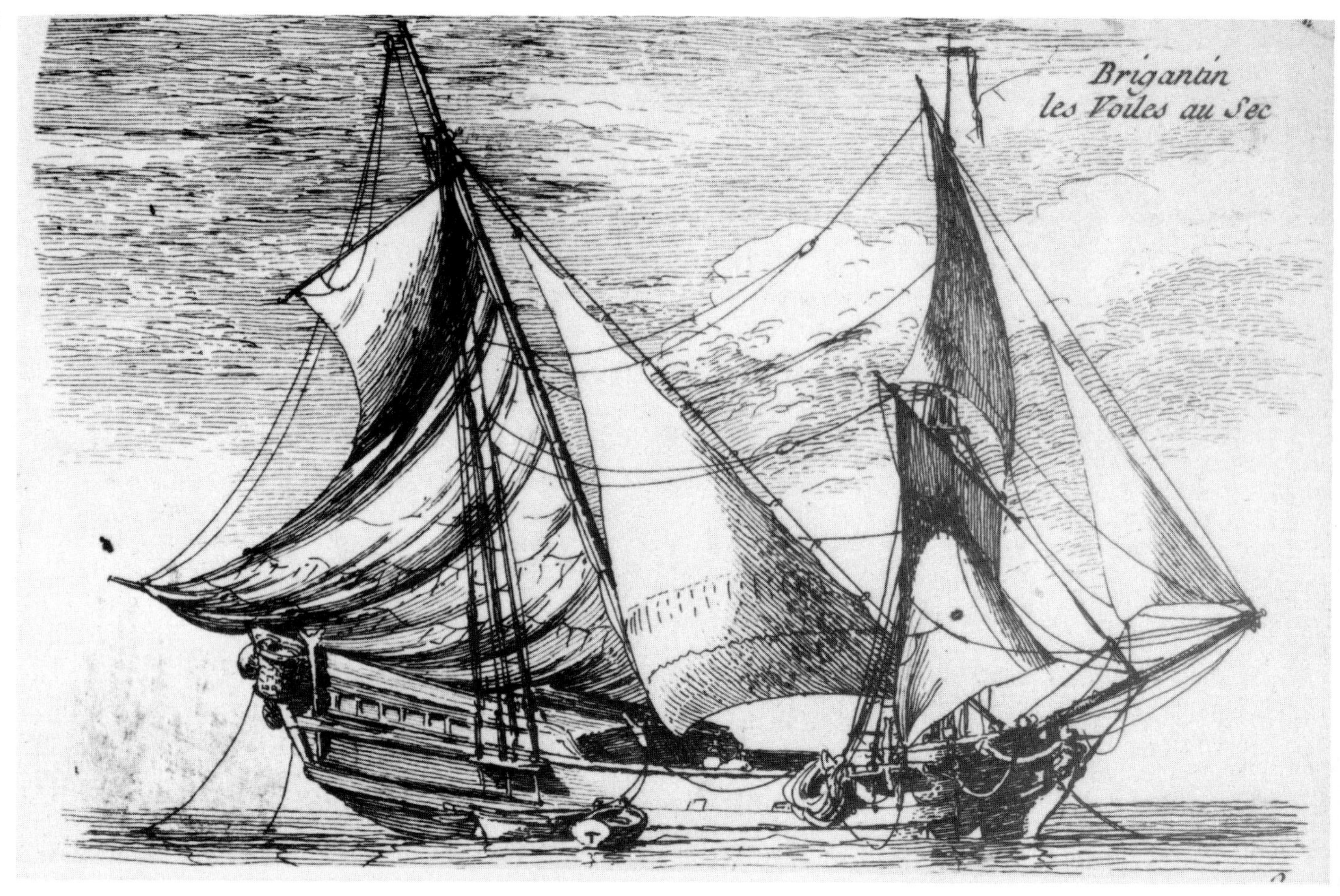

93

Fig 92. Another of Ozanne's engravings which is full of life. This is entitled 'Brigantine' and shows her at anchor, drying her sails. The steeply raking mainmast is a feature of this rig.

Fig 93. Detail of a painting by George Webster of shipping at the entrance to the Dardanelles. This brigantine is similar to the Portuguese 'patache' which Baugean engraved (plate 43 in Collection ... de Bâtiments de Guerre et de Bâtiments Marchands*); even the ensign is similar.* (Courtesy Malcolm Henderson)

Fig 94. A small brig running before the wind under easy sail, and the crew hoisting the boat aboard with the aid of tackles. Etching by Pierre Ozanne c1770.

plan has been re-drawn as figure 89 and the waterlines plotted on the half-breadth plan – the original plan had none – and a sail plan has been reconstructed from the spar dimensions. The vessel measured 62ft 0in length of keel, 22ft 0in extreme breadth, 10ft 3in depth in hold, 1ft 0in 'waste' [sic], 3ft 9in between decks, and 159⁵²⁄₉₄ tons. The body plan has rounded floors and slack bilges with some tumblehome; the profile is fairly typical for the mid-eighteenth century, and there is a loading port in the 'tween decks.

Finding spar dimensions to accompany an actual lines plan of a bilander is a rare event. These measurements show that the fore yard and 'crossjack yard' are both 42ft long and that the 'yard' of 45ft entered against the 'main mast' must be the bilander's yard for the fore-and-aft mainsail. The use of the word 'crossjack' answers William Salisbury's comment. All the yards on the main mast are identical in length to those on the fore, and so are the topmasts and topgallant masts, only the lower masts being of unequal length. Illustrations of bilanders reproduced here have provided details to reconstruct the sail plan in figure 91.

There are several instances in the eighteenth century of small brigantines with two square sails on the foremast and only a gaff sail on the main, as the following cases illustrate. A French brigantine of about 1720 was featured in a book describing a voyage to the West Indies: on the foremast there were only two square sails, and the mainsail had the very short gaff common in seventeenth and early-eighteenth century schooners.[84] An identical rig appeared in N M Ozanne's book of etchings in the 1760s, except that the main gaff was somewhat longer. Ozanne labelled this rig '*Brigantin*'. His version of a brig resembles Chapman's

94

LIST OF SPAR DIMENSIONS INSCRIBED ON LINES PLAN OF BILANDER IN CHAPMAN COLLECTION AT STOCKHOLM

	Mast	Yard	Yardarm	Head
Main lower mast	66ft 0in	45ft 0in	1ft 6in	8ft 0in
Main topmast	32ft 6in	30ft 0in	1ft 8in	3ft 4in
Main topgallant mast	18ft 6in	20ft 0in	1ft 4in	2ft 0in
Fore lower mast	55ft 0in	42ft 0in	2ft 2in	7ft 0in
Fore topmast	32ft 6in	30ft 0in	1ft 8in	3ft 4in
Fore topgallant mast	18ft 0in	20ft 0in	1ft 4in	2ft 0in
Crossjack	–	42ft 0in	1ft 6in	–
Bowsprit	37ft 0in	30ft 0in	1ft 6in	–
Jib boom	28ft 0in	–	–	–
Spritsail topsail yard	–	20ft 0in	1ft 4in	–
Bowsprit to steeve 6½in in a foot				

Notes: Rake of masts not stated; yard on bowsprit is the spritsail yard; yard on main lower mast is the fore-and-aft yard; crossjack yard spreads foot of main topsail; no diameters given.

drawing if the topgallants and jibboom are removed.[85] The oft-published picture of the Salem schooner *Baltick*, dated 1765,[86] indicates the close connection in the middle of the eighteenth century between a schooner, and a brigantine with a fore-and-aft mainmast: remove the gaff foresail of the *Baltick* and we have Ozanne's *brigantin*. A drawing entitled 'A Yarmouth Brig' is taken from Edward Gwyn's sketchbook of about 1780 and provides another example of a brigantine with a fore-and-aft mainmast.[87] Her rig closely resembles Ozanne's *brigantin*. In Gwyn's careful pen-and-wash drawing the type of rig is probably of greater importance than the word 'brig' describing it, particularly as many descriptions prove the unreliability of rig nomenclature to determine a hard-and-fast rule. The absence here of a fore topgallant reminds one of a Bideford polacca. Thomas Luny sketched a similar brigantine near Teignmouth and Topsham in about 1799.'[88]

These four widely-spaced examples indicate that the brigantine with a fore-and-aft mainmast existed throughout the eighteenth century and that it continued through the nineteenth, although the masts increased in height to permit topgallants and royals to be carried on the foremast and a gaff topsail on the main. Nevertheless the close similarity between a brigantine with a fore trysail and a schooner having a heavily square-rigged foremast persisted. The brigantine with a square main topsail must also have been in use, but the comparative rarity of examples suggest that the rig was much less common. However, after about 1790, illustrations of this variety of brigantine grow in frequency for a few decades.

The two-masted square-rigged craft were mostly square-sterned by 1775, or if they had a round stern with the wales taken to the sternpost, then they were cats with a square counter supporting stern windows. The pure pink stern was going out of favour in England after about the 1760s, although it and the round-sterned successors to the flute remained popular on the Continent. Schooners were not much used for cargo carrying in Europe or America, but rather as privateers or dispatch boats, and in consequence had fine-lined hulls with large sail plans. On the other hand, sloops carried cargo both on coastal and short sea voyages, and had hulls very similar to those given to the two-masted square-rigger.

An example of a brig with a pink stern is the *Industry*,

95

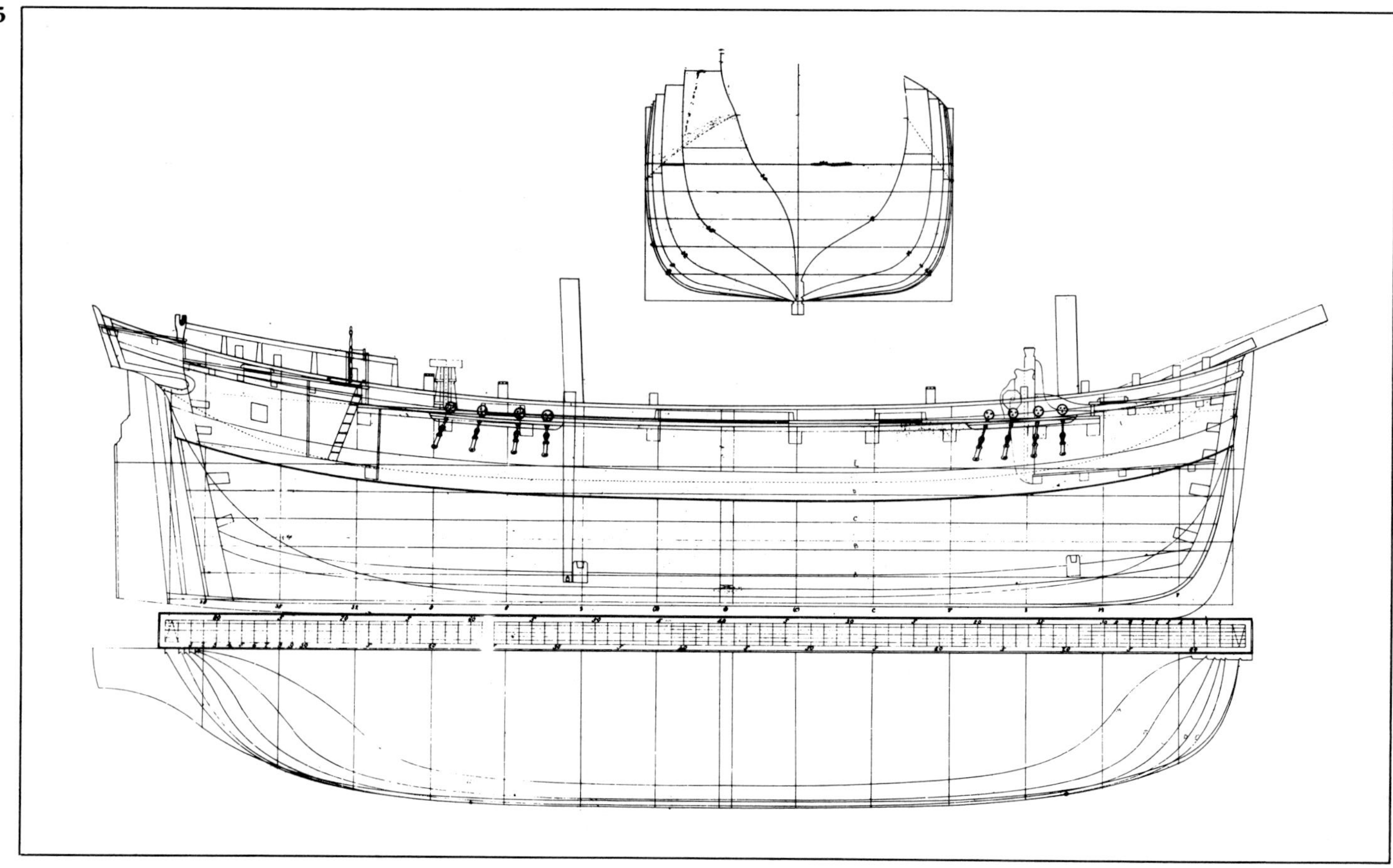

Fig 95. Industry. *Lines plan, dated 'Dec 1765'. Redrawn by Paul Roberts from an Admiralty draught. Dimensions on the plan: 83ft 9in (length on deck), 24ft 7in (extreme breadth), 12ft 8in (depth in hold), 222 tons burthen. Rigged as a brig. No deck plan or spar dimensions.*

whose lines were taken off by the Royal Navy at Deptford in 1765, presumably after her purchase for use as a transport. Her dimensions are 83ft 9in length on deck, 24ft 7in extreme breadth, 12ft 8in depth in hold, and 221$^{50}/_{94}$ tons. She has very full lines, a plain stem, flat floors, practically no tumblehome, a narrow lute stern overhanging the rudder head, bulwarks only a foot high, the deck at four different levels, a windlass abaft the foremast, and a capstan abaft the mainmast.[89] No spar dimensions are listed on the plan but these could be calculated from standard proportions. The transport *Plymouth* built in 1741 of 163 tons, was very similar in hull-form but her floors were rather less flat, and her lines plan includes spar dimensions.

Shipbuilding costs of brigs are scattered through various archives. At Northam, near Southampton, Thomas Raymond built the brig *Wight* in 1787 at £7 10s per ton on 151¾ tons, which the accounts worked out as £1136 5s; to this was added the sum of £997 12s 5½d for various tradesmen. The total amount of £2133 17s 5½d makes the cost per ton £14 1s, which seems expensive. There was a further £121 7s 1d for expenses connected with the launch, crew's wages, pilotage, launch dinner, etc. I am grateful to Alan Jamieson for these extracts from the 'Disbursement book for ship *Wight* 1787-92' in the Shipping Files of Priaulx Library, St Peter Port, Guernsey. The *Wight* was registered in Guernsey and traded to Quebec in these years.

SCHOONERS

Sufficient evidence has been collected to show that schooner yachts were much in use in Holland by the middle of the seventeenth century, and probably in England by 1700. In America, the first mention of a schooner was in a launch account of a new vessel at Gloucester, Massachusetts, in 1713, and from 1725 pictures of schooners appear in engravings of American ports with increasing frequency. All these illustrations are of fore-and-aft schooners. The first representation of a schooner with square sails is thought to be of the Portuguese dispatch vessel *St Ann* which reached Portsmouth in 1736 and had her lines taken off the following year. She is reported to have been built in America and sold to Portugal, but the lines plan made of her was collected by Chapman on one of his three visits to England and is now in the Chapman Collection at Stockholm.[90]

Howard Chapelle has drawn out her lines and reconstructed her sail plan from the spar dimensions recorded, which show her to have been an exceedingly fine-lined craft, with a long, narrow hull, hollow floors and large deadrise, her length at the rail being 58ft 2in, breadth (moulded) 11ft 10in, depth from keel rabbet to deck 6ft 10¼in, and tons burthen 36$^{41}/_{94}$. So she was quite small, but

Fig 97. A modern model of the schooner Sultana, *built at Boston in 1767 and purchased by the Royal Navy in 1768. Dimensions: 50ft 6in (deck) × 16ft 0¾in (moulded × 8ft 4in; and 52⅔ tons. She was shorter and broader than* Chaleur, *and had a head and less drag aft. She was steered with a tiller.* (Model Shipways, Bogota N J)

97

96

Fig 96. A Dutch schooner and a British cutter at Curaçao in 1786. The Mariner's Museum at Newport News has a painting done the previous year of an almost identical schooner at Curaçao but flying British colours. The schooner seen here has a ringtail boom rigged out, but there are no yards crossed. (Parker Gallery)

very narrow. She was rigged with two head sails, two gaff sails with short gaffs, and three square sails on the foremast, the topgallant yard being also termed a 'pigeon' yard reminiscent of the French word *perroquet* meaning parrot, but also topgallant. The foremast was stepped right up in the bows and the mainmast amidships. Howard Chapelle considers the square canvas to have been for use in light weather and that the sails were furled to the yards which were then lowered to the deck. The square sails were thus additions to a basically fore-and-aft rig.[91]

Another school of thought put forward by E P Morris in *The Fore-and-Aft Rig in America* is that square sails were the earliest sails in any rig and that fore-and-aft canvas was always added later as an auxiliary sail. On this hypothesis he argued that the schooner with square sails was developed from the brigantine, and that a gaff sail added to the foremast later became the principal sail there. He cites a correspondingly similar development in square-rigged ketches where the addition of a gaff sail eventually resulted in a pure fore-and-aft rig.[92]

The first schooner registered in the Royal Navy was apparently the *Barbadoes*, a Virginia-built vessel of 130 tons, which was purchased at Antigua in 1757, but no plans o her exist. In the next decade, the Navy purchased si Marblehead schooners ranging in size from 90 to 121 tons t protect the Colonial fishing fleets. Of these, the plans of th *Chaleur* have survived, and Howard Chapelle ha reconstructed the lines and sail plans.[93] Her lines were take off at Woolwich in 1768 and show a moderately full-bodie schooner with flat floors but very rounded bilges, a shor sharp entrance and longer run, all of which suggest she wa a cargo carrier. She was 70ft 8in along the deck, 20ft 4i moulded breadth and 7ft 9½in depth in hold, and of 12 tons. Spar dimensions indicate that she carried squar topsails on each mast and the lower yards are terme 'crossjack' yards; there was a boom to spread the foot of th tall, narrow square sail on the foremast; the gaffs ha increased in length, and the fore gaff sail was set on a boom The masts had practically no rake and the foremast was stil stepped right up in the bows. A plan of the *Halifax*, buil about 1765, shows a similar type of hull.

The trend in American schooners, to judge fro surviving plans and spar dimensions, was for the hulls to ge increasingly finer, with longer hulls and frequently with a big draft aft, while the masts raked considerably and th yards of the square sails became longer. In the schooners *Si Edward Hawke* and *Earl of Egmont*, built to the order of th Admiralty at New York in 1767-68, we can see this tren already in operation.[94]

By 1775 there seem to have been two types of schooner i

98

Fig 98. Two American schooners off Virginia in 1794, painted by G Tobin. The one on the left is a two-topsail schooner with deep topsails but small topgallants; she has long lower masts which result in large gaff sails. There is a boom at the foot of the foremast to which the square sail, furled on the fore yard, could be sheeted. Stunsail booms are also run in on top of this boom. The leward part of the main stay has been slacked off to pass clear of the foresail. On the right is a shallop without a bowsprit. (Parker Gallery)

99

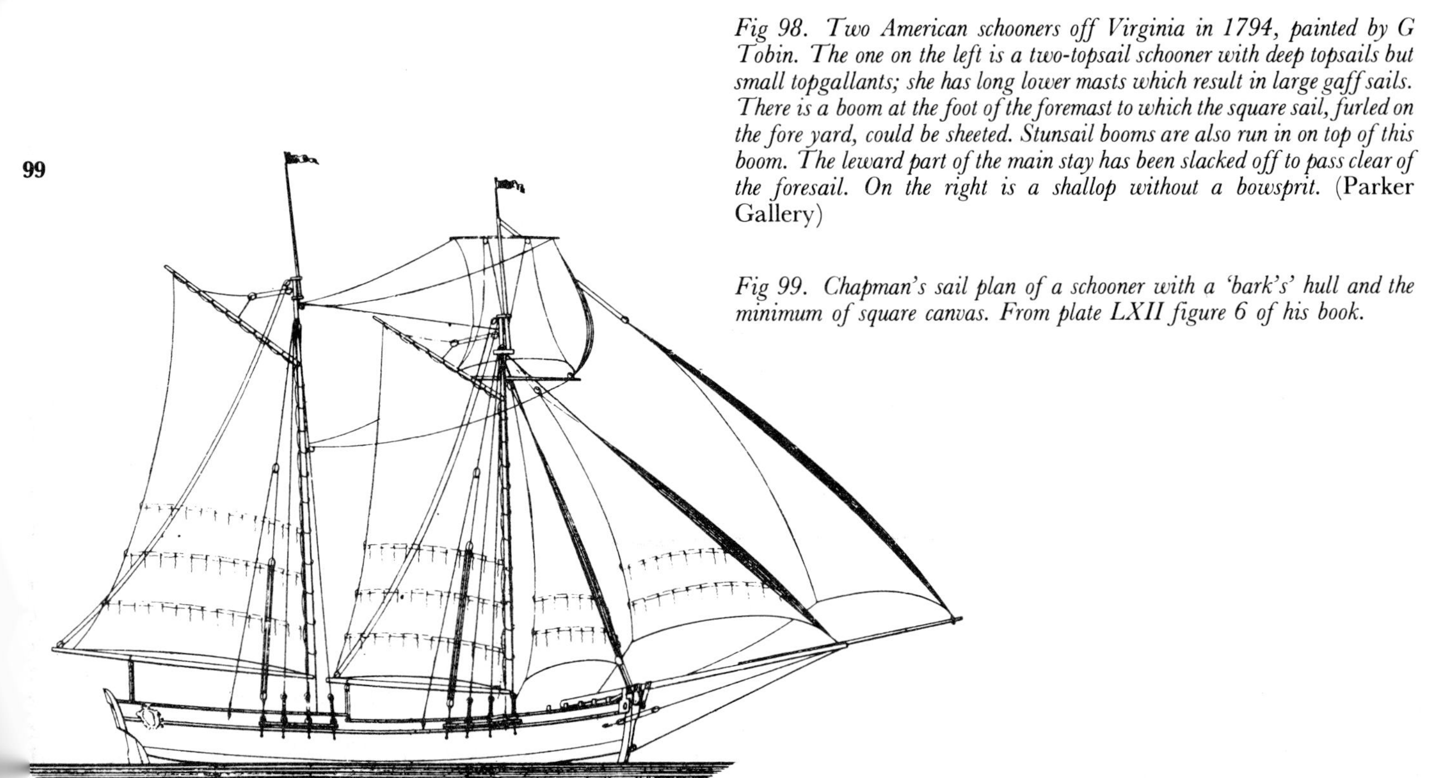

Fig 99. Chapman's sail plan of a schooner with a 'bark's' hull and the minimum of square canvas. From plate LXII figure 6 of his book.

use: one was the ocean-going model, usually built on fine lines, with a large amount of square canvas often on both masts, and invariably heavily armed; the other variety was of smaller size, either full or sharp-built but without any square sails, mostly employed as tenders, fishing boats or pilot boats, and some shallops carried this rig.

In Europe, Chapman (1768) illustrated a schooner's sail plan with three headsails, two gaff sails, and a square topsail on the foremast (figure 99). In his lines plans, he assigns the schooner rig to eight hulls in all: a frigate's hull, a bark's hull, two 'packet boats', two 'pleasure vessels', and two privateers. With the exception of the first two, all have hollow floors, large deadrise and very sharp lines. The schooner-rigged bark has a hull-form that is very similar to the Dutch flute on the same page (plate XXVII).[95]

Groenewegen (1789) has only one engraving of a schooner, and she is described as a *Kanonneer boot* with square topsails on each mast.[96] Falconer (1769 and 1780) illustrates a schooner with a similar engraving. Lescallier (1777) says that schooners are mostly used in England and America, and that the sails resemble the mainsail of a brigantine or cutter. He continues to explain that there are two or three jibs and sometimes a topsail set flying on each mast; in addition a square sail is set when running before the wind.[97]

In England, there is a drawing by Edward Gwyn (c1780) entitled 'A Topsail Schooner', see figure 102, in which the topsails are deeply roached and sheeted to a spread yard some distance below the gaff jaws. This was a practice adopted in some cutters, as illustrated in *Fast Sailing Ships*, figures 17 and 18, but it is hard to know how common it was in schooners.

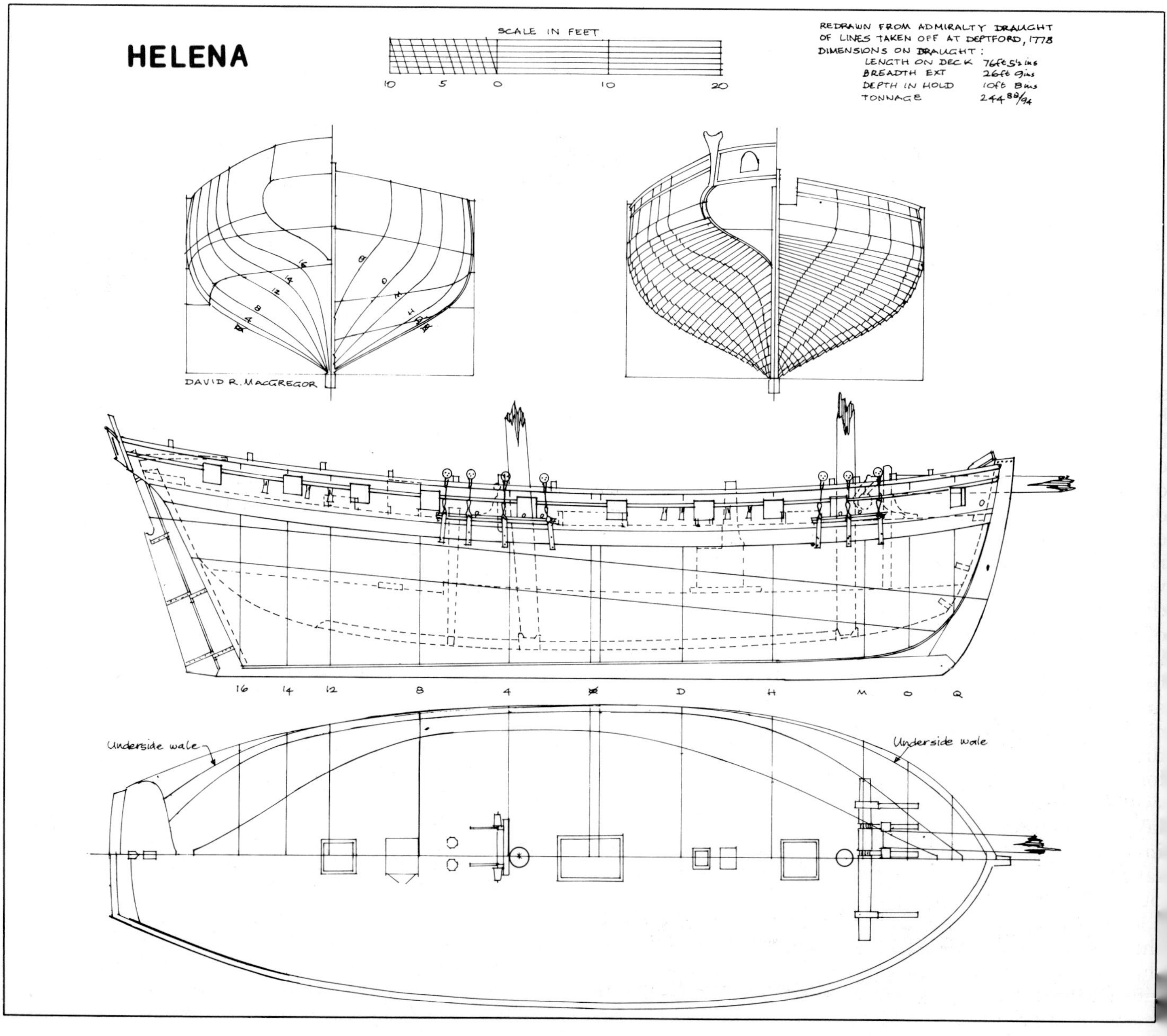

Fig 100. Helena. *Lines plan, general arrangement and planking, redrawn from an Admiralty draught at the National Maritime Museum, Greenwich. She was built in 1778. Dimensions on the plan: 76ft 1½in (length on deck), 56ft 5½in (length of keel for tonnage), 26ft 9in (extreme breadth), 10ft 8in (depth of hold), and 215 tons. Reconstruction: deck plan combined here from a separate drawing and plan layout re-arranged. See text for the history of this schooner.*

100

101

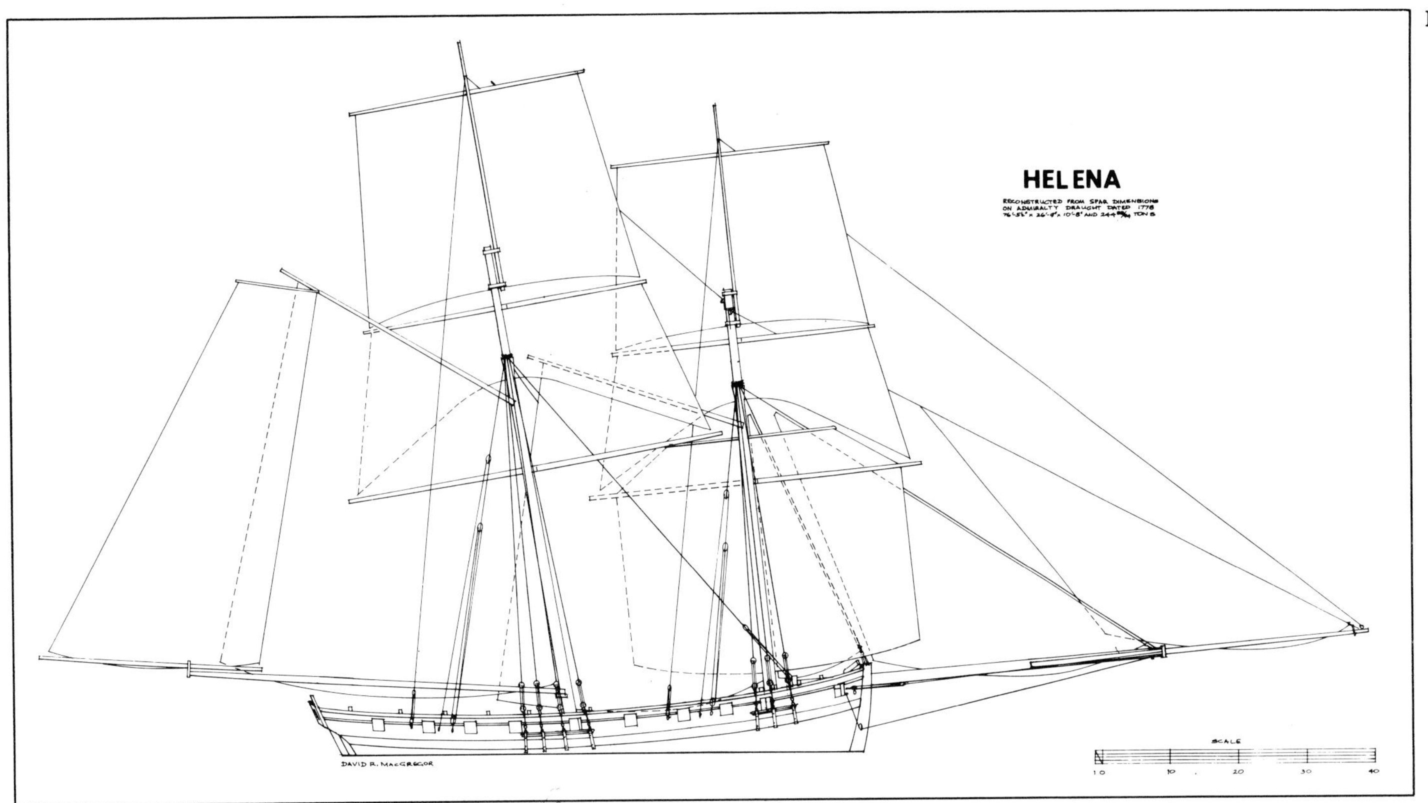

Fig 101. Helena. *Sail plan, entirely reconstructed from spar dimensions listed on an Admiralty draught, as tabulated in the text; mast positions and rake of masts taken from original. Not given in spar list: head yard to square fore sail, doublings of masts and jibboom. See text for further comments on reconstruction.*

An English example of a fast-sailing, heavily-rigged schooner can be had in the *Helena* of $214\frac{88}{94}$ tons, clinker-built, with topsails and topgallants on each mast, a plain bow and a narrow stern with a square tuck. She had a cutter's hull, and the bowsprit was mounted on the port side of the stem head. Her dimensions were 76ft 1½in length on deck, 56ft 5½in length on the keel for tonnage, 26ft 9in extreme breadth and 10ft 8in depth in hold. She has steeply rising floors with the maximum beam just above the load waterline and is really outside the scope of this book but for the fact that it is rare at this date to find the spar dimensions of a named schooner with an accompanying lines plan. The keel is slightly rockered forward, where it is also deeper below the rabbet than it is at the heel of the sternpost. There are end elevations drawn on the plan showing the run of the clinker planking, a style employed on several Admiralty draughts at this date.[98] She drew 13ft 9in aft and 7ft forward, was pierced for ten guns on the starboard side, and was fitted with a windlass. The deck layout and internal layout shown on the longitudinal section depict the manner in which she was fitted out, presumably at the time she was taken into the Navy. She was built in 1778, for what purpose has not been established, but presumably to obtain a letter of marque; however she was captured by the French the same year, re-taken in 1779 and added to the Navy in that year under her original name. The spar dimensions, given below, must then be her original ones. The lower masts are certainly massive sticks; it is instructive to read that the lower yards are termed 'spread yards' and that there are no topmasts, only 'topgallants'. The base of this sail plan is of immense length, and the full suit of sails can have been set only in moderately light breezes. Sometimes the term 'topgallant' mast indicates one fidded abaft the lower mast, but this is more likely in cutters or schooners with smaller spars, and so it has not been done here.

SPAR DIMENSIONS OF SCHOONER *HELENA* INSCRIBED ON ADMIRALTY DRAUGHT (No 4523 Box 64) AT NATIONAL MARITIME MUSEUM, GREENWICH

	Length	Diameter
Mainmast	81ft 0in	22½in
Main topgallant mast	36ft 0in	7⅞in
Main topgallant yard	35ft 0in	6¾in
Main topsail yard	42ft 0in	8½in
Main spread yard	55ft 6in	9¼in
Main gaff	38ft 0in	10in
Main boom	54ft 5in	12⅞in
Fore mast	71ft 0in	19½in
Fore topgallant mast	32ft 0in	7½in
Fore topgallant yard	32ft 0in	6½in
Fore topsail yard	38ft 4in	6¾in
Fore spread yard	49ft 0in	8¾in
Fore gaff	32ft 0in	8in
Bowsprit	56ft 5in	19in
Jibboom	50ft 0in	9in
Ring tail	33ft 9in	8in

Ring tail dimension refers to the boom.
Not given in above list: lengths of stunsail booms; length of crossjack yard or head yard to spread head of square sail; lengths of doublings or head of lower masts; length of jibboom inside bowsprit.

Reconstructing the sail plan of the *Helena* has proved something of a problem as there were so few contemporary examples of schooners but, after trying various arrangements of spars and sails, the only logical solution

102

seemed to be that of a cutter's rig on each mast, which makes the result look like Edward Gwyn's schooner. The deeply-roached topsails set on spread yards halfway down the mast are certainly peculiar to one variety of cutter. This rig set a square sail whose head fitted into the roach of the fore topsail, and so it has been drawn here. A variation was to have the head laced not to a short yard but to a longer crossjack yard which was slung on the after side of the topsail. However, as no crossjack yard is listed amongst the *Helena*'s spar dimensions, it was decided not to employ this form. The stem head is drawn with holes bored through it to take the fantail end of a stay and so the fore stay is set up at this point, thus making it difficult to decide on the sizes of staysails between the foremast and the outer end of the bowsprit. The jib – or flying jib – is hoisted to the head of the lower mast, so that no headsail goes to the 'topgallant' mast. At this date, fore-and-aft topsails do not appear to have been carried by cutters and so none has been drawn above the main gaff. However, a main topmast staysail could have been carried.

Some examples of the smaller type of schooner carrying only fore-and-aft sails include the boat sailing out on the starboard tack towards the *Resolution* and *Adventure*, which are depicted on an engraving as they set out in 1771 at the commencement of Cook's second voyage of exploration. This schooner carries three sails: a jib laced to a boom which

Fig 102. A tinted drawing by Edward Gwyn entitled 'A Topsa Schooner'. A date of c1780 has been asigned to his drawings. Th drawing provides the authority for reconstructing the Helena *in the mann I have adopted. Gwyn's schooner appears to have a square stern whic terminates her pronounced sheer.* (National Maritime Museum)

pivots on the outer end of the short bowsprit; and a foresa and mainsail each set on a boom with a short gaff. The there is the *Peggy*, whose hull and spars still survive a Castletown, Isle of Man, where she was built in 1791. She i referred to at greater length in Chapter 3. Edward Gwy drew an elevation of a much large fore-and-aft schoone which mounted a broadside of seven guns, and carried tw headsails. The fore gaff was as long as the boom, and longe than the main gaff; the short topmasts were lashed to th foreside of the lower masts, without cheeks or trestletrees An example of a shallop built in 1806 appears in figure 141 and is described in the next chapter. It was really this smal type of schooner which David Steel described in his *Riggin and Seamanship* (1794) ending with these words: 'Schooner sail very near the wind, and require few hands to wor them. Their rigging is light, similar to a ketch's, th topmasts fix in iron rings abaft the lower mast heads.[99] I should be noted that gaff topsails were not in common us until the end of the eighteenth century, but Thomas Lun sketched a small schooner with one in 1799.[100]

VESSELS WITH ONE OR TWO MASTS

To anyone who comes to study single-masted and small two-masted craft prior to 1815, the rarity of plans is immediately apparent, and the researcher is obliged to seek out paintings and engravings to supplement the meagre scale drawings available. In the Admiralty Collection of draughts at the National Maritime Museum, Greenwich, there is an assortment of sloops and single-masted hoys which are mostly in the form of lines plans with spar dimensions in tabular form, but some sail and rigging plans of these or similar craft actually exist in the Chapman Collection at the Maritime Museum in Stockholm. I am grateful to David Lyon for drawing my attention to these Swedish plans which must have been collected by Chapman when he visited England. In addition, his published work, *Architectura Navalis Mercatoria* (1768), supplements some of these plans by providing lines plans as well as one sail and rigging plan of each type of craft. Ignoring the ships' boats and pleasure yachts, his book gives nine sail plans of vessels covered by the section now under discussion, of which five have two-masts and the remainder one. These examples are of European craft only, but American vessels are covered adequately by William

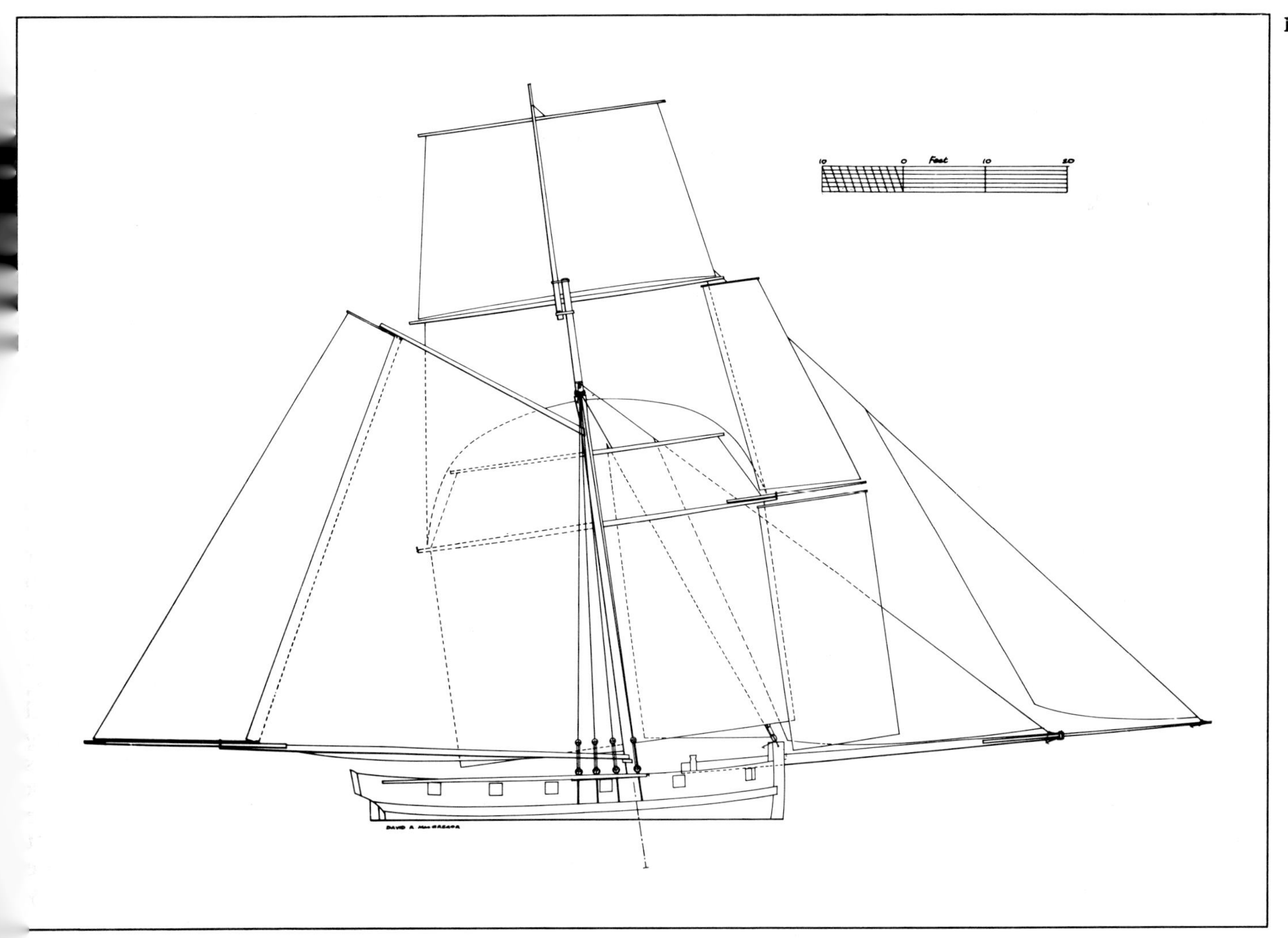

103

Fig 103. HMS Fly. *Sail plan. She was bought into the Royal Navy in 1763. Measurements on the plan: 51ft 6in (overall) × 20ft 10½ft (extreme) × 8ft 1¼in (hold) and 78⅓ tons. The plan was reconstructed from spar dimensions on Admiralty draught at the National Maritime Museum, Greenwich, and from the sheer elevation, which gave mast position and rake. This sail plan shows the style of a heavily-rigged cutter at this date, which has been utilized in the* Helena's *reconstruction.*

104

Gouillette
les Voiles au Sec
1er Cah
No.

105

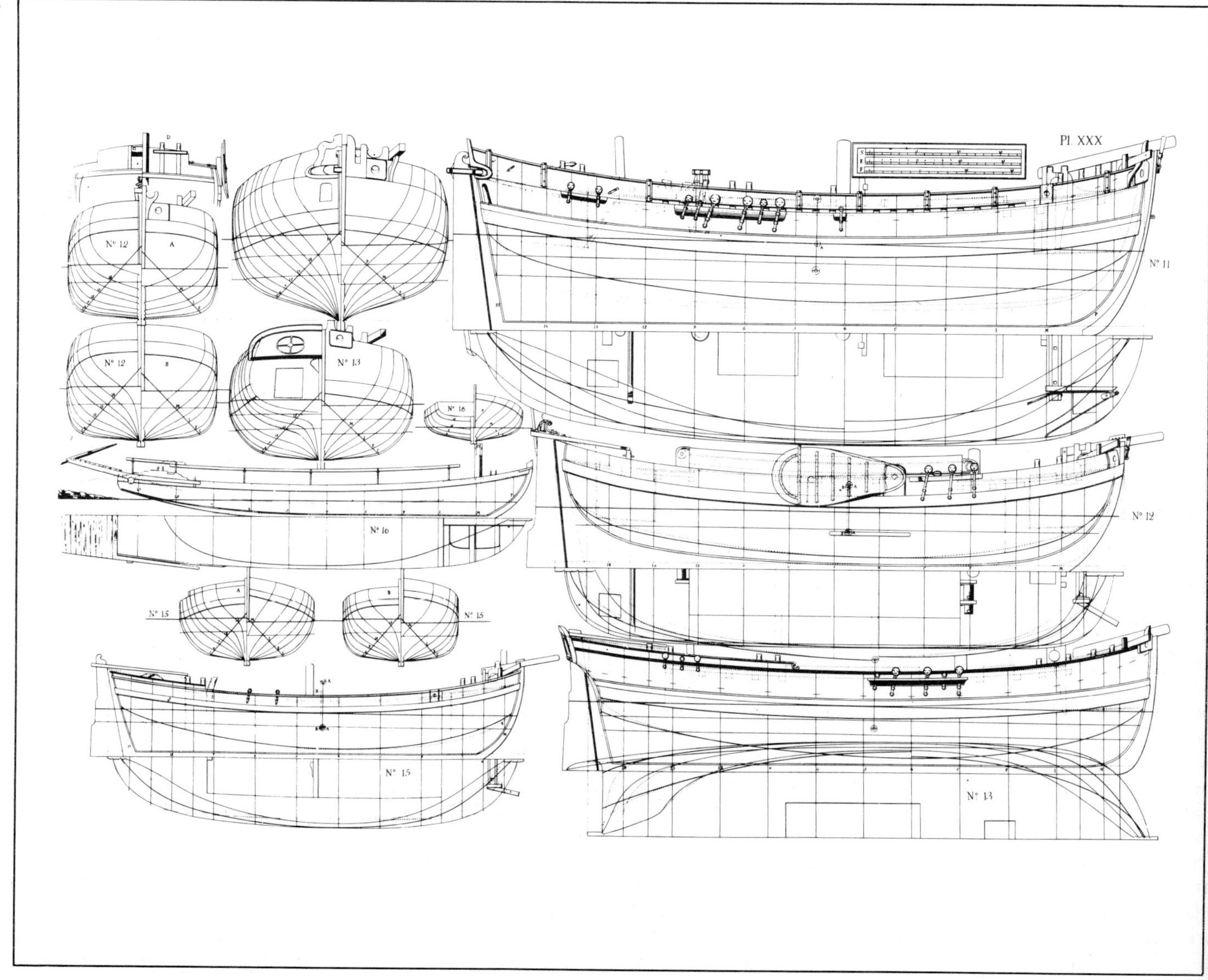
PL. XXX
No 11
No 12
No 13
No 16
No 10
No 15

Fig 104. Wearing a British flag, this schooner is pictured (c1770) by Ozanne at anchor, drying her sails. She is a short, full-bodied craft with a pink stern; there is a crutch against the poop for the main boom to rest on, and the poop reaches to the mast; the jibboom has been run in; the main topmast is fidded abaft the lower mast, and the drawing of it is unfinished at the head. (MacGregor Collection)

Fig 105. Small Craft. *Lines plans reproduced from plate XXX in* Architectura Navalis Mercatoria *by Fredrik af Chapman (1768). The types of vessel are as follows:*
No 11 Pink *rigged as a ketch of 137 tons burthen.*
No 12 Hoy *rigged as a 'chalke' of 110 tons burthen. (A 'chalke' has one mast and is No 13 on Chapman's plate LXII or figure 120).*
No 13 Bark *rigged as a galleas of 93 tons burthen. (This is No 9 on Chapman's plate LXII or figure 107).*
No 15 Lighter *but no rig stated; of 41 tons burthen.*
No 16 Ferry.

106

E Smak onder zeyl gaande 4

Fig 106. Groenewegen's engraving of a Dutch smack (1789) with leeboards and a full bodied hull. The small topgallant has been cast loose on the fore side of the topsail, ready for hoisting and the crew are manning the halliards of the foresail as it rises up the stay.

Baker's *Sloops and Shallops*,[101] by Howard I Chapelle's works, and also in the book by E P Morris. The last two have been quoted in the references.

Of the rigs recognized by *Lloyd's Register* which were listed at the beginning of the section on Two-Masted Square-Rigged Vessels, there were a number whose exact definition it would be hard to determine because they covered a multiplicity of rig variations, but many of them can be considered under the general English term of ketch.

The evolution of the ketch rig in its fore-and-aft form requires a careful study of the eighteenth century to trace the various rigs and how they combined in the first half of the nineteenth, so that it is possible to give here only a few examples to suggest the line along which the ketch might have evolved. R Morton Nance has written and illustrated several lines of development[102] and William A Baker has cited examples of the rig up to the early years of the eighteenth century in his work entitled *Colonial Vessels*. These humbler ships rarely obtained a portrait to themselves before 1825 and one is therefore obliged to examine an artist's sketches, a dictionary illustration, or the various ancillary craft littering the painting of a river or harbour, when the principal subject is a castle or a ship-of-the-line.

By the end of the eighteenth century, it would appear that the construction in England of the fully square-rigged ketch or 'ship without a foremast', as the rig has been styled, had practically ceased. A distinction should be noted between the merchant ketch, shown in figure 108, and the bomb ketch or yacht ketch. In the former, the mainmast was placed one-third of the length from the bow, which permitted a much larger gaff mainsail to be carried, and likewise a sizeable gaff mizen; in the bomb ketch the mainmast was amidships. Cutters and sloops were frequently shown with a small mizen or jigger mast stepped at the stern and setting a lug or lateen sail, and these 'dandy-rigged' craft may well have provided a direct link with the pure fore-and-aft ketch. It was only a matter of time for the mizen to increase in size and the mainsail to be reduced although it appears to have been a very slow process.

Of the ketch rigs illustrated by Chapman in 1768, E P Morris wrote that they 'are alike in essentials...but differ endlessly in details', and he goes on to point out that Chapman's five types are not an exclusive choice but really a chance selection of rigs which were changing all the time, the use of certain names being almost accidental.[103] Some idea of how contemporaries ignored the precision of nomenclature can be had by comparing the Swedish, English and French equivalents for each of the five ketches, as listed in Chapman's Table of Contents.

ENGLISH EQUIVALENTS OF KETCH RIG FROM PLATE LXII IN CHAPMAN (1768)[104]

	Swedish	**English**	**French**
No 3	ketch or hooker	ketch	ketch or dogger
No 7	Dutch fishing hooker	dogger	Dutch dogger
No 8	galliot	Dutch hoy	Dutch hoy
No 9	galleas	galleas used in the Baltic	German galleas
No 11	hooker yacht	ketch-yacht used in the Baltic	hooker-yacht

Of these five, Nos 3 and 11 have three-piece mainmasts setting three square sails as well as a gaff sail; No 7 sets three square sails on a pole mast, but without a gaff sail; Nos 8 and 9 have a preponderance of fore-and-aft canvas, and whereas No 8 has a deeply roached topsail which has to ride over two stays, No 9 is more nearly the equivalent of the ketch which finally appeared in the mid-nineteenth century. As to the hull shape, Nos 3, 9 and 11 have square sterns, but 7 and 8 are round-sterned with outside rudders.

SAIL PLANS OF CHAPMAN'S FIVE KETCHES *(Plate LXII)*

Fig 107. 'Galleas used in the Baltic'. The nearest equivalent to the ketch of a century later. (Chapman No 9)

Fig 108. 'Ketch-yacht used in the Baltic'. Also used in cargo vessels. (Chapman No 11)

Fig 109. 'Ketch'. This is the bomb-ketch. (Chapman No 3)

Fig 110. 'Dogger'. Used in Holland. (Chapman No 8)

Fig 111. 'Dutch Hoy'. (Chapman No 7)

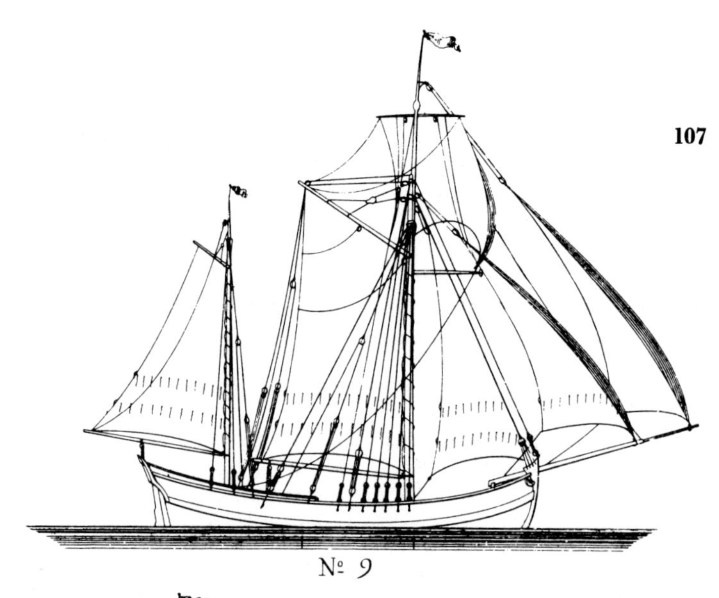

107

108

109

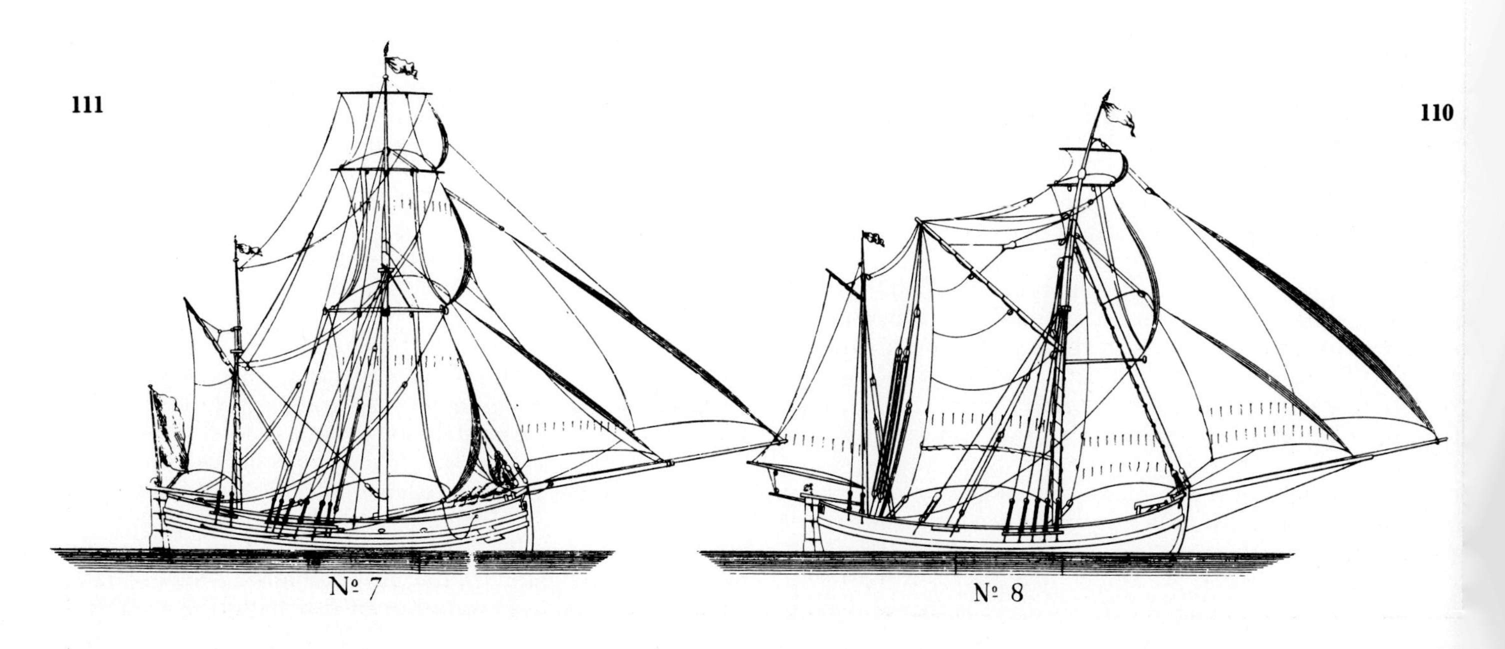

111

110

112

Fig 112. An engraving by Pierre Ozanne *(c1770) with a title that may be translated, 'Dogger running free'. She seems to have a Dutch flag, but the sails do not accord exactly with any of the plans in figures 107–111. Below the topsail is a square sail that is twisted with the port sheet hauled aft and the starboard tack taken to the chess-tree, the wind being on the starboard quarter; this makes the starboard leach line up with the gaff and causes confusion. The pink-sterned hull of the dogger resembles the trading hoy in figure 113.* (MacGregor Collection)

Fig 113. Trading Hoy. *Lines plan, unidentified, but probably c1750–1775, and redrawn by Paul A Roberts from a plan in the Science Museum, London, which I traced. No deck plan or spar dimensions exist but a reconstructed sail plan has been attempted in figure 114. Dimensions scaled off the plan: 50ft 6in (tonnage length) × 17ft 3in × 7ft 5in. The presence of iron hanging knees suggests that she might have been an East India Company's hoy and as such might have been built under the supervision of Gabriel Snodgrass who strongly advocated the use of iron knees. For a modern rigged model of a similar hull, see Roger Finch,* Coals from Newcastle *(1973) page 59.*

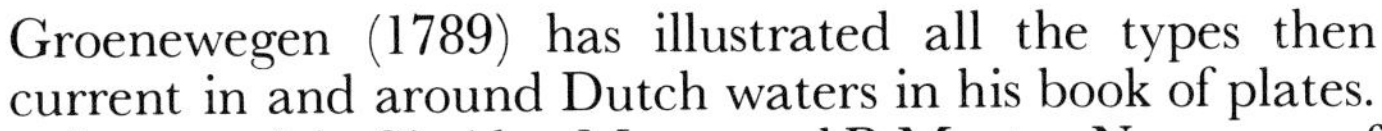

Groenewegen (1789) has illustrated all the types then current in and around Dutch waters in his book of plates.

In an article, Sir Alan Moore and R Morton Nance say of the dogger that 'the rig most commonly associated with her name is a modification of the eighteenth century ketch'.[105] John Lyman has suggested that 'any round-sterned, apple-bowed vessel with some kind of pole-masted ketch rig was referred to as a dogger by English-speaking mariners in the period 1770–1805'.[106]

The four single-masted rigs given by Chapman in the English list of contents are sloop (No 12), Dutch tjalk (No 13), English hoy (No 14), and English cutter (No 15). The sloop is a lofty craft setting a topsail and topgallant on a pole mast; the tjalk is round-sterned with leeboards, a sprit-mainsail and a square topsail; the English hoy carries no square canvas and is a simple gaff-rigged sloop; the cutter has four yards like HMS *Fly* in *Fast Sailing Ships*, (reproduced here in figure 103) with the square sail set on a crossjack yard hoisted up into the roach of the topsail.

Hoys were regularly employed in English waters to carry cargo around the coasts and up the estuaries, and had a variety of hull shapes. A lines plan of one with a pink stern is

113

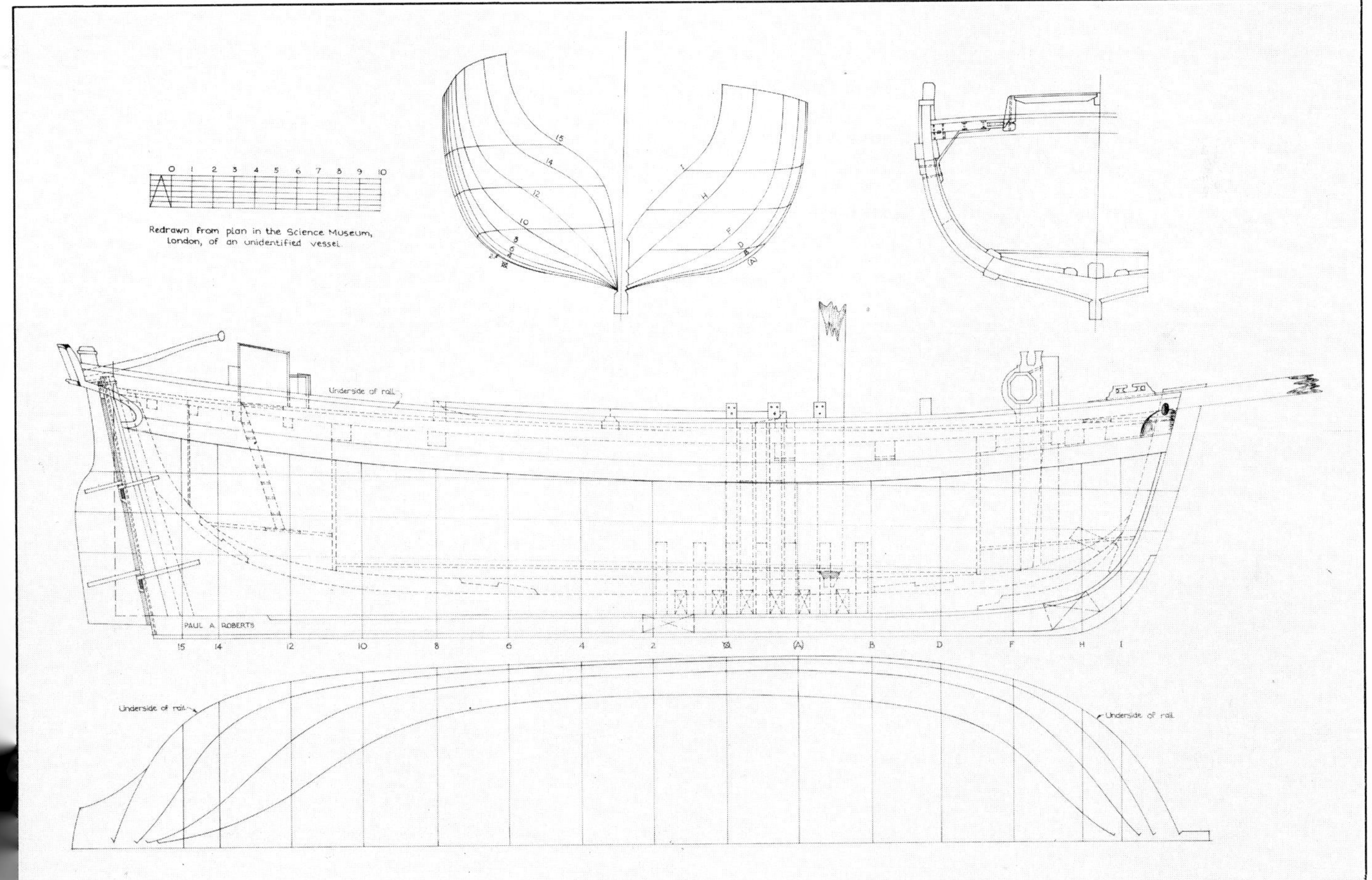

in the Science Museum, London; unfortunately it is unnamed and undated. This has been redrawn as figure 113 to show a plain bow, moderately fine entrance and run, hollow floors, slack bilges, sides flaring outwards with no tumblehome, a narrow lute stern with little overhang, a flush deck, a hatchway 16ft long, and a single mast. An unusual feature is that three of the timbers have been continued a foot above the bulwarks and pierced with three holes like deadeyes to accept the lanyards of the rigging.

Fig 114. Trading Hoy. *Sail plan, entirely reconstructed, using a sail plan in the Chapman Collection at the Sjöhistoriska Museum, Stockholm, of an 'East India Company's Hoy' as the source. The hoy had her sails furled and the bowsprit heaved up, but here the sails are drawn as set and the bowsprit is lowered.*

Dimensions scaled off the plan give 50ft 6in tonnage length × 17ft 3in × 7ft 5in. A cross-section shows the use of iron hanging knees, which would suggest a date at the end of the eighteenth century.[107]

One of the English plans collected by Chapman is entitled 'East India Company's hoy' and it shows a single-masted vessel which is double-ended, having a very short pink stern and a long hatchway; the mainsail is brailed in, the gaff has not been lowered, and the bowsprit is topped up. All the standing and running rigging is clearly drawn. This plan has been liberally employed to reconstruct a sail and rigging plan for the trading hoy, and the result appears in figure 114. It is worth noting that Chapman's sail plan described above is remarkably similar to the one he published in *Architectura Navalis Mercatoria* as figure 14 on

114

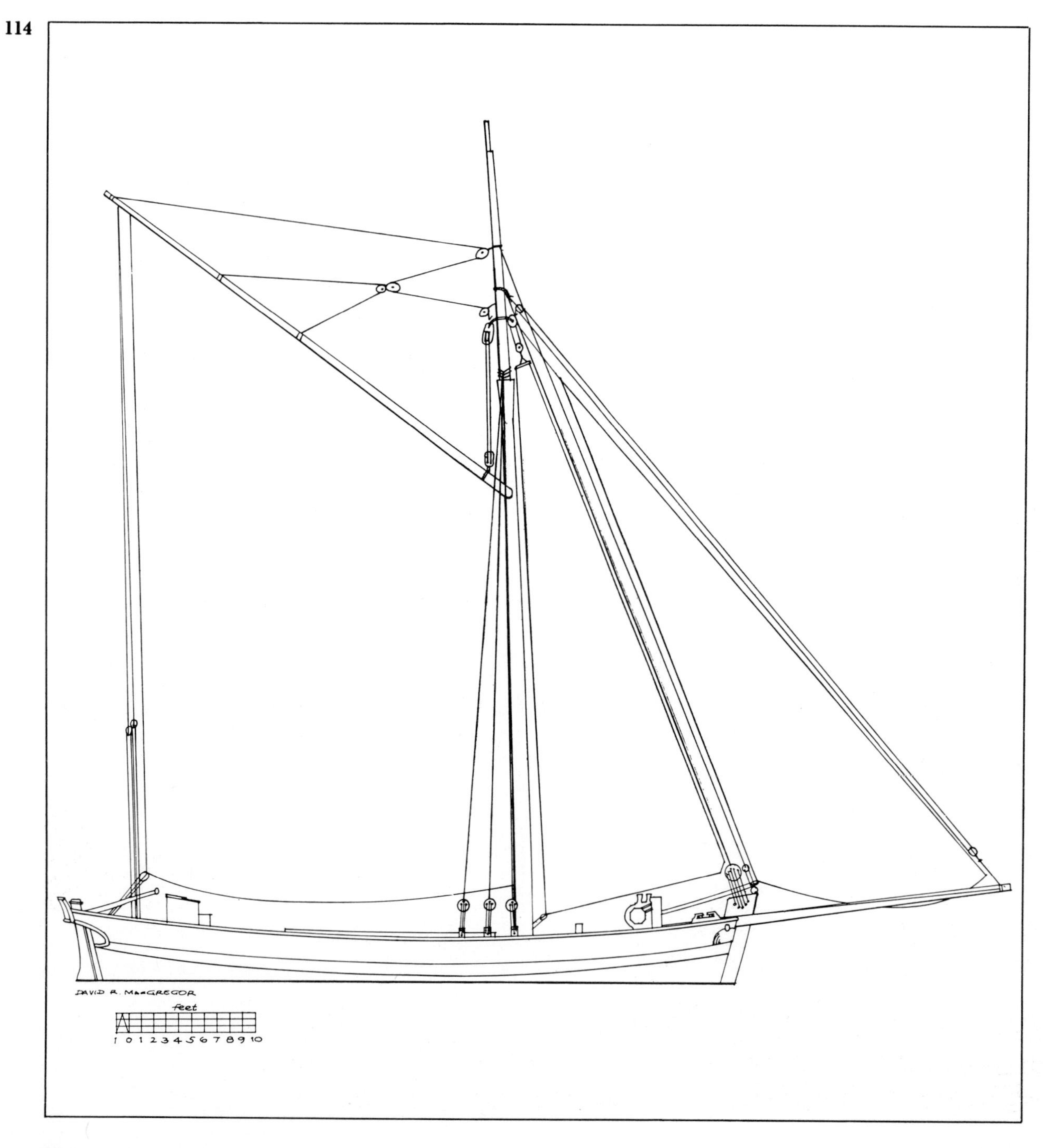

Fig 115. Ballast Lighter. *General arrangement and sail plan, redrawn from a plan in the Chapman Collection at the Sjöhistoriska Museum, Stockholm. No dimensions have been written on the plan, but a note states: 'a Clean run aft'. She is extremely broad for her length, there being only about $2^1/_4$ beams to length. She is sprit-rigged with no bowsprit.*

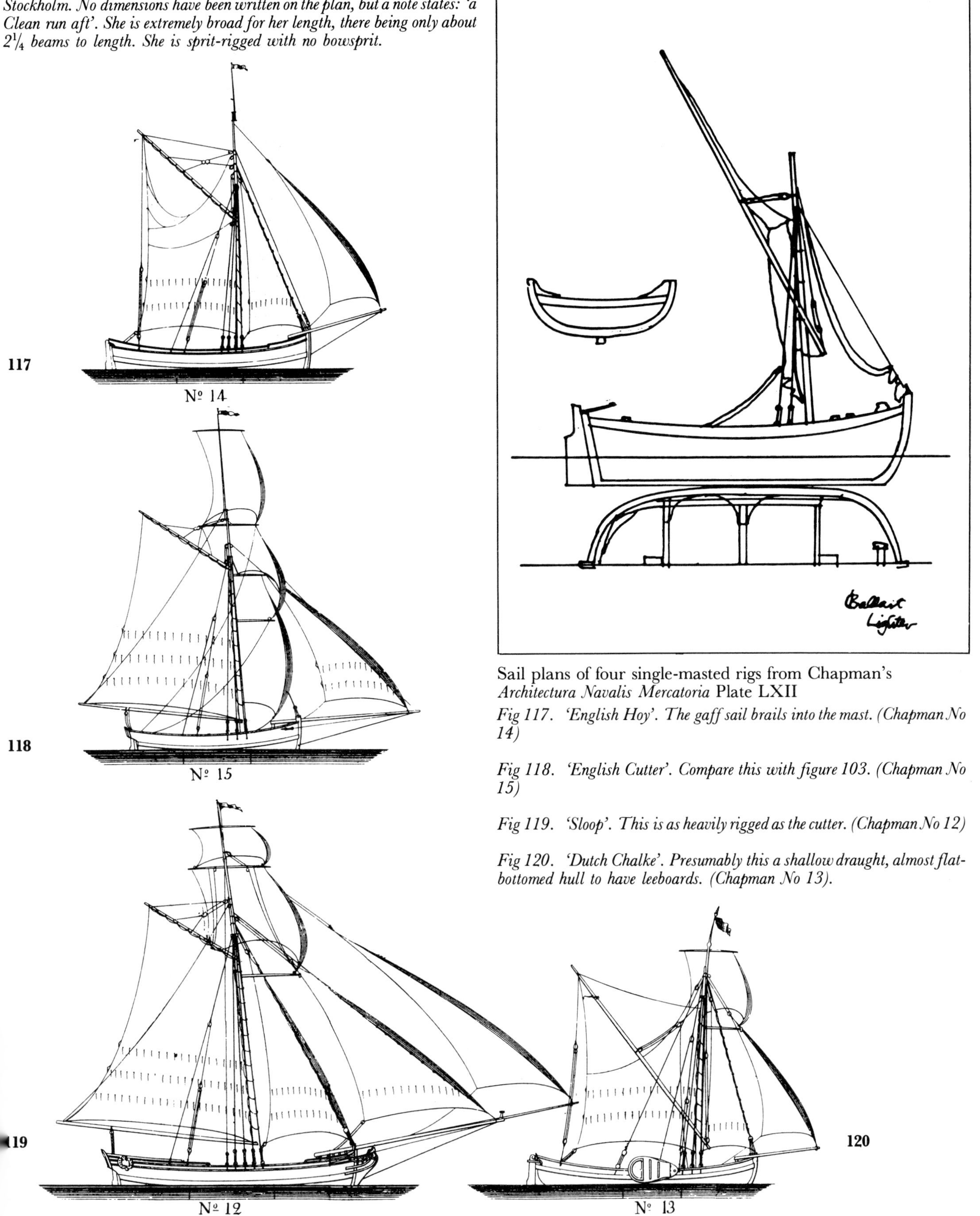

Sail plans of four single-masted rigs from Chapman's *Architectura Navalis Mercatoria* Plate LXII

Fig 117. 'English Hoy'. The gaff sail brails into the mast. (Chapman No 14)

Fig 118. 'English Cutter'. Compare this with figure 103. (Chapman No 15)

Fig 119. 'Sloop'. This is as heavily rigged as the cutter. (Chapman No 12)

Fig 120. 'Dutch Chalke'. Presumably this a shallow draught, almost flat-bottomed hull to have leeboards. (Chapman No 13).

plate LXII.

Amongst other plans in the Chapman Collection at Stockholm Maritime Museum are a 'French Trader of 75 tonns' for which there is a body plan with rounded floors, a sheer elevation and a deck layout; in addition there is a mast and rigging plan which includes all the running rigging. There are a topsail yard, spread yard and a fidded topmast raked aft. She probably has a fixed bowsprit and so is not a cutter. Another plan (figure 115) is of a 'Ballast Lighter' with just over two beams to length and rigged with a sprit on a short mast. A third plan (figure 116) is entitled 'Chalk Barge' and shows a flat-bottomed swim-header of chine construction which has leeboards and is rigged with a sprit. The hull is probably similar to that in figure 13 on plate L of Chapman's book of plans, which is entitled 'Chalk barge' in the list of plates. These plans and some others in the collection provide remarkably good details on rigging and masting techniques.

Many cutters were purchased by the Admiralty in the 1760s and their plans have survived, but they are all too fine-lined for consideration here, and in any case, they were illustrated in my earlier work, *Fast Sailing Ships*. In the Act of 1784 to prevent smuggling, cutters, luggers, shallops, wherries, smacks and yawls were proscribed if they were not 'square-rigged' or fitted with a standing bowsprit; and, further, no traveller was allowed on the bowsprit, nor was the setting of a flying jib. Other restrictions were that the length of the bowsprit must not be more than two-thirds the distance between the stem and sternpost at deck level; clinker construction was prohibited; the proportion of beams to length must not exceed three-and-a-half to one; no armament must be carried. The evasion of this Act was widespread, but it did make hulls broad for their length and gave encouragement to the rigs of sloop and brig for merchantmen.[108]

In America, some of the sloops were based on the

116

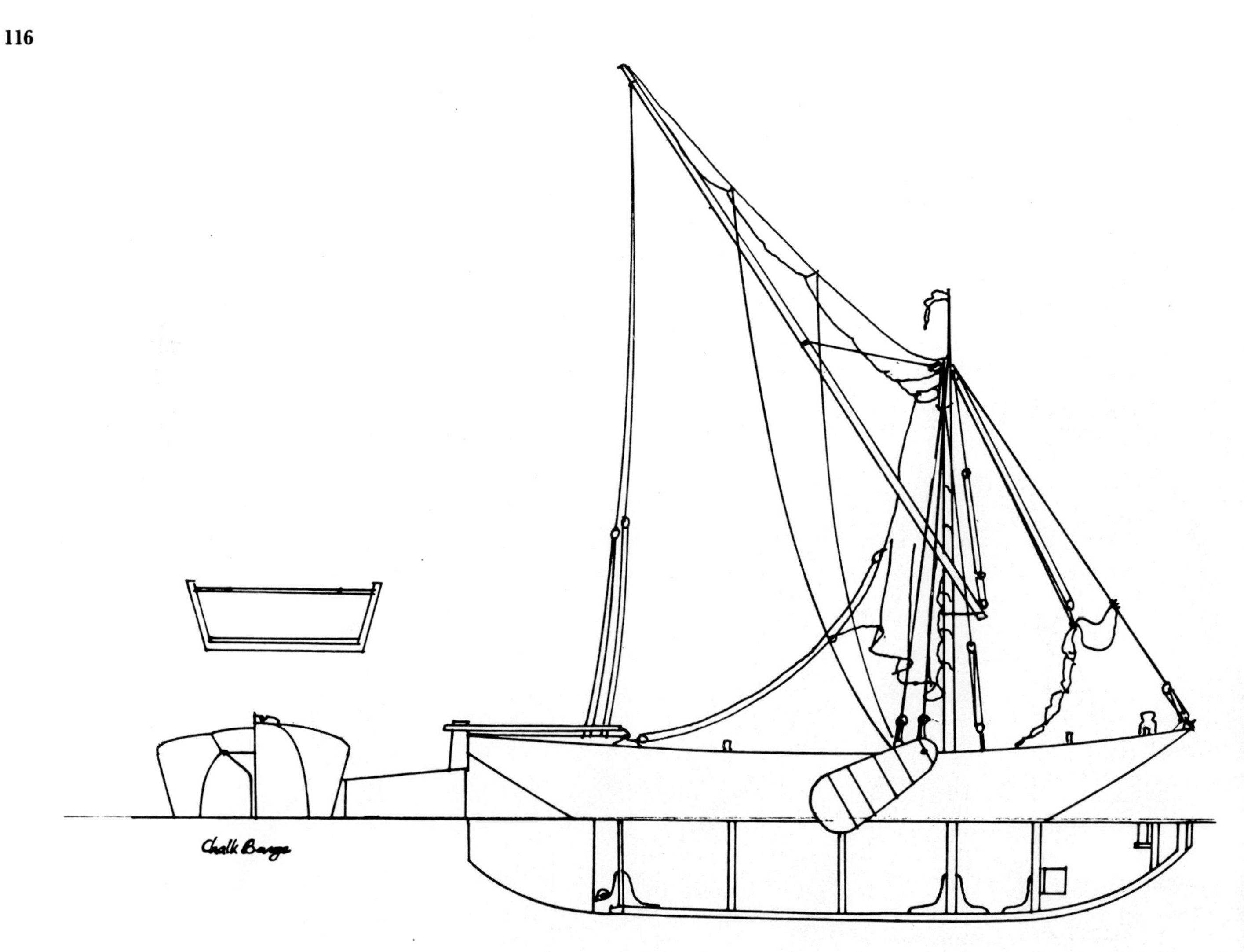

Fig 116. Chalk Barge. *Deck plan and sail plan, redrawn from a plan in the Chapman Collection at the Sjöhistoriska Museum, Stockholm. Similar to 'Chalk Barge, an English Vessel' in figure 13, plate L, in Chapman's work. She has the hull of a swim-header, and the base of the hull forms the centre line for the deck layout. I am grateful to David Lyon for drawing my attention to this plan and also the one in figure 115.*

Bermudian model such as the *Mediator* of 104 tons, purchased by the Royal Navy in 1745, with large deadrise, flaring sides, sharp entrance and run, rounded stem, and raking sternpost. The most prominent feature of her rig was the great length of the bowsprit and the main boom, which made the hull look comparatively short. There were a tall lower mast and a short topmast; two yards were carried, setting a topsail and a tall narrow square sail, and there were three headsails.[109] Other sloops would have had a hull built on fuller lines, but the sail area, although not so extreme, would have been large.

After the War of American Independence, two-masted shallops were built to replace the larger fishing schooners lost in the War, and these became known as 'Chebacco boats' after the Chebacco Parish of Ipswich, Massachusetts, later called Essex. Many boats had a pink stern which resulted in the survival of the term 'pinky' for this type of fishing schooner.

The development of small craft is a fascinating subject, but so complicated, with an infinite number of variations in each locality, that there is insufficient space here to treat the matter in anything but the broadest outline.

Fig 121. Two of the crew are climbing the rigging to furl the square topsail which is being clewed up, but it is strange that the topgallant has not been taken in first. This sloop has a jibboom which overlaps the bowsprit for half its length and the rig is generally very similar to that of Chapman's sloop in figure 119. The wind is from astern. In this engraving by Pierre Ozanne c1770, he writes 'barque' as a caption – a word he employs to denote a small vessel.

121

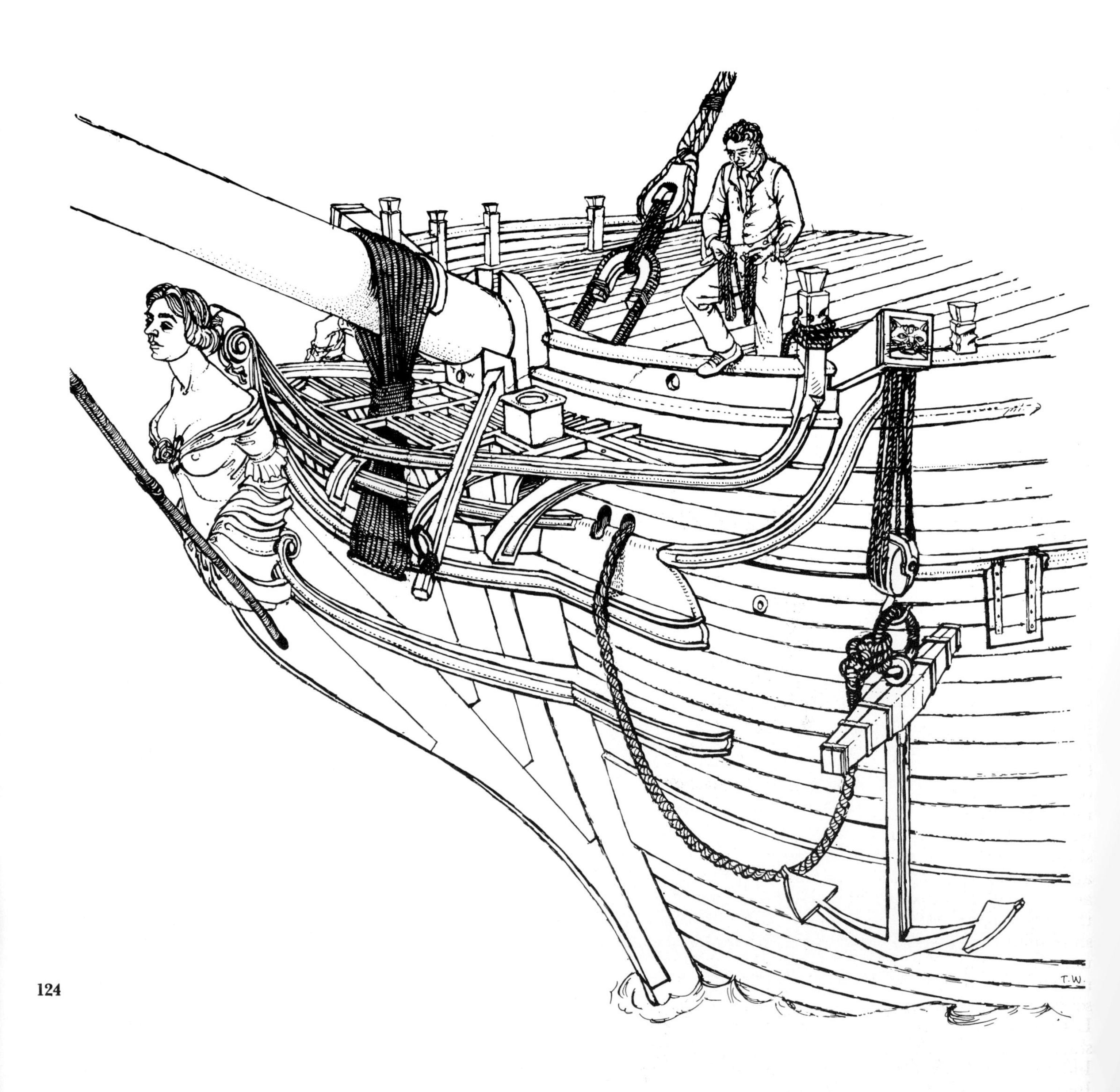

124

Fig 124. The head and figurehead of a merchant ship of about 1800, drawn by T W Ward. This is based on plans of the ship of 330 tons as illustrated here; a suitable figurehead has been reconstructed. The artist has drawn 'a seat of ease' next to the bumpkin.

3

SQUARE RIG AND FORE AND AFT 1793-1815

WEST INDIAMAN OF 330 TONS

The importance of published books of plans in moulding shipbuilders' thoughts was stressed in *Fast Sailing Ships 1775-1875*, Chapter 1, and a number of titles published in the eighteenth and nineteenth centuries were given. Other than Chapman's sixty-two plates in *Architectura Navalis Mercatoria* (1768) which was referred to extensively in our last chapter, the two English books with the largest collection of scale plans to appear before 1815 were Marmaduke Stalkartt's *Naval Architecture* (1781) and David Steel's *Elements and Practice of Naval Architecture* (1805). In France the Marine section of *Encyclopédie Méthodique* (1783-7) incorporated plates from existing books, including Chapman's, and the plates on shipping occupied most of one volume. In Steel's work, thirty-eight plans of naval and merchant ships were issued in a separate folio. This book was in its third edition by 1882 and was used in many shipyards as a standard work of reference.[1] The fact that the author categorically states that many of the plans represent actual vessels and that additional ships had been built from the same plans could only further endear it to practical shipbuilders. The merchant ship plans, which are all unnamed, consist of an East Indiaman of 1257 tons, a merchant ship of 544 tons, a collier brig, two Virginia schooners, a Bermuda schooner, a Berwick smack, a London trading smack, a Southampton hoy and various ships' boats. There are also tables of scantlings for three East Indiamen, of 1257, 1000 and 818 tons, and for three West Indiamen of 544, 440 and 330 tons.

Bearing in mind the author's reference to the draughts being taken from actual vessels, it is surely more than a coincidence to discover that the Blackwall Yard launched several ships of the very tonnages enumerated. The following were launched by 1805, the date of publication: of 1257 tons - *Alnwick Castle* and *Marquis of Ely* in 1801, *Royal George* in 1802, and *Essex* in 1803; of 818 tons - *Walpole* in 1798, *Lady Burgess* in 1799, *Wyndham* in 1800, and *Europe* in 1803; of 544 tons - *Harriott* in 1802.[2] (Although *Harriott* was launched for the East India trade, Steel's draught of a ship of this tonnage states that she is suitable for either the East or West India trade.)

A smaller work, *The Shipwright's Vade-Mecum*, also published by David Steel, appeared in 1805 and was in its second edition in 1822. This contained the lines plan of a 74-gun ship and three plans actually devoted to a 330-ton merchant ship. On the hypothesis that Steel may have obtained some of his plans from the Blackwall Yard, a manuscript list[3] was consulted which showed that, of the vessels built there in the twenty years prior to 1805, the ship with a tonnage closest to 330 tons was the *Three Sisters* of 329 tons. She was built in 1788. Her measurements, taken from the London Custom House register, give 103ft 6in (extreme length aloft), 27ft 11in (extreme breadth above the wales) and 5ft 9in (depth between decks); depth of hold is not stated. These dimensions agree very closely with those given by Steel on plate 2 which consists of 103ft 3¾in (between perpendiculars), 27ft 6in (extreme breadth) and 12ft 0in (depth of hold). In the London Custom House register the tonnage increases slightly to 333. '[The ship] of 330 tons, of which the dimensions are given,' writes David Steel, 'is peculiarly adapted for the West India trade; and has been found to answer so well that several ships have been built from the draught.'[4] There were of course many other yards on the Thames from which Steel could have obtained his data but the evidence assembled here suggests that the ship selected by him as an example could have been the *Three Sisters*. Similarly his table of scantlings and offsets must undoubtedly apply to the same vessel.[5]

The manuscript indicates that the ships built at Blackwall after the *Three Sisters* and nearest to her in tonnage, were the *Amity Hall*, 314 tons, built 1789; the *St. Vincent*, 340 tons, built 1797; and the *Walker*, 341 tons, built 1799 as a South Sea whaler. The first two ships were West Indiamen. See Appendix 3 for list of ships built at the Blackwall Yard.

Whether these plans actually represent the *Three Sisters* or some other vessel is largely immaterial, but the important points are that they do depict a typical merchant ship of 330 tons and that large numbers like her were afloat in the years 1790-1820. The lines, deck layout and longitudinal section given in figure 122 show a normal two-decked vessel with a

122

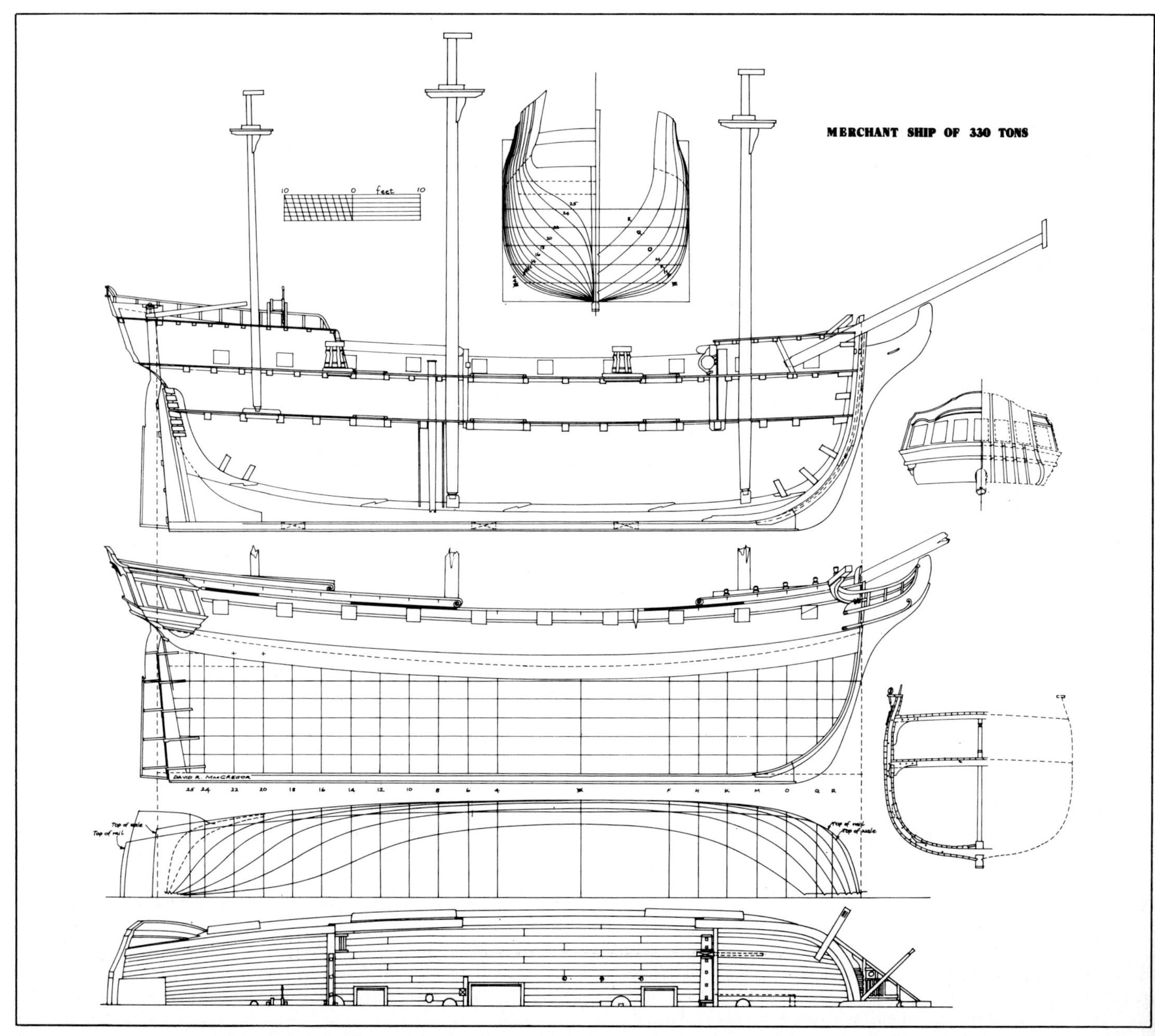

square stern, ornamental head, foc'sle and poop. She has flat floors and a barely discernible hollow at the garboard rising up to easy rounded bilges with wall sides from bilge to wales and above that a sharp tumblehome. There are a full convex entrance and a hollow run, and between the ends the middle body was designed without any dead flats. No centres of arcs are marked on the body plan to sweep in the bilges, nor are any buttock lines drawn.

As to fittings, there are two capstans on the upper deck, the windlass is abaft the foremast and no deckhouses are shown. This was still the era of war when decks with unrestricted views for fighting the ship or resisting attack were essential, but because of the low bulwarks, the gun ports are rather close to the deck. The chain plates are composed of two iron links, the middle link connecting to the deadeye, and the toe link to the preventer plate which was bolted top and bottom to the ship's side. The hanging knees are still of wood; in fact, no iron straps or knees are to be seen inside the hull. The deck line has little sheer. There is a round-headed rudder, which was first introduced in 1779. The register assigns to her a woman's figurehead and William Ward's drawing in figure 124 gives a possible interpretation. He also depicts, the solidity of the timber construction in the bluff bows. No long boat is drawn here but it would have been a substantial boat standing on deck between the fore capstan and the bitts by the mainmast; Steel gives the plan of a 19-foot boat in plate 4 of *The Shipwright's Vade-Mecum*, but there is space for only a 17-foot boat here. Steel indicates no ladderway on the outer planking nor any billboard, but many Admiralty draughts of merchant ships include both these features.

Sail and rigging plans to accompany the lines plans rarely exist for merchant ships prior to 1830, and there are very few for warships. Some spar dimensions are occasionally to be found on the draughts themselves, but recourse must usually be made to published works that either list spars, according to the rig and tonnage, or else give rules for finding their length, based on a given

Fig 122. Merchant Ship of 330 Tons. *Lines, sections and deck. Not positively identified but possibly the* Three Sisters *built 1788 at Blackwall, London, of 329 or 333 tons. Redrawn from plans in* The Shipwright's Vade-Mecum *by David Steel (1805). Some deck fittings have been reconstructed, but more details could be added. Dimensions on the plan: 103ft 3¼in (between perpendiculars) × 27ft 6in (extreme) × 12ft 0in. Further details are given in the text.*

Fig 123. Merchant Ship of 330 Tons. *Frame and Planking Expansion Plan, reproduced from plate 3 in* The Shipwright's Vade-Mecum *by David Steel (1805). The line of the planking can be followed, likewise the frames; the wide dark lines are the spaces between the frames. Stem, sternpost and keel are omitted. Below is Steel's plan of the Upper Deck, which was used in figure 122. Here the deck planking and deck beams are drawn.*

Fig 125. This painting by Francis Holman is dated 1784 or 1794 and depicts the ship Three Sisters *off Harwich. This was a popular name for a ship at the time, so that it cannot be said to portray the ship of which Steel provides plans, although it certainly does resemble her in many respects. The ship in the painting could set royals on fore and main as well as a mizen topgallant, but she does not have a dolphin striker. The hull also has similarities with that in figure 122. I had not seen this painting when I drew out Steel's plans* (Rutland Gallery)

123

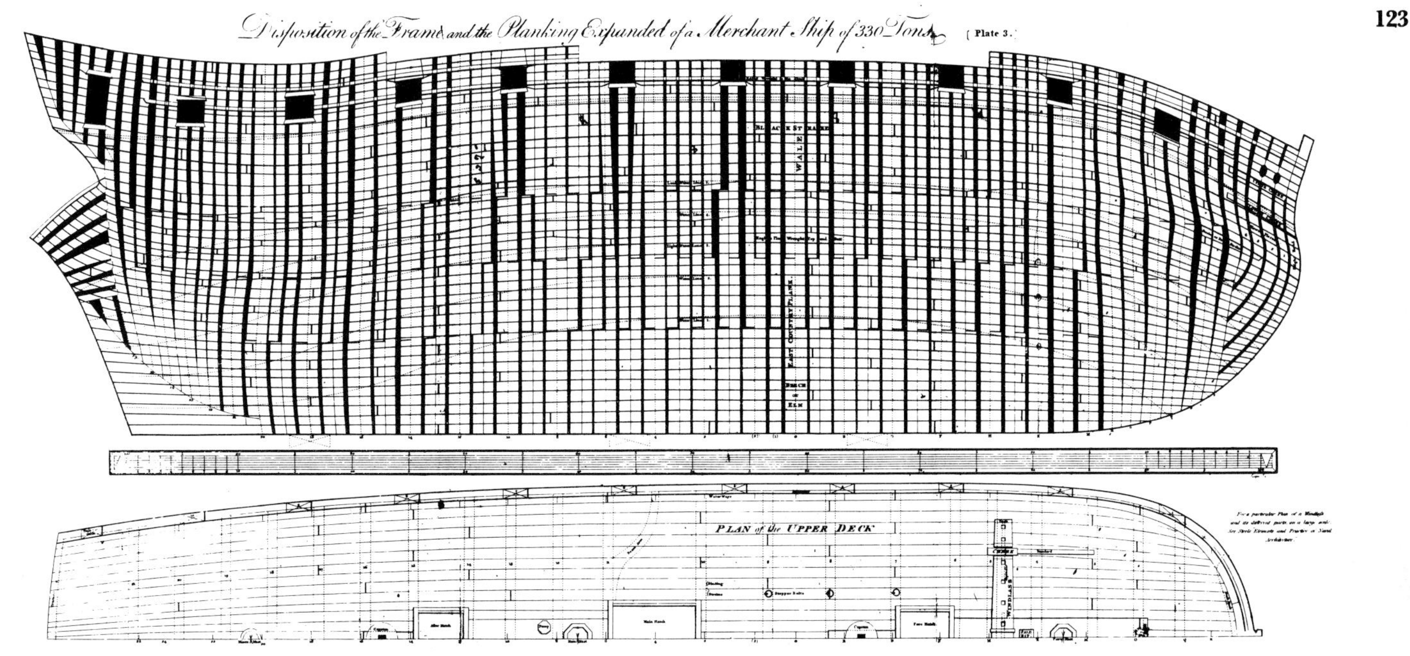

125

126

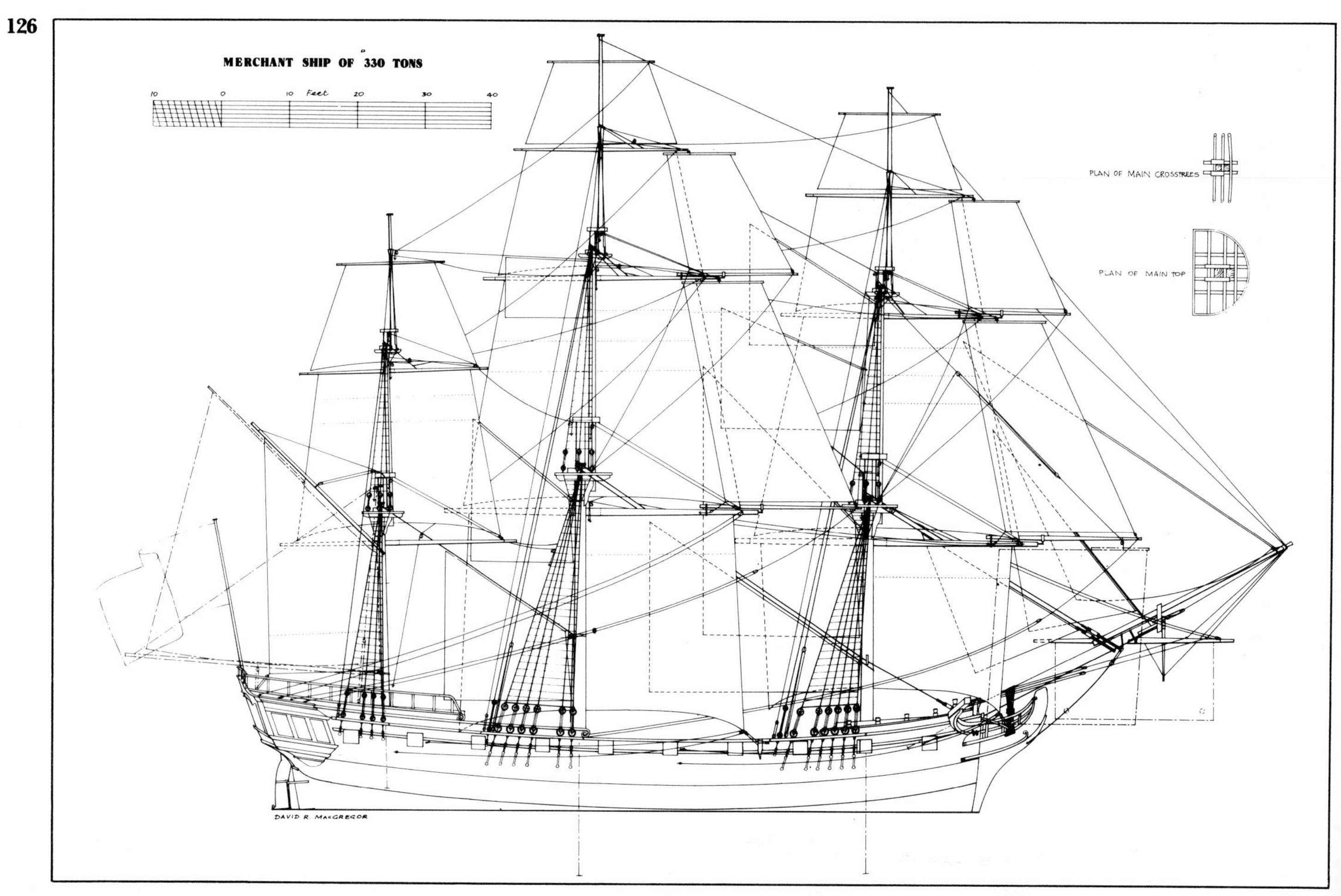
MERCHANT SHIP OF 330 TONS
10 0 10 Feet 20 30 40
PLAN OF MAIN CROSSTREES
PLAN OF MAIN TOP
DAVID R. MACGREGOR

127

Fig 126. Merchant Ship of 330 Tons. *Sail plan. This is possibly the* Three Sisters *built at Blackwell, London, in 1788 of 329 or 333 tons. The plan was entirely reconstructed from the following sources: sheer elevation from the lines plan; spar dimensions from Steel's* Rigging and Seamanship *(1794), vol I, table for ship of 300 to 330 tons; sails and rigging from the same work and Darcy Lever's* Sheet Anchor *(1808); contemporary paintings.*

Fig 127. A ship getting under way in Pegwell Bay near Deal, as painted by Thomas Whitcombe in 1810. The ship is coming from the right, and in the centre of the painting she has got the royals loosed and ready for hoisting; the stunsail booms are being run out and men are aloft overhauling the gear; many of the staysails are set. On the left of the painting, she is seen under a cloud of canvas. She carries a broadside of six guns. It is interesting to note that there is a bobstay above and below the spritsail yard, thus making it impossible to set a sail here.

Fig 128. A spirited engraving by Jean Baugean of two very different vessels running before the wind. The one on the right he labels 'Tartane'. The one on the left, 'Merchant vessel', has stunsails out to starboard on the foremast, and out to port on the main; the sheets of the topgallant and royal on the main have been let fly to allow wind to blow under the bellying sails to those on the foremast. As it is, the fore topsail has no wind in it and is driving back against the mast as the ship creams along. She has lowered all her headsails but has a spritsail set. A crossjack yard and mizen topsail can be seen through the gaps in the sails on the mainmast. The tartane has also got her flying kites set, with a large jib boomed out to port and raffees above her topsail yard.
(*Published in 1814 by Baugean as plate 52 in* Collection de Bâtiments de Guerre et de Ba Bâtiments Marchands)

SPAR DIMENSIONS OF MERCHANT SHIP OF 330-300 TONS FROM STEEL'S *ART OF MAKING MASTS, YARDS &c (1816 ed)*

	Masts or Booms		**Yards**	
	Length	Dia.	Length	Dia
Main mast and yard	66ft 0in	19in	47ft 0in	12in
Main topmast and yard	38ft 0in	12in	35ft 0in	9in
Main topgallant mast and yard	19ft 0in	6½in	26ft 0in	6
Main royal yard	13ft 0in	4½in	16ft 0in	4
Fore mast and yard	61ft 0in	19in	45ft 0in	11½in
Fore topmast and yard	37ft 0in	12in	32ft 0in	8½in
Fore topgallant mast and yard	18ft 0in	6½in	25ft 0in	5¾in
Fore royal yard	12ft 0in	4½in	15ft 0in	4
Mizen mast and gaff	58ft 0in	13in	26ft 0in	6½in
Mizen topmast and yard	28ft 0in	9in	28ft 0in	7
Mizen topgallant mast and yard	15ft 0in	4½in	16ft 0in	4
Bowsprit	42ft 0in	19in	30ft 0in	7
Jibboom	33ft 0in	9in		
Driverboom	38ft 0in	7½in	20ft 0in	5
Crossjack yard			35ft 0in	7
Lower studdingsail boom and yard	25ft 0in	6in	15ft 0in	4½in
Main topmast studdingsail boom and yard	24ft 0in	5¾in	12ft 0in	4
Main topgallant studdingsail boom and yard	18ft 0in	4¼in	10ft 0in	3½in
Fore topmast studdingsail boom and yard	23ft 0in	5¾in	12ft 0in	4
Fore topgallant studdingsail boom and yard	19ft 0in	4¼in	10ft 0in	3½in
Ensign staff	26ft 0in	5½in		
Jack staff	13ft 0in	4		

128

dimension of the hull.

The two principal reference works in English for reconstructing a sail plan at this date are David Steel's *Rigging and Seamanship*, first published in 1794 but with many subsequent reprintings, and Darcy Lever's *The Young Sea-Officer's Sheet Anchor*, first published in 1808. Contemporary models, paintings and drawings give valuable corroborative evidence.

The reconstructed sail and rigging plan in figure 126 for the merchantman is based on the above sources, and the lengths of the masts and spars are taken from Steel's tables for a merchant ship of 300 to 330 tons.[6] The same lengths appeared twenty years later in a reprint of 1816 but between the two editions the word 'topgallant royal' had changed to 'royal'. It should be noted that the published plans have the heel of the mizen mast stepped on the lower deck as in the *Cupid* of 1777 (figure 77). This arrangement was none too frequent. Steel's table makes no allowance for a short mizen lower mast, and so the length has been taken as though the mast stepped on the keelson, otherwise the top would have been unacceptably high. No mizen royal yard or mast is given, and so the topgallant mast is drawn with a common pole head. As dimensions are given for the short mizen gaff, as well as the driver boom and yard, the latter has been drawn dotted for better clarification. By 1805, some merchant ships would have adopted the mizen royal and the spanker as standard features. The evolution of the spanker is covered in Chapter 2 (*see* Masts, Sails and Rigging in Three-Masted Vessels). In 1794, Steel showed a dolphin striker or martingale in one of his plates which suggests that it had been in use for at least ten years, as he is hardly likely to have indicated any fittings on his plans that were not well-proven in practical usage. It has accordingly been incorporated here. Nicholas Pocock also drew a vessel in 1794 with one.[7] The standing jib was the principal headsail and hooked on to a traveller on the jibboom; the jib stay was shackled to this traveller before leading out to a sheave in the end of the jibboom and thence back to the bowsprit cap or the bows, where it was set up with a tackle.

The painting by T Whitcombe getting under way illustrates the changes which were taking place in about 1800. Compared with Steel's merchantman, there is no evidence of a short, old-style mizen gaff and so the spanker must be the regular sail. A mizen royal is set; the fore and main royals have braces; a main middle staysail is set; and the main topmast staysail sets up on a spring stay. Men are aloft, standing on the footropes and rigging out the stunsail booms. The spritsail yard has a bobstay above and below and cannot therefore set a sail.

Fig 129. William Miles. *Lines plan and details. She was built in 1808 at Bristol by J M Hilhouse. Dimensions: 127ft 8in × 32ft 4in × 24ft 8½in, and 577 tons. Redrawn by Paul A Roberts from a photostat of the builder's plan in the possession of Charles Hill & Sons. Reconstruction: masts, bowsprit, channels, elevation of deck fittings from a plan of* St Vincent *(1804). Also included on the sheet is a part cross-section of* Nelson *(1806) and a bow construction of* St Vincent*, both built by Hilhouse.*

129

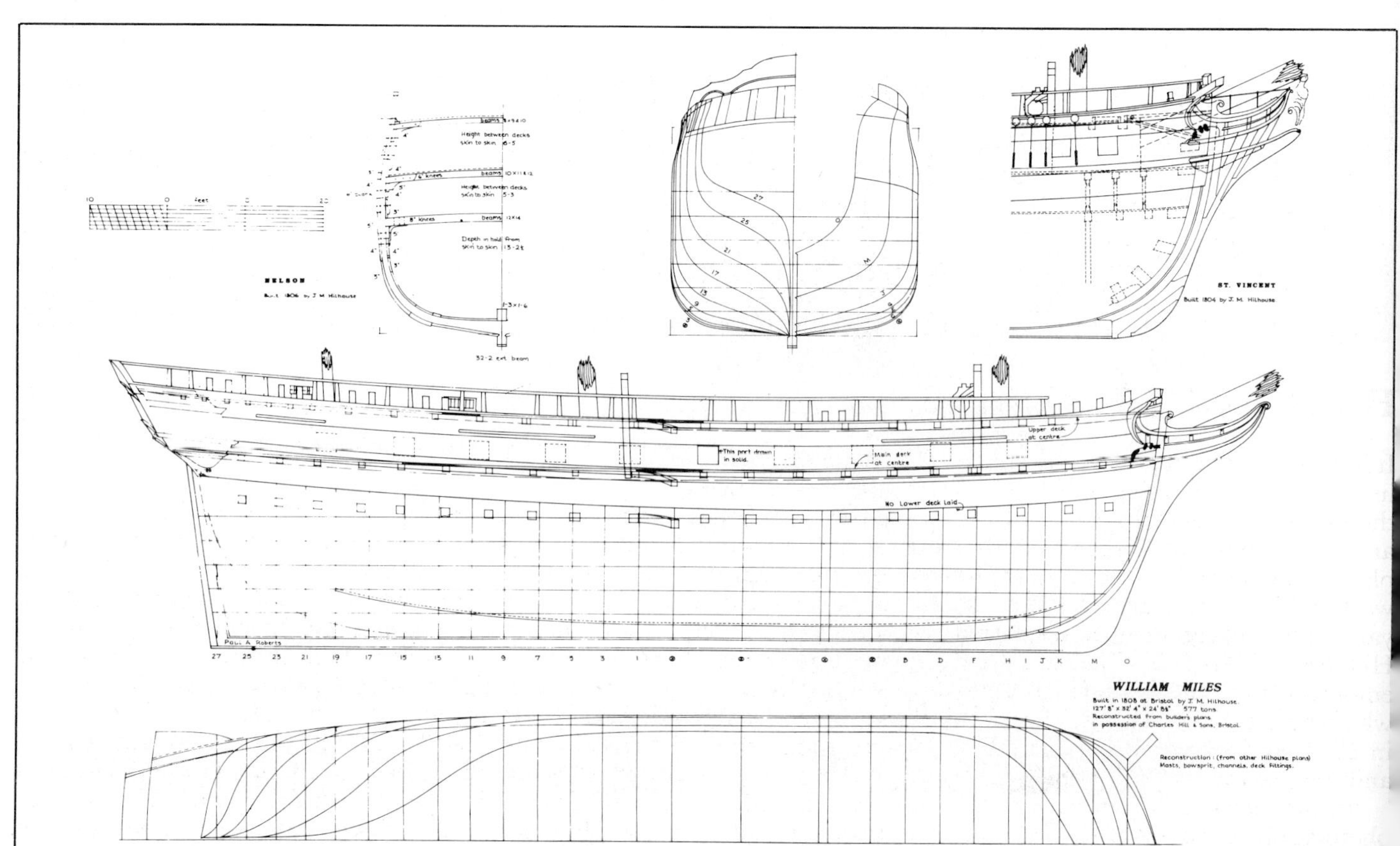

130

HILHOUSE OF BRISTOL

Fig 130. Photograph of the second William Miles, *built at Bristol in 1816, originally as a ship of 324 tons. The tumblehome, bluff entrance, and open bow port can be clearly seen.* (Nautical Photo Agency)

It is fortunate that representative sets of plans have survived in the case of several shipbuilders. Among them, those from the yards of Adams of Buckler's Hard, Hilhouse of Bristol and Brocklebank of Whitehaven are more numerous than plans from other builders. It makes comparisons more worth while if there are several to examine from the same yard. The collection of plans formed by James Martin Hilhouse (1748–1822) is particularly interesting as it embraces not only his own ships, but also other vessels which he measured. He had opened his shipyard at Bristol in 1772, and was soon busy building both merchantmen and men-of-war.

At the Science Museum, London, one can examine photographs of many of the Hilhouse draughts, although they scarcely do justice to the beautifully executed originals which I was able to examine through the kindness of John C G Hill when in possession of Charles Hill & Sons. It should be noticed that the folio numbers assigned by the Science Museum do not correspond with those on the actual plans, and it is the builder's folio numbers which are employed here. The plans cover a period of sixty-five years from 1776 and form a valuable comment on merchant ship design, although spar dimensions are virtually non-existent.

When James Martin Hilhouse died in 1822, his son George took control. In 1825 he admitted Charles Hill into partnership and the title of the firm became Hilhouse, Hill & Co. The firm owned and operated a number of ships they had built, which traded to the West Indies, India and

131

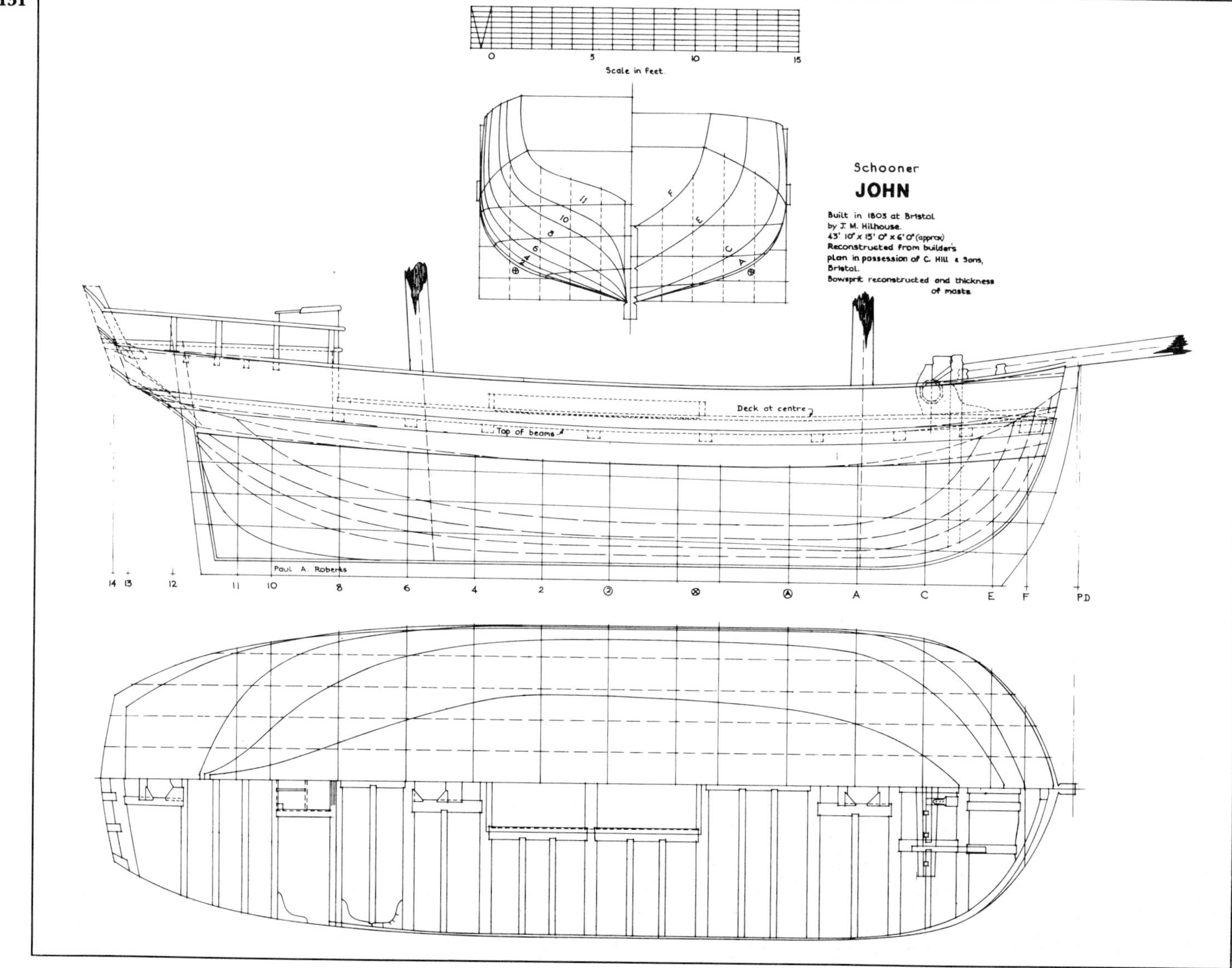

Fig 131. John. *Lines and deck of a schooner built in 1803 at Bristol by J M Hilhouse. Dimensions scaled off the plan: 43ft 10 in (for register) × 15ft 0in (moulded) × 6ft 0in (approx); 43 or 50 tons. Redrawn by Paul A Roberts from the Author's tracing of the builder's plan when it was in the possession of Charles Hill & Sons. Reconstruction: bowsprit and mast thickness.*

Fig 132. An intriguing perspective by Robert Hilhouse of an unidentified craft, but presumably a brig or brigantine, to judge by the fore top. It is rare at this date to get such informative three-dimensional drawings of deck fittings. (Photographed from the original which was in the possession of Charles Hill & Sons, through the courtesy of John C G Hill.)

China. In 1845 George Hilhouse decided to let his partner Charles Hill take control of the whole business, as there were no young members of his family to carry on. The name of the firm was altered to Charles Hill & Sons, which has been retained to the present day.[8]

In *Fast Sailing Ships*, I described at length the steep-floored and fine-lined ships, schooners and cutters either built by the yard or whose plans were collected, and two such plans were reproduced: a Post Office packet in figure 38, and the fruit schooner *Sappho* in figure 61. In the present volume, a plan of the full-bodied *Exeter* was given in figure 65 in the last chapter, and it will be seen that her waterlines were less full than those of the *William Miles*, reproduced here.

Many of Hilhouse's ships were designed to carry the maximum amount of cargo with scant regard to their sailing qualities. This was achieved by giving them a square box-like section for half their length. After a very full entrance, the *William Miles* carried this parallel middle body for some thirty feet before it turned quickly into a hollow run. Her lines plan in figure 129 shows this clearly and also the wall-sided midship section. There was a flush upper deck, surrounded by an open rail, making three

132

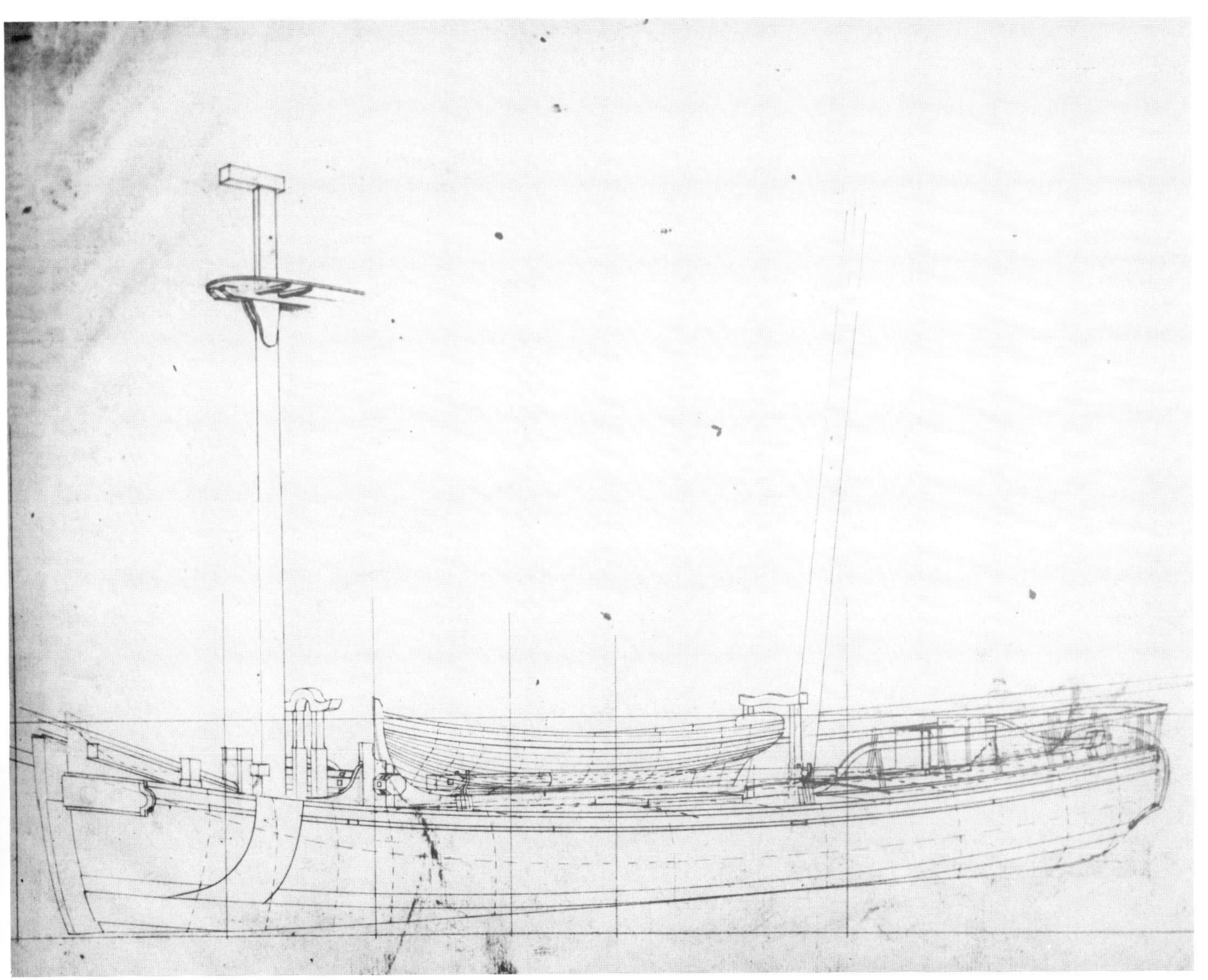

decks together. This third deck was added for convenience in cargo stowage, enabling certain goods to be kept separate where there was a risk of damage and preventing other cargoes, such as hogsheads of sugar, from being crushed in the lower tiers by the weight above. In this case, the height of the lower 'tween decks was 4ft 10in. The *St Vincent* (1804) and *Nelson* (1806) were built on very similar lines. In 1809 the *William Miles* was described as a 'well armed running ship', and this in spite of her full body. When she stranded on the falling tide in the River Avon in 1813 – her crew having suddenly deserted her on catching sight of the press gang – a Bristol newspaper called her a 'burthensome ship with a remarkable convexity in her hold'.[9] The *St Vincent* survived until 1860.

The *William Miles* was originally built for the West Indies trade, but after her sale to London owners in 1817 she entered the India trade. She was built at Bristol in 1808 by J M Hilhouse to the order of Philip John Miles, who owned several ships built by Hilhouse. She measured 127ft 8in × 32ft 4in × 24ft 8½in (below the upper deck) and 577 tons. A fair estimate of her cost can be deduced from the first cost of the *Nelson*, launched by Hilhouse for the same owner two years earlier and of very similar tonnage; this is given as £10,600,[10] which results in £18 9s 3d per ton on 547 tons.

In 1815 there were from 700 to 900 ships engaged in the West Indies trade,[11] but the majority of them were slow ships, built to carry the maximum amount of cargo and in war time they always sailed in convoy, a system which did not encourage fast, weatherly vessels. However, fast well-armed ships could obtain licences to sail independently. Such vessels were termed 'running ships' and were sure of good employment in any trade.

In 1828 the *William Miles* carried 192 convicts to Tasmania, making the passage in 127 days, under barque rig. Care must be taken not to confuse her with a second ship of the same name, built in 1816 at Bristol for the same owners. The second ship was probably so named to replace the earlier one which was on the point of being sold. A photograph of the second *William Miles* (figure 130) shows the very bluff bows given to bulk carriers of the period, as indicated by the waterline and run of the planking. The timber port beside the stem reveals the trade in which she was engaged.

With one exception, all the Hilhouse plans of schooners are of steep-floored vessels, but the exception is the *John*, built in 1803. No doubt others like her were produced, but no plans have survived to prove it. The register for *John* has not survived in the Custom House, but dimensions scaled off the plan give 43ft 10in register length, 15ft 0in moulded breadth and 7ft 3in top of deck to bottom of rabbet amidships; depth of hold would be approximately 6ft 0in. When loaded, she drew 7ft which gave a freeboard of only 2ft 2in. Tonnage according to *Lloyd's Register* (Underwriters' Green Book) was 43, but the Shipowners' Red Book gives 50. She was sheathed with copper in 1803 and sailed for Barbados in October, presumably remaining there in the inter-island trade.

The lines plan in figure 131, shows a hull with appreciable deadrise, slack bilges and very little tumblehome, but her great beam gave big stowage capacity. For a schooner, she was very full-bodied with a proportion of only 2.92 beams to length. Brocklebank's shallop built in 1806 for the West Indies (figure 140) had a proportion of 3.06 beams to length; and the plan prepared in 1803 by the Admiralty to build a small schooner at Port Jackson has 3.11 beams to length.[12] The latter had less deadrise than the *John* but a slightly finer entrance and run; she has the same long hatchway between the masts, but the deck is flush, and there is a square tuck stern with no counter. The Brocklebank shallop is discussed in a following section.

The *John* has a large overhang to the counter for a small vessel and the counter timbers are shown, but no wing transom. The wales presumably terminated at quarter pieces. Although the break of the poop is 2ft 6in high and a companionway is drawn, no floor is given to the after cabin; indeed, the builder's drawing contains no constructional details below deck level. A perspective drawing, probably done by Robert Hilhouse of a somewhat similar type of hull, is illustrated in figure 132. The principal differences are that there is no poop and that the windlass is abaft the foremast. However, the perspective gives a good idea of the shape of the Hilhouse deck fittings and the large longboat provided. The two crutches mounted just inside the bulwark to hold a spar are just visible, but the planking of the longboat has been superimposed, in one place by dotted lines and at the bows by solid lines, which is confusing. Like that in the *John*, the mainmast is placed rather far aft because of the long hatchway which makes a big overhang to the main boom. Another similarity is the noticeable after-rake given to the mast. In the perspective, the top on the foremast indicates a fully square-rigged mast; on the mainmast, the cap and top have been drawn in pencil but never inked in. The rig of brig without a square main course is probable here with lower masts of almost equal height.

Robert Hilhouse, James's third son, drew a number of other perspectives which included several cutters, a swim-headed spritsail barge, a Dutch tjalk and a man-of-war. He undoubtedly redrew plans to a small scale for this purpose in order to get his vanishing points on one sheet of paper. One plan probably reduced for this purpose is the schooner or shallop in folio 51. Drawn to ⅛in scale, the keel is about 7in long. The two lower masts are drawn and their gaffs are just discernible. The deck layout and hull shape bear

133

considerable similarities with the perspective view in figure 132. This shallop has steep floors, unlike the *John*. The latter was described as 'schooner' on the builder's plan, and could presumably have had some square canvas on the foremast, unlike Brocklebank's purely fore-and-aft rigged shallop.

The craft described as 'shallop' on the Hilhouse plans were all single-masted, and a number were built, presumably for use in the West Indies, where they were probably taken on a ship's deck and rigged on arrival. In the present case, the shallops were really enlarged longboats and, with the exception of its counter stern, the same could be said for the *John*. For ease of comparison, the following table lists the dimensions of the *John*, two shallops and a longboat whose plans have been examined.

COMPARISON OF MEASUREMENTS ON FOUR HILHOUSE PLANS OF SIMILAR HULL-FORM

Name and type	Date	Dimensions
John Schooner	1803	43ft 10in register × 15ft 0in moulded × 6ft 0in approx
Clara 'Shallop no 2' (one mast)	1796	34ft 6in keel & forerake × 13ft 0in moulded × 6ft 4in
'Shallop no 13' (one mast)	?	28ft 6in to 33ft overall × 10ft 0in moulded × 5ft 8in
'Longboat no 4'	1807	23ft to 28ft overall x 9ft 0in moulded x 4ft 6in

The number of hogsheads that could be carried was left blank in two cases. The *Clara's* mast measured 46ft 11in from heel to truck, the bowsprit 31ft 2in, the boom 34ft 3in, and the gaff 18ft 0in.

BROCKLEBANK OF WHITEHAVEN

Daniel Brocklebank (1751–1801) had built five ships in New England between 1770–75, before he returned post-haste to his home town of Whitehaven as tension mounted between the Colonists and the British troops. The first ship that he built in his own yard at Whitehaven was the brig *Perseverance*, launched in 1788, and thereafter he produced an average of two vessels each year. In *Fast Sailing Ships*, a lines plan of the *Jupiter* of 1793 was reproduced in figure 33, with comments by Daniel Brocklebank on her performance and hull-form. He considered the lower part of the entrance as made 'very sharp and thin with considerable hollow', and indeed she was so, compared with the bluff-bowed *Irton*

Fig 133. This Norwegian ship with a bark's hull is the Jakob Kielland & Søn *of Stavanger, built in 1799. This watercolour by N Camillieri depicts her off Marseilles in 1805. She appears to be flush-decked, but the solid bulwarks do not run forward of the main rigging.* (Maritime Museum, Kronborg)

Fig 134. Cumberland. *Lines plan. A full-rigged ship, built in 1800 at Whitehaven by Daniel Brocklebank. Dimensions: 98ft 6in (aloft) × 27ft 4in (moulded) × 18ft 6in and 341 tons. The plan was reproduced from a tracing made of the original builder's plan in the Liverpool County Museums.*

134

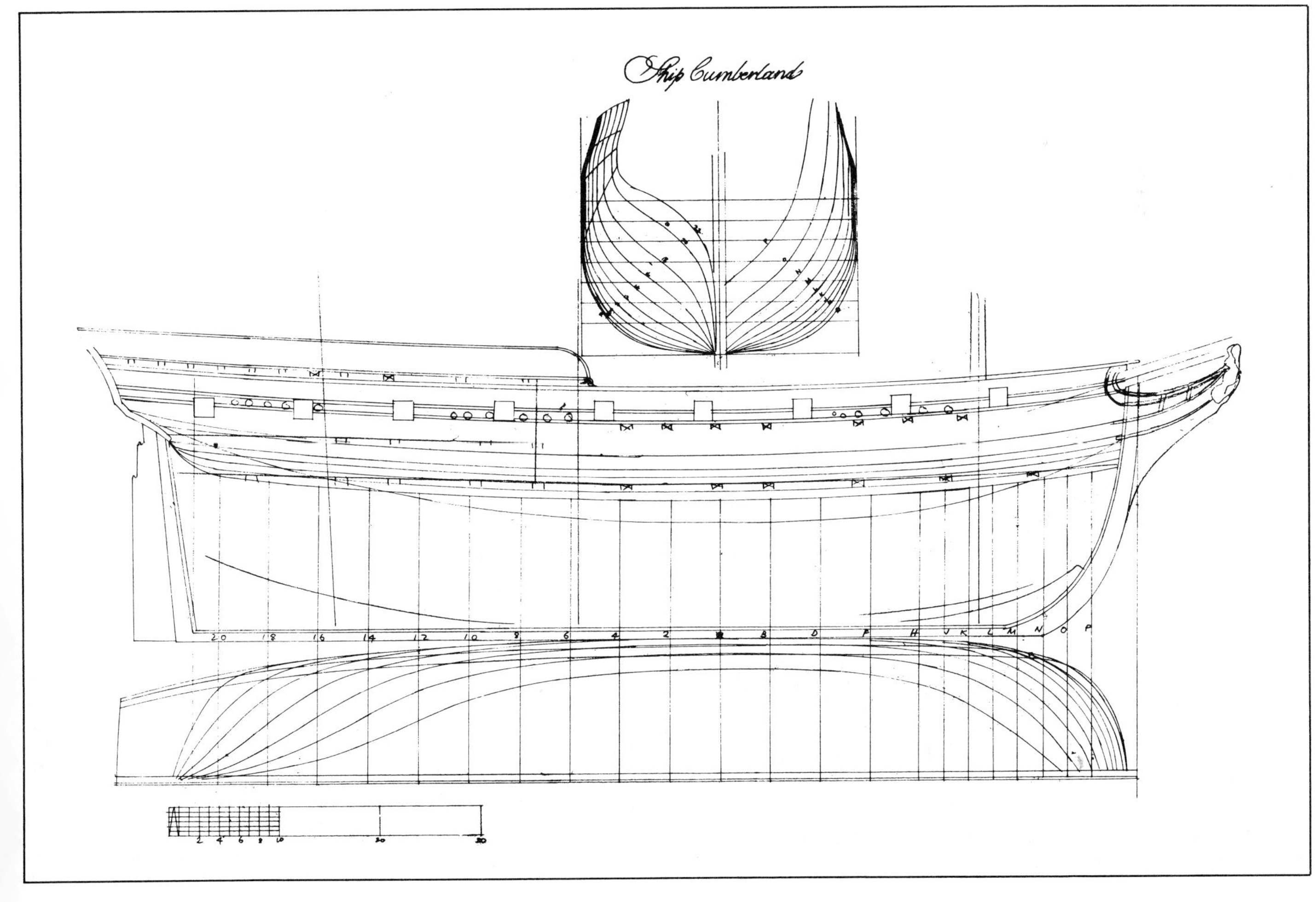

135

Fig 135. Here is one of Brocklebank's ships, the Antigua Packet, *starting to take in sail by lowering her stunsails; she is pictured off the land, probably inward bound, and there is a pilot lugger under her lee in the left-hand view. This ship was constructed in 1815 at the company's own yard at Whitehaven and measured 272 tons. Vessels of this size were often being rigged as barques from then on.* (Merseyside County Museums)

(1793) and other brigs of the 1790s, but certainly not when compared with the average Baltimore clipper schooner. The *Jupiter's* midship section is rounded all the way up, whereas the other surviving plans have vertical topsides and flatter floors.

These Brocklebank plans were first inspected at the Company's offices at Liverpool in the 1950s; later they were examined in greater detail at the Liverpool Museum through the courtesy of Michael Stammers, Keeper of Shipping. The plans are mostly drawn on Whatman paper in sepia ink, and the waterlines in the half-breadth plan and on the sheer elevation were often dotted in thc 1790s. All the plans were drawn to show the starboard side, with one exception, an unnamed brig drawn on paper with an 1810 watermark. The scale varied: often it was a proportional one, not fractional, and at other times no scale was either drawn or specified.

The published history of the firm, *Brocklebanks 1770–1950*, by John F. Gibson, is an invaluable guide to the story of the ships and it includes a detailed list of all those built;[13] but the numbers assigned to each in order do not correspond with the yard numbers to be found in the notebook begun by Daniel Brocklebank. This manuscript book in the Museum's archives lists particulars of nearly all the ships on one or more pages, beginning with the *Jupiter* of 1793 and closing with the brigantine *Ariel*, No 150. The particulars usually include the ship's measurements and the spar dimensions and, starting with No 49, there is nearly always an accompanying table of offsets. No costs are given in this notebook, but Gibson's history occasionally refers to values and prices. It would appear that the yard was almost entirely concerned with new work because there are only occasional references to alterations. Presumably the yard was operated entirely for the company's own fleet, but whether they carried out repairs there after each voyage is unknown.

Up to 1815, half the production of the yard was in brigs or snows, as the following totals show: 16 ships, 40 brigs, 2 snows, 1 schooner, 2 cutters, 1 sloop. Sizes of each varied greatly, but the largest brig was the *Balfour* of 310 tons and the largest ship was the *Volunteer* of 353 tons.

The full-rigged ship *Cumberland*, yard No 27, was built in 1800 for John Hartley & Sons and registered 340 $^{90}/_{94}$ tons, which makes her almost their largest ship of this period. Her dimensions were 98ft 6in length aloft, 27ft 4in moulded breadth, 18ft 6in depth of hold, and 4ft 9in height between decks. The hull-form on her plan is of a deep, broad ship with a moderately full entrance but a finer run, flat floors that quickly round up into slack bilges with vertical sides above, and marked tumblehome. The original plan in ink embodies only a plain stem, but a head has been added in pencil. Nine ports are cut in the side and the poop runs almost to the mainmast. No royal masts or yards are specified in the spar dimensions. The height of the mainmast from deck to head of the topgallant mast is 92ft 6in; that of the foremast is 86ft 0in; on the mizen the height is 57ft 6in to the head of the topmast, as no topgallant mast or yard is listed. The main yard is 45ft 0in between the cleats, the topsail yard 33ft 0in and the topgallant yard 23ft 0in. Brocklebank's ship *King George*, built in 1804, had a similar midship section although not quite so deep.

The great depth of hold in relation to register length is a typical feature of most Brocklebank ships, which were built to carry their owner's cargoes, and where any inducement to make a fast passage was unnecessary. In any case, depth of hold was not measured for tonnage, and so this proportion was untaxed. A table on page 134 lists ratios of even deeper ships built at Greenock by Steele & Carswell.

Ships continued to be built with only a two-piece mizen but crossing two yards, and the *Montgomery* of 1799 was a small ship of this type registering only 190 tons and measuring 84ft 0in × 22ft 9in × 15ft 5in. The mizen lower mast was shorter than the main lower mast, being 27ft 0in deck to hounds, as against 32ft 6in on the main and 29ft 6in on the fore. On the mizen there were two yards: a crossjack yard of 25ft 6in (cleated) and a topsail yard of 19ft 0in (cleated). There was no trysail gaff on the foremast, but the main boom was exceptionally long and measured 42ft and the main gaff 27ft; whereas, on the mizen, the boom measured only 27ft and the gaff 18ft. The rig was really that of a brig with an additional mast. According to Gibson's history of the firm, the first barque was the *Crown* of 1821.[14]

The largest brig, the *Balfour* of 310 tons was bigger than many of the full-rigged ships. Built in 1809, she had the following measurements: 97ft 10in (aloft) × 27ft 0½in (extreme) × 18ft 6in. The design was fairly similar to that of the *Cumberland*, but had a more upright stem. A longboat made for her in about 1812 measured 24ft 6in × 8ft 6in (extreme) × 4ft 2in and was schooner-rigged like the sail plan in figure 141, with masts 23ft high, gaffs 5ft long and a main boom of 18ft.

The *Balfour's* spar dimensions make the lower mast on the main 4ft 6in longer than on the fore, but otherwise the masts and yards on the foremast were identical in length to the corresponding spars on the main. The width of the tops is given as 13ft 9in. The cleated length of the lower yards was 40ft. This 'cleated' length excludes the yardarms, or distance between the cleat – to which the head earing is secured – and the extreme end of the yard. An incomplete sail plan feintly drawn in pencil was found on the back of the *Balfour's* lines plan, but the hull size is smaller, unless drawn to a different scale. Its chief feature is the large size of the fore trysail.

Of the other brigs, many were of the conventional type with a head and trail boards, bulwarks, a fairly full entrance but a finer run, and a rounded cross section. *Scipio* of 242 tons, built in 1797, was of this kind. But there was also another basic hull-form of a deep full-bodied carrier, of

Fig 136. Irton. *Lines plan. The brig was built in 1793 at Whitehaven by Daniel Brocklebank. Dimensions: 83ft 6in × 24ft 0in (moulded) × 16ft 0in and 201 tons. Redrawn by Paul A Roberts from the Author's tracing of the builder's plan in the Liverpool County Museums. Reconstruction: stern elevation of similar brig; roughtree rail; knightheads. Body plan and waterlines in half-breadth plan were drawn dotted on the original.*

136

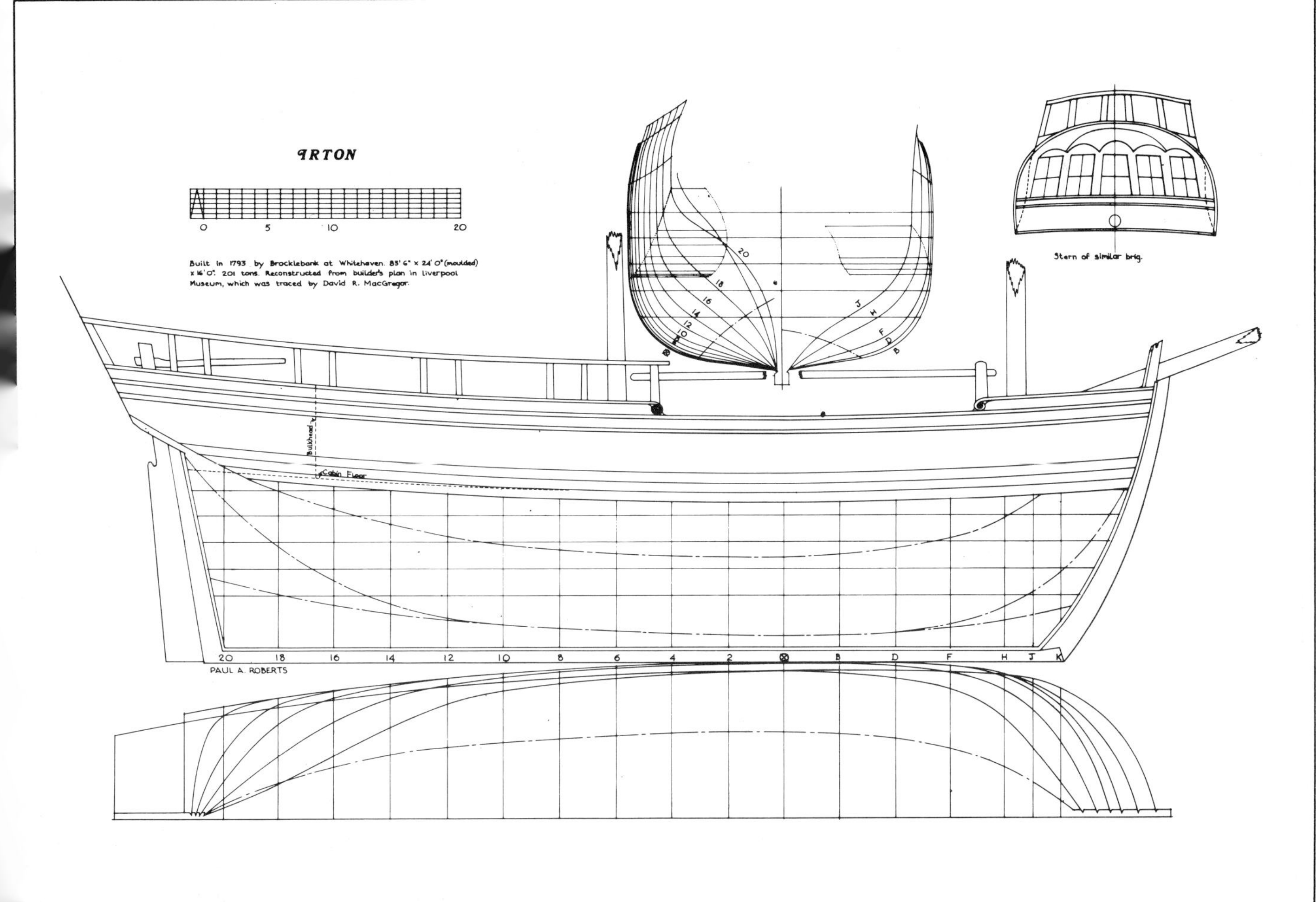

137

138

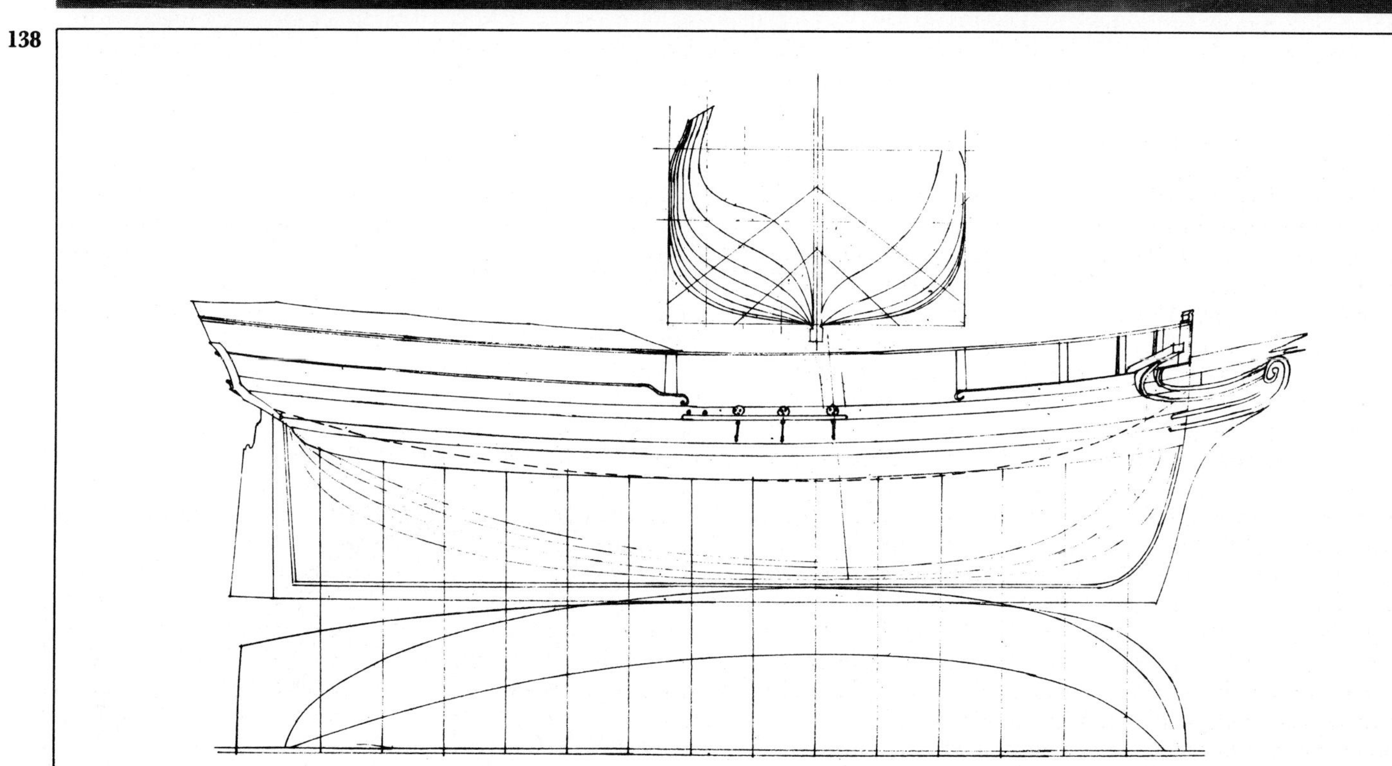

Fig 137. This painting of the Alice *pictures a craft rather similar to the* Irton *in figure 136, for which there is no sail plan.* Lloyd's Registers *of 1812–13 list two brigs and two snows named* Alice, *all of about 160 tons, one of each rig being built in America. A possible candidate is the snow of 159 tons that was built at Barmouth, Wales, in 1804 with a draught of 12ft and owned in London by J Bedwell. In 1807 she sailed to Gibraltar.* (Parker Gallery)

Fig 138. Brocklebank Sloop or Cutter. *Lines plan, unidentified, but possibly the* Earl of Lonsdale *built in 1798 at Whitehaven by Daniel Brocklebank. No scale has been drawn or specified. The plan is reproduced from a pencil tracing I made of the original builder's plan in the Liverpool County Museums, by courtesy of Michael K Stammers. The half-breadth plan has diagonals projected, but no waterlines.*

Fig 139. Sail plan of an unidentified cutter or sloop in the Brocklebank archives. No scale has been written or drawn. This is reproduced from a tracing of the original plan which I made in the Liverpool County Museums.

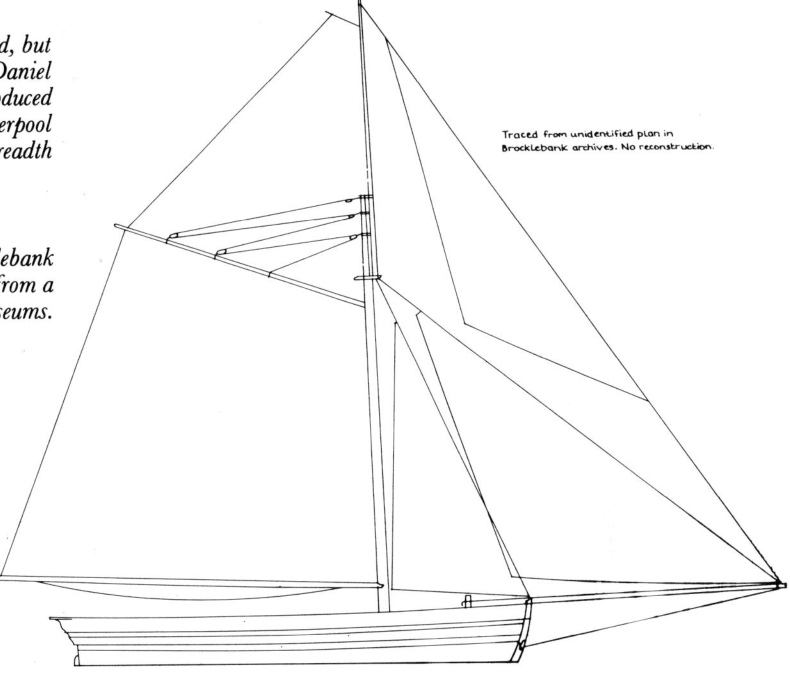

which the brig *Irton*, built in 1793, is a good example (figure 136). She was lengthened 4ft 6in during the course of construction and the final dimensions were 83ft 6in length aloft, 24ft 0in breadth moulded, 16ft 0in depth in hold, and 201 tons. She has a plain stem with no gammon knee, a heavy square counter stern, a flush deck with open bulwarks, and a foremast stepped right in the bows and only a few feet abaft the forefoot. There is slight deadrise, accompanied by very rounded bilges, vertical topsides and some tumblehome; the entrance is very full and so is the run. The great depth of hold is a noticeable feature. Of similar hull-form and drawn in the same manner were the following: *Mary Ann* (1794, brig, 155 tons); *Jane and Sarah* (1795, snow, 158 tons, but with figurehead); *Carrier* (1796, brig, 127 tons); *Dryad* (1801, ship, 256 tons); *Balfour* (1809, brig, 310 tons); two unnamed brigs and one unnamed ship. When tracings of the body plans of *Irton* and *Balfour* are superimposed, the shape of tumblehome and topsides, and the curve of the bilge correspond exactly, and it is only *Balfour's* additional breadth of 3ft that makes any difference.

The *Ceres*, built in 1799 of 93 tons, was of shallow draft, had dimensions of 66ft 3in × 18ft 1in × 10ft 5in, and was rigged as a brig. Daniel Brocklebank's notebook has no particulars entered on her page. She would have been suitable for the Baltic trade, having flat floors, hard bilges and vertical sides, but she was captured by the French in the very year she was built. There is no scale on the plan. The ratio of register length divided by depth is 6.36.

Somewhat similar is an unnamed plan of a single-masted vessel drawn on Whatman paper with a watermark dated 1794. Although no scale is specified on the plan, it can be shown by proportion that if the moulded beam was 16ft then the register length would be 50ft 6in, which would agree fairly well with the dimensions of the cutter *Earl of Lonsdale*, namely, 51ft 0in length aloft, 16ft 11in breadth extreme, 8ft 8in depth of hold, and 61 tons. The only other single-masted vessel built in the years 1788–1809 was the *Mackerel* of 1790 with a length of 30ft and a beam of 10ft 10in. The *Earl of Lonsdale* was an Isle of Man Packet with a head, a raking mast, and slightly more deadrise than *Ceres*. As no yard is listed in the spar dimensions, she can have carried only fore-and-aft canvas. There is considerable similarity between the Brocklebank sloop's plan and that of Chapman's Timber Hoys, which are in the 100–200 tons range. If you ignore the bulwark rail added to the Brocklebank plan, the sheer elevation is somewhat similar, as also are the midship section and shape of the head. There are no spar dimensions or sail plans of the timber hoys.

Another plan of an unnamed cutter is of quite a different hull-form with hollow garboards, very steep deadrise, a drag aft and fine lines. There is not even a drawn or written scale on the plan. In addition, there are two small sail plans of unnamed cutters one of which is drawn to ⅛in scale, which gives the hull a register length of 57ft and the height of the mast from rail to cap as 48ft. The only other single-masted craft built before 1815 was the *New Triton* of 1814, and her length is only 50ft 10in. Also built in the Brocklebank yard were four two-masted shallops, described below, and the schooner *Experiment* of 1802 (*see* Two-Masted Schooners).

SHALLOPS

Although there are two plans of single-masted shallops in the Hilhouse collection, the most common arrangement was for them to be schooner-rigged, with or without a bowsprit. In his Dictionary, William Falconer calls them 'a sort of large boat with two masts, usually rigged like a schooner'. The shallop was one of the proscribed rigs in the Acts for the prevention of smuggling, so it must have been a common form.

Brocklebank's yard at Whitehaven built four shallops in the period 1788–1810, but neither names nor yard numbers are attributed to them in Daniel Brocklebank's notebook. Their particulars are listed below:

All four were constructed for John Hartley & Sons to carry hogsheads of sugar, presumably in the West Indies between the shore and the ship, and it is assumed the shallops were shipped out on the decks of a larger vessel and rigged on arrival. The yard book entry for the 1801 shallop states 'per *Cumberland*' which would confirm this.

Only one set of plans has survived, and it is for the shallop built in 1806, which could carry 21 hogsheads. A note on her lines plan reproduced in figure 140 states: 'Much approved of being of an Easy Draught of Water and Sailing Fast'. She is a beamy craft with short, sharp ends that have marked hollow in the lower waterlines, and the sections are very rounded up to the load line and straight above that. No scale is drawn but the ratio works out at ½in to 1ft. A sail plan drawn on the reverse at half scale is assumed to be of

Date built	**Length overall**	**Breadth moulded**	**Depth in hold**	**Mast Height gunwale to hounds**		**Bowsprit outside stem**	**Gaffs**
				Fore	**Main**		
1799	37ft 0in	12ft 6in	6ft 0in	30ft 0in	32ft 6in	12ft 6in	11ft 6in
1801	27ft 6in	9ft 6in	5ft 4in	23ft 6in	25ft 6in	13ft 0in	9ft 0in
1804	32ft 6in	11ft 2in	5ft 10in (gunwale to ceiling)	30ft 0in	31ft 0in	11ft 0in	10ft 6in
1806	39ft 6in	12ft 10in	6ft 0 in	36ft 0in	38ft 6in	15ft 0½in	11ft 0in

140

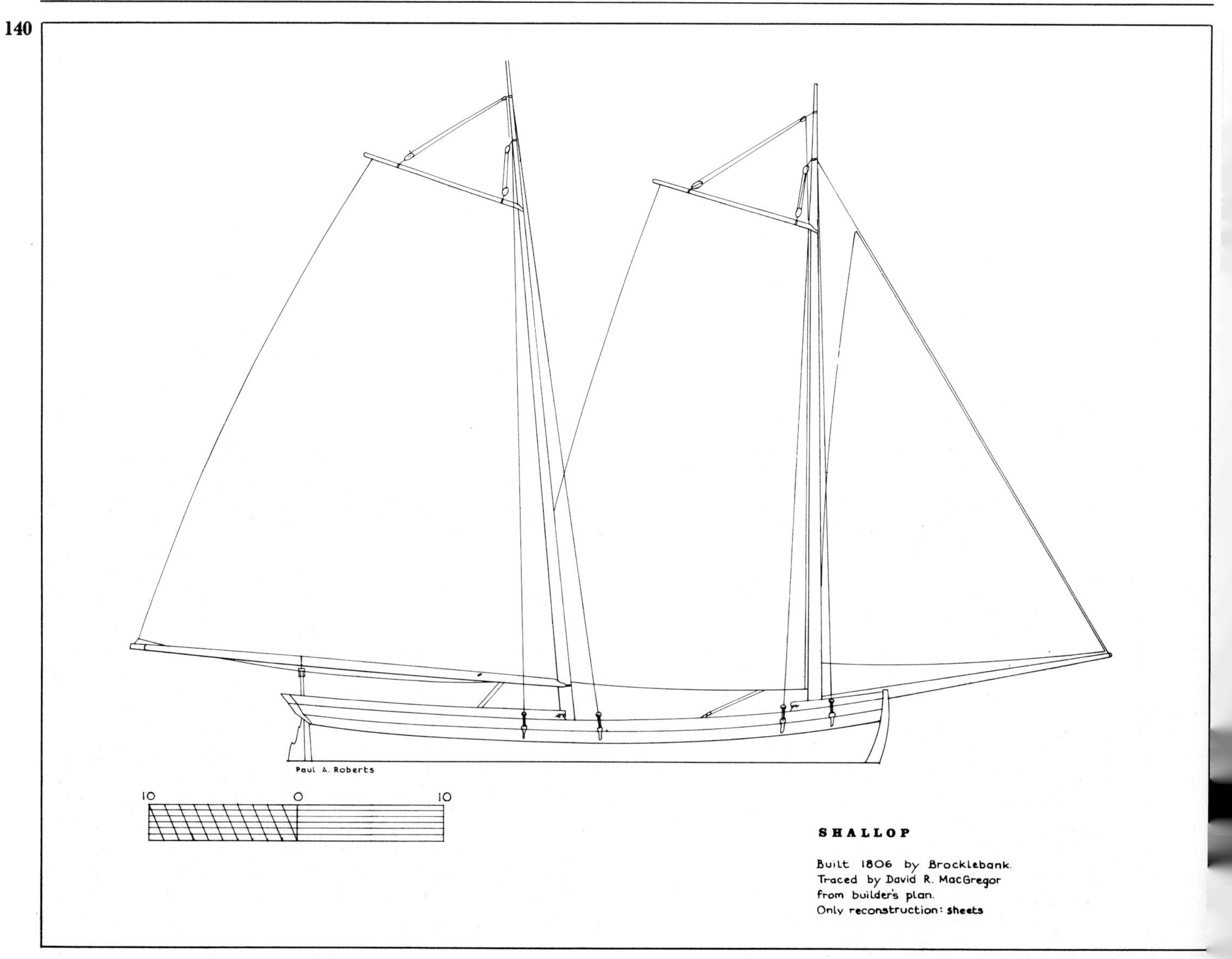

Fig 140. Shallop. *Lines plan. The vessel is unnamed, schooner-rigged, and was built in 1806 at Whitehaven by Brocklebank. The dimensions are as listed here in the table. The plan was drawn by Paul A Roberts from a tracing made by the Author of the builder's plan in Liverpool County Museums. Reconstruction: position of masts made to agree with sail plan. The dotted lines on the half-breadth plan are presumably deck beams.*

Fig 141. Shallop. *Sail plan. She was built in 1806 by Brocklebank, and has been drawn by Paul A Roberts from a tracing made by the Author of the builder's plan in Liverpool County Museums. Reconstruction: sheets added.*

the same vessel, and no doubt all four craft were similarly rigged. It is a very simple form of sail plan with pole masts and the minimum of rigging. The foresail was boomless in each case, but there was a main boom and both gaffs were always of the same length. There were only two shrouds to each mast with but a single stay from the foremast on which was set a large staysail. The peak and throat halliards have a single tackle in each case; no sheets are drawn on the original, and no reef points indicated.

These Brocklebank shallops were somewhat similar to the square-sterned 'Chebacco dogbody' of New England from which the Saint John woodboat developed later in the nineteenth century. William A Baker lists examples of each type in his book *Sloops & Shallops* from which it may be noticed that whereas the 'dogbodies' were of similar dimensions to the Brocklebank shallops, the woodboats were often twice as large.[15] The origins of the pink-sterned Chebacco boat were mentioned at the end of Chapter 2. The chief difference between the Brocklebank shallops and the dogbodies was that the latter had longer gaffs to each mast and no bowsprit; but the sail plan of the shallop was similar to a West Indies type or the American pilot boat.

A surviving example of a two-masted shallop in the British Isles is the *Peggy*, built in 1791 at Castletown, Isle of

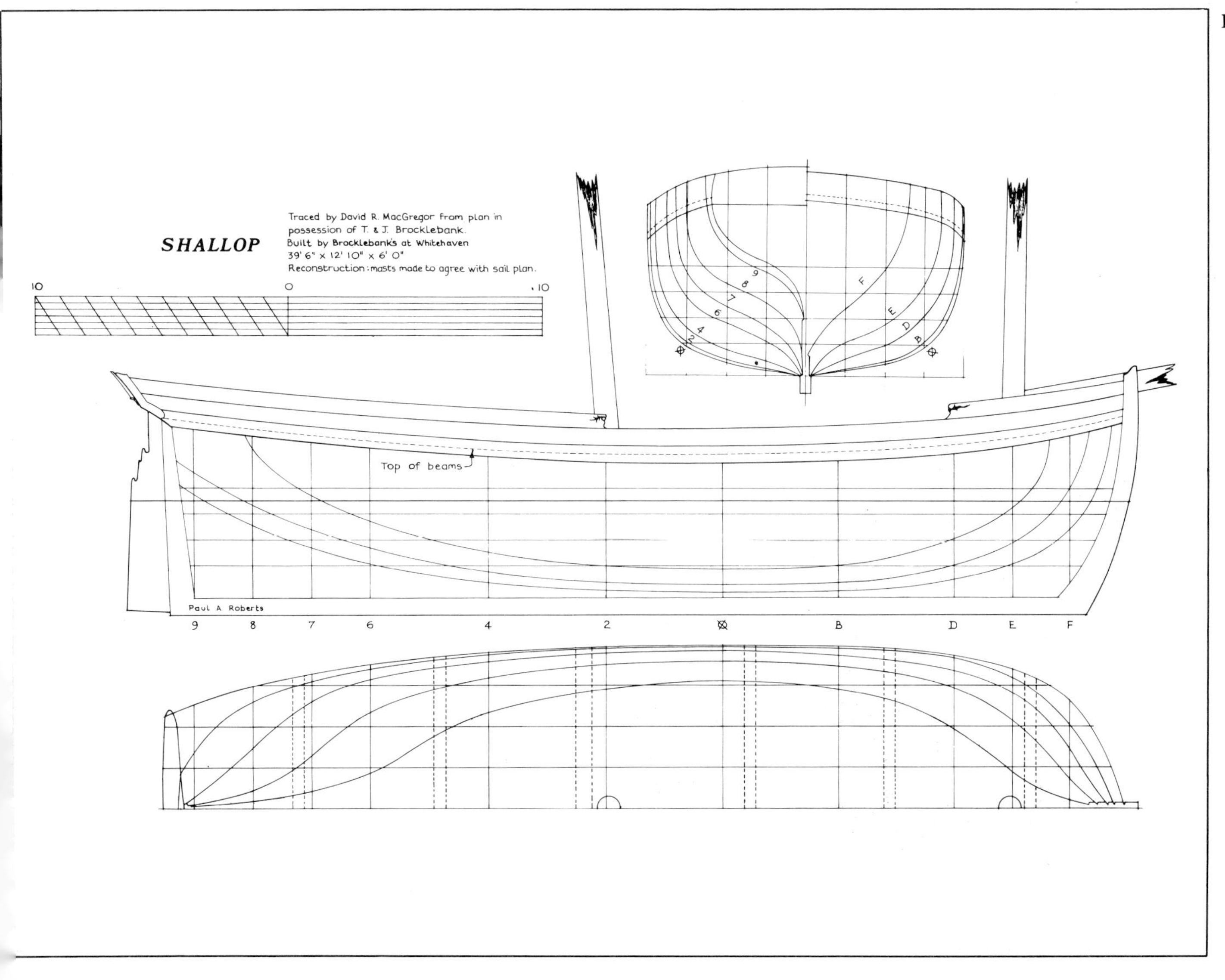

Man, where she is still preserved. She was measured in 1969 by D K Jones and W Clarke, and her dimensions are 26ft 5in length overall, 7ft 6in moulded breadth and 4ft 1½in inside depth. Of shallow draft but with considerably more deadrise than the Brocklebank shallop, she has a counter stern with a slight round to the transom, and there is a square tuck. She was clinker built and originally had two drop keels. Surviving spars are the two masts, main gaff and boom. The foremast measures 16ft 10in from original gunwale to hounds, and the mainmast 18ft 4in between the same points; the main gaff measures 9ft 6in to inside the jaws and the main boom 17ft 9in. The fore gaff and bowsprit are missing, but the latter has been reconstructed to measure 9ft 6in. The *Peggy's* hull-form bears some resemblance to the Virginia pilot boat model although this was double the length.

In a sketchbook dated 1799, Thomas Luny made two pencil drawings of a shallop in the neighbourhood of Teignmouth and noted that she had 'tanned sails'.[16] The

142

Fig 142. This drawing of a shallop by William Daniell (1769–1837) agrees generally with figures 140 and 141. Note the dimensions writen on mainmast and main boom; the number of cloths in the sail may therefore be accurate. The drawing is undated and is re-drawn from a pencil sketch in the National Maritime Museum, Greenwich.

Fig 143. Cleopatra *(?). Lines plan. The ship was built at Whitby, probably by Barry. The name attribution is uncertain, as* Lloyd's Register *calls her a brig. The date of build is given as 1817, and she is of 267 tons. The plain bow is typical of Whitby ships. The plan is reproduced from the tracing made of a plan in Whitby Museum. Dimensions scaled off plan: 96ft 0in × 26ft 3in (moulded) × 14ft 6in.*

National Maritime Museum, Greenwich, has an undated drawing by William Daniell (died 1837) of an undecked shallop (figure 142). He has written dimensions of 30ft on the mainmast and 20ft on the main boom. Daniell's engraving of Loch Ranza in the Isle of Arran, dated 1817, depicts a smaller shallop in the foreground, but she has no bowsprit. Small examples of this rig survived until the early years of the twentieth century in the open-decked boats used as lighters in the River Camel to bring cargoes up to Padstow.

Two large three-masted shallops, the *Bermuda* and *Milford*, were built at Bermuda in 1804–5 to supply fresh water from tanks on board to naval vessels on the Jamaica station. They were 73ft long overall, 23ft moulded beam, and 9ft 6in moulded depth, and of 148 tons. A plan in the Admiralty draughts at the National Maritime Museum has been redrawn by Howard Chapelle in *Search for Speed under Sail*, plate 47. The hull-form is that of an enlarged shallop. The rig consisted of short masts with sails set on gaffs and booms.

SHIPBUILDERS IN THE NORTH OF ENGLAND

Whitby continued as a centre for shipbuilding, and many vessels of between 300 and 450 tons were built there. A number of the larger ones were taken up as transports in 1814 for the war in America. Of the many prolific builders, John Barry (1763–1826) built some thirty ships of all sizes from 1792 to 1814, being succeeded by his son Robert in 1815, while he continued as shipowner. John's father, also Robert, had launched his first vessel at Whitby in 1787, and his two uncles, John and Francis, were both shipbuilders.[17]

Lines plans of several ships built by John Barry and his son, Robert, are preserved at the Whitby Museum in the H W Smales Collection, but unfortunately they are not accompanied by deck layouts, sail plans or even spar dimensions. Copies were made of the following for study purposes:[18]

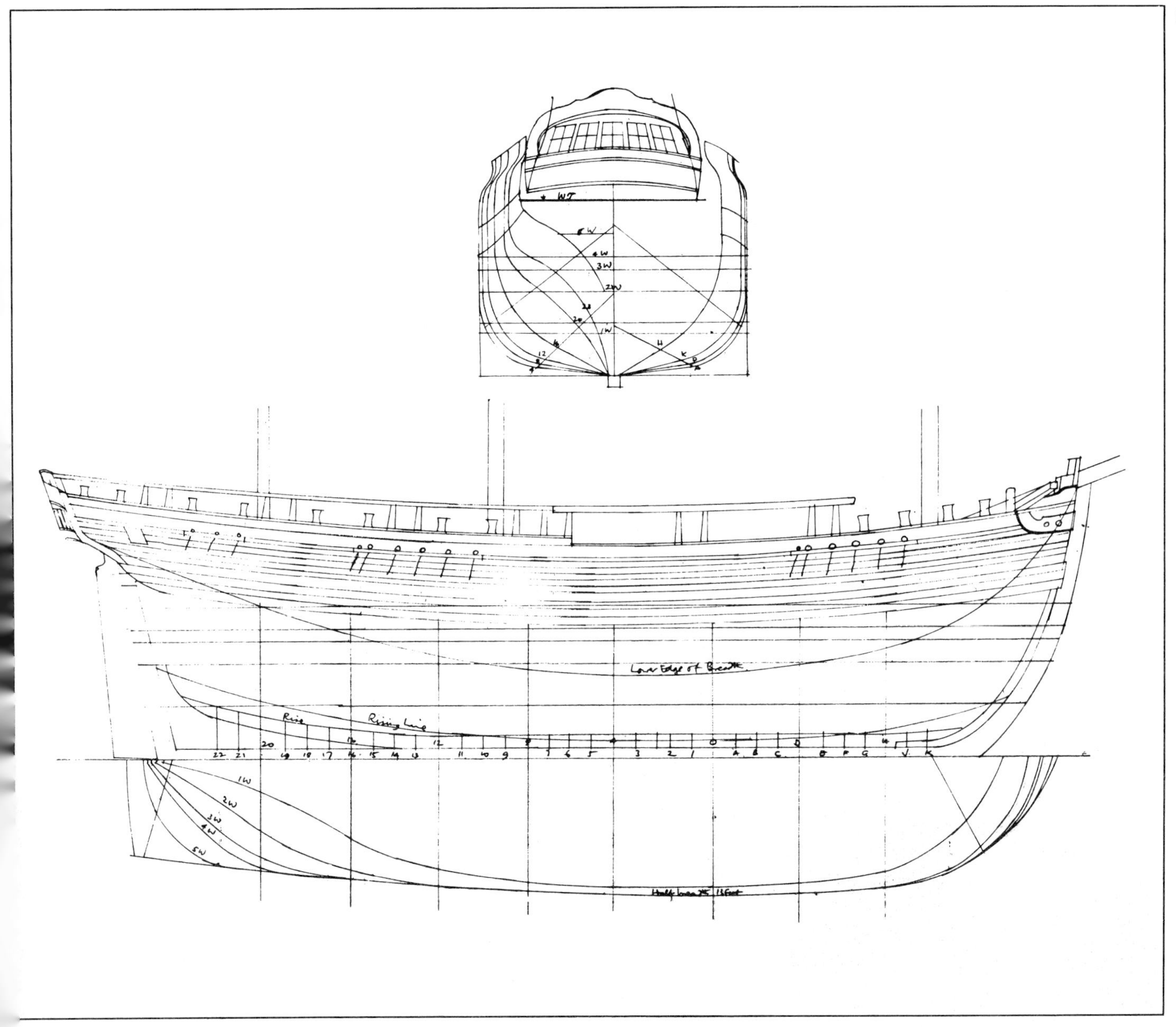

143

Orient	built 1810	110 tons	brig; shallow draft
Hyperion	built 1810	468 tons	ship
Thetis	built 1811	252 tons	ship, but plan has two masts
Brilliant	built 1813	237 tons	ship
Clio			
either	built 1813	82 tons	sloop { both still listed
or	built 1816	86 tons	sloop } in 1821 in *L R* (red)
Cleopatra (?)	built 1817	267 tons	brig, but plan has three masts

The *Cleopatra* may have been an older vessel with her quarter-badge or window and her rough-tree rail amidships. The plan was unnamed and Smales has written on it: 'Suggest 1817 *Cleopatra* 267 tons brig'.

A comparison of the styles of draughtsmanship in the plans of the above ships reveals that two or more diagonals were laid down on the body plan, although they were not always projected on the half-breadth plan. The spacing of the waterlines for projection on the half-breadth was irregular, and the most common aspect of all shipbuilders' plans were the body plan and the positions of the sections which comprised it. Barry's sheer elevations contained the rising line, which indicated the upper ends of all the floor timbers, but only one had the 'lower height of breadth' drawn on it.

The principle of John Barry's design can be seen in the plan of *Hyperion*, in which the full entrance and run are plainly to be seen and there is 10ft of dead flats. There is little deadrise and the slack bilges round up into wall sides with sudden tumblehome. All Barry's plans have a plain bow and open bulwarks and the inference is a flush deck. Other points of interest are the knightheads and pairs of mooring bitts made prominent by the open rail; the timber loading port in the stern, indicated on the body plan; the position of the mainmast which is further aft than usual, thus making a long gap between it and the foremast. Dimensions scaled off the plan give 107ft 6in register length, 28ft 4in moulded breadth and approximately 18ft 6in depth of hold. In 1819 she drew 18ft which would give a freeboard of 5ft. She was built with fifteen pairs of iron standards and knees. She was employed as a transport in 1814, and like many another big ship was diverted to the India trade about 1817. In Robert Dodd's engraving of 'North Country Shipping off Flamborough Head', dated 1797, the portrait

Fig 144. Oil painting by W J Huggins (1781–1845) of the ship Fortitude. *A likely candidate would be the ship built at Whitby in 1814 of 389 tons and owned in London. Also for consideration is the ship built at Scarborough in 1799 of 403 tons and owned there.* (J & J Rumens of Woodstock)

Fig 145. An English merchant ship running before the wind. She has done her best to reduce sail on the mizen without actually taking in the sails, so as to let more wind reach the sails on the mainmast and, even on the main, the course is furled and the topgallant partially lowered; all the sails on the foremast are just full and drawing. The artist is Jean Baugean and this engraving was published in 1814 in Collection ... de Bâtiments de Guerre et de Bâtiments Marchands *(plate 15). There is a brigantine on the right.*

Fig 146. The Freya *was built at Flensburg in 1802 and this picture was painted 31 years later. It is odd that there is no main trysail gaff, although there is one on the foremast.* (F Holm-Petersen)

144

Vaisseau marchand anglais, venant de mettre a la voile.

146

147

Fig 147. Photographed dried out on the beach at Flimby, south of Maryport, is the old barque Lady Gordon *which was built at Whitehaven in 1817. Her hull is typical of many of the vessels described in this chapter and the retention of single topsails and the plain vertical stem further heightens the illusion that we are viewing a ghost from the past. She was originally a full-rigged ship of 285 tons with a draught of 14ft. The house abaft the mizen with its rounded sides must be a later addition; later developments too, are the shortened fore topgallant mast and the loss of the fore royal. The jibboom has been hauled in-board here and the dolphin striker hinged up under the bowsprit. She was still afloat in 1863.* (Nautical Photo Agency)

Fig 148. This is a painting by Robert Salmon, dated 1809, and the Lady Gordon *could well have looked like this when new. The ship in the centre is the* Betsy, *hove-to off Liverpool, but it has been impossible to identify her, as* Lloyd's Register *had five ships of this name with Liverpool as the surveying port, and three of them were built in America. The ship is typical of her period, and a brig on each side completes this delightful painting by Salmon.* (Parker Gallery)

of the ship on the left resembles the *Hyperion*, although the absence of a dolphin striker would have been unacceptable in 1810. The plan of the sloop *Clio* is really a scaled-down version of these bigger ships (fig 196).

Fishburn & Brodrick's yard at Whitby continued to construct large ships, amongst which may be cited the *Coverdale* of 579 tons, built in 1795 and measuring 118ft 11in keel and fore rake, and 33ft 2in breadth; also the *Culland's Grove* of 599 tons built in 1801 with dimensions of 130ft 9in length on deck, 127ft 2in keel and fore rake, and 32ft 4in beam.[19] Such vessels obtained good remuneration in the transport service which attracted many Whitby shipowners, so that the whaling trade went into decline during the Napoleonic wars. The activities of privateers and the press gang added to the problems of the whaling fleet. Perhaps this was the reason why two ships were offered for sale at Sunderland in 1798. One was the *Ariel* of 334 tons which could carry 26 keels of coal or 420 loads of timber; she was also armed and, at the time, was fitted out complete as a whaler. The other was the *Hunter* of 253 tons, which could also carry coal or timber and was armed. The would-be seller might advertise his vessel as 'calculated for the Baltic. Greenland, coal or coasting trade on a light draught of water, takes the ground well, shifts without ballast' and hope to get a good price for a general-purpose ship.[20] Hulls such as this were economical to build, as the wall sides and parallel body restricted the amount of grown timber bends required, thereby reducing the cost of construction and maintenance. During the long periods of wars, building costs were rising steadily and an indication of these can be gleaned from various ship-building records.

148

149

The CAST IRON BRIDGE over the RIVER WEAR, built by ROWLAND BURDON ESQ.R M.P.
Span 236 ft. Height 100 ft. Spring of the Arch 33 ft.

John Brockbank, who operated at Lancaster from 1791–1820, built the ship *Penelope* of $222\frac{87}{94}$ tons in 1796 at a finished price of nearly £9 3s per ton; the ship *Mars* of 394 tons built in 1799 cost £11 8s per ton; the ship *Pusey Hall* of $312\frac{50}{94}$ tons built in 1808 cost £13 11s 4d per ton. In September 1815 he estimated that the cost of building a 240-ton ship for the North American timber trade would be £22 10s per ton. By contrast, two brigs built on speculation, and sold, cost less: the *Barbadoes Packet* of 196 tons (1802) cost £10 14s; and the *Alexander* of about 160 tons (1815) cost £14 per ton.[21]

Elsewhere in north-west England, Thomas Wood of Maryport built the ship *Postlethwaite* in 1797 of 258 tons at £14 9s per ton. At Whitehaven in about 1800, Brocklebank's were asking £10 10s to build a brig. In 1813 the cost of building a vessel at Whitehaven 'complete with everything requisite for sea except warlike stores, sheathing and provisions' had risen to no less than £28 per ton. This was the equivalent price being paid for East Indiamen built at the Blackwall Yard on the Thames.[22]

A launch at Maryport in October 1803 afforded some entertainment, to judge by a local account:[23]

> *Shiplaunch* – On the 3rd inst a fine new ship was launched from the building yard of Messrs Fletcher, Fawcett, Peat & Coy at Maryport (called the *Anthorn* built for Captain Scaife) which for the rumour of it, novelty and the uncommon fineness of the weather attracted an amazing concourse of people, a greater number it is supposed than has ever been seen at that place since it became a town. The launching was not in the usual manner, the vessel descended broadside foremost into the water from a perpendicular height of between three and four feet and afforded a very curious as well as pleasing sight to the numerous spectators.

Presumably there was a restricted width of the harbour which obliged a sideways launch.

On the north-east coast of England, shipbuilders were busy along the River Wear at Sunderland and upstream at Hylton. The Goodchild family operated a yard for 149 years until 1821. Thomas Burn, Henry Rudd, Benjamin Heward, James Crown and the Hall brothers were some of the other builders. In 1792 Thomas Havelock built the *Themis* of 574 tons, which was considered a large ship, but her size was easily exceeded by the *Lord Duncan* which Havelock launched six years later from his Southwick yard and which measured no less than 925 tons. For a ship that was not an East Indiaman, she was colossal. In 1806 she was chartered for the West Indies and accidentally blown-up at Port-au-Prince. John Laing and his son David opened a shipyard on the Monkwearmouth shore in 1793. After David's death in 1796, John's younger brother Philip joined the yard, and their first vessel was the brig *Affiance*; later, in 1804, a dock was acquired near the Wearmouth Bridge.

150

Then, after a short period of building at South Shields, the Laings returned to the River Wear, first to a yard at Southwick, and in 1818 to another at Deptford on the south side of the River. It was there that they launched Sunderland's first East Indiaman, in the shape of the comparatively small *Caledonian* of 414 tons.[24] There were nine shipyards at Sunderland in 1801 and a Parliamentary Report of 1806 records the local output.

NUMBER AND TONNAGE OF VESSELS BUILT AT SUNDERLAND[25]

Year	Total number built	Average tonnage	Largest tonnage
1790	19	144	312
1791	6	202	356
1804	51	163	349
1805	36	163	337

Of course, in an era when many vessels were comparatively small and when shipwrights were possessed of great skill in the ways of working in wood, small craft were constructed in backyards and on pieces of waste ground some distance from the nearest water, which resulted in heroic tales of endeavour to propel these vessels towards what reporters of the day liked to describe as 'their native element'.

Fig 149. The first cast-iron bridge was constructed in 1777 over the River Severn near Coalbrookdale and other, similar bridges followed, such as this one over the River Wear at Sunderland. Inspection of the engraving will reveal a number of interesting craft underway on the river, including a shallop just ahead of the brig. On the left-hand shore, a shipyard is being laid out. (MacGregor Collection)

Fig 150. The Duke of York *was a lofty ship, setting skysails on each mast, with topgallant and royal stunsails even set on the mizen. She was built at Shields in 1811 of 346 tons. She is flying a blue ensign.* (Parker Gallery)

151

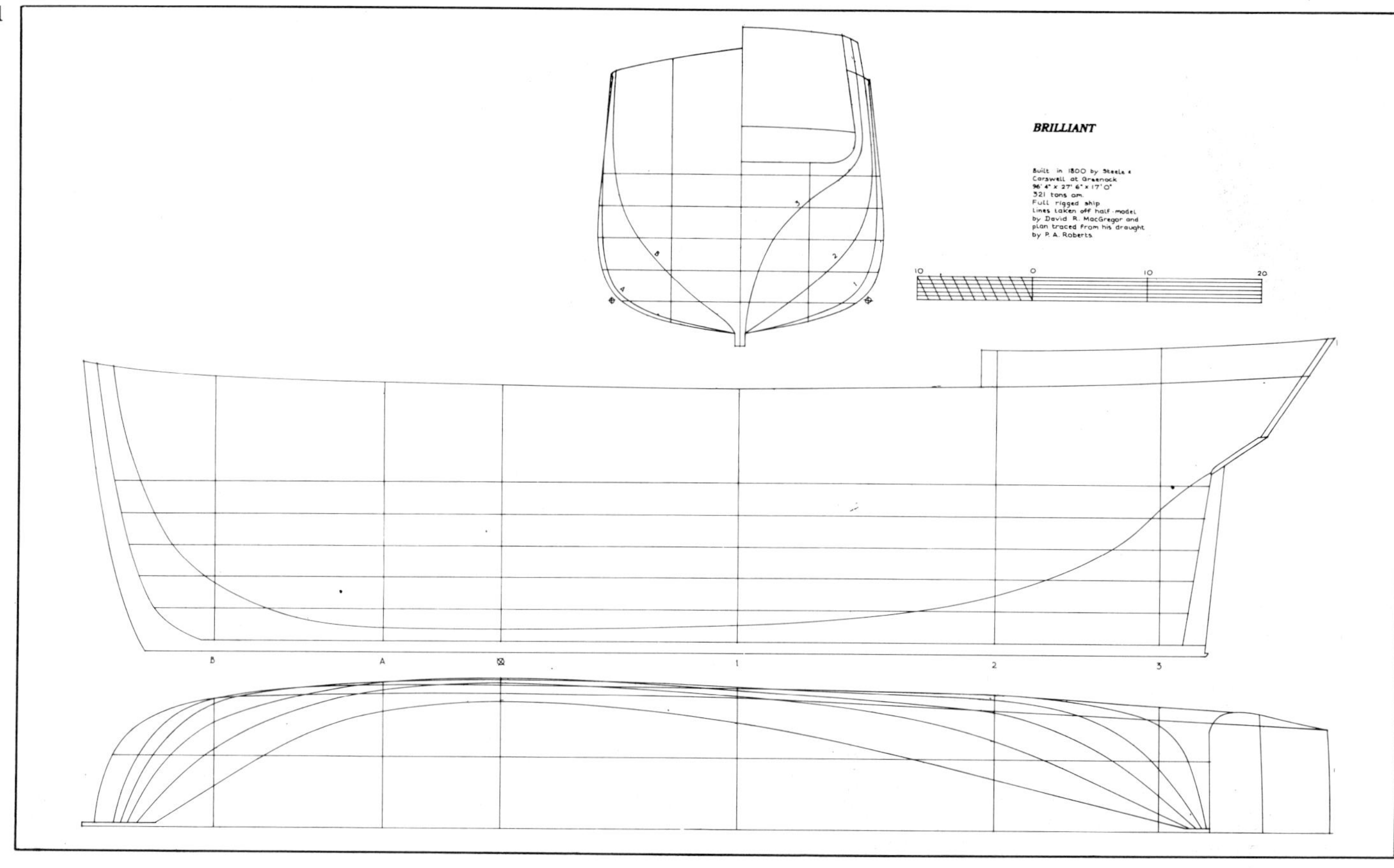

STEELE & CARSWELL OF GREENOCK

The notable shipbuilding firm of Robert Steele & Co had its humble beginning in 1796. Robert Steele (1745–1830) had built small fishing boats at Saltcoats, Ayrshire, with his father, but moved to Greenock sometime after the latter's death and entered into partnership with John Carswell in 1796. Under the name of Steele & Carswell they built 35 vessels between 1796 and 1816, of which there were 12 full-rigged ships, 10 brigs, 2 schooners, 8 sloops and 3 Excise or Customs yachts of no given rig.[26] (See Appendix 1).

Bracket half-models have survived for the ship *Brilliant* (1800) and the brig *Spinster* (1804), the lines of which were taken off through the courtesy of the late James Steele. The present whereabouts of the models is unknown. As can be seen in figure 151 the *Brilliant* showed the port side of the ship, which is relatively uncommon either for a model or a plan. She was somewhat of the cod's head and mackerel tail type, having a very full entrance, with the maximum beam placed one-third of the length from the bow, but a longer and finer run. The floors were slightly rounded with appreciable deadrise and rounded topsides. There was none of the sudden tumblehome found in the designs of Hilhouse and Barry. The *Brilliant* was deep for her length, measuring 96ft 4in × 27ft 6in × 17ft 0in and 321 tons; height in the 'tween decks was 5ft 1½ins.

No doubt the *Brilliant's* design was broadly similar to that of other ships built by Steele & Carswell in these years, and a number had a greater depth of hold. As a ship's depth was not calculated for tonnage, a deep ship could obviously pay her owners handsomely, provided she could enter harbour successfully and perform satisfactorily at sea. The following particulars illustrate the great depths given to some of their ships:

DEEPEST SHIPS BUILT BY STEELE & CARSWELL

Name	Date	Rig	Dimensions from Yard Book (length is 'Keel and fore rake')	Tons	L/D	B/D	L/B
Ariadne	1799	S	85ft 10in × 24ft 0½in × 16ft 4in	219 51/94	5.25	1.47	3.57
Sisters	1801	S	95ft 6in × 27ft 3in × 18ft 10½in	312 48/94	5.05	1.44	3.50
**Spinster*	1804	bg	80ft 0in × 23ft 2in × 16ft 2in	188 51/94	4.95	1.43	3.45
Mariner	1805	S	91ft 2½in × 26ft 2½in × 18ft 5in	278 33/94	4.95	1.43	3.48
Rebecca	1816	S	95ft 2in × 26ft 11½in × 18ft 2in	305 33/94	5.24	1.48	3.52
Albion	1818	S	119ft 0in × 30ft 9in × 23ft 6in	505 66/94	5.06	1.30	3.86

**Herald* (1804 brig) had identical dimensions, except that depth of hold was ½in less.
Rebecca and Albion actually built by Robert Steele & Co, the firm having been renamed.
Note: Right-hand column has ratios for length (L), breadth (B) and depth (D).

The *Brilliant* was less deep than any of the above examples, her three proportions being respectively 5.66, 1.61, 3.50. The upper limit in the ratios has been taken as 5.25 for L/D and 1.50 for B/D. Here the ratios show *Mariner* to have been the deepest vessel for her length, but *Albion* for her breadth. Brocklebank's deep ship *Cumberland* (1800) had ratios of 5.32 for L/D and 1.47 for B/D.

The sloops built by Steele & Carswell were undoubtedly trading smacks, such as the *Eliza* launched in August 1813 of $51\frac{19}{94}$ tons with dimensions of 48ft 9in × 16ft 8in × 8ft 10in. At a distance of 6ft from her keel, her floor had risen 1ft 2in. Robert Steele wrote a book entitled *Report on the Admeasurement of Shipping for Tonnage* which was published in 1834 by the Greenock Chamber of Commerce, and in a table on page 15 he lists the rise of floors for seven of his own ships. Most had fairly flat floors, except for his smallest full-rigged ship, the *Leander* (1799), in which the rise was 2ft 5in at a distance of 6ft from the keel. She was in the Newfoundland trade and measured 188 tons with dimensions of 77ft 1in × 23ft 8½in × 14ft 9½in and 4ft 6in height between decks.[27]

The largest full-rigged ships were the *Clyde* (1813) and *Bengal* (1815) with very similar dimensions. The *Bengal* measured 103ft 11in keel and fore rake × 29ft 7½in × 19ft 8in and 402 tons. Robert Salmon executed a fine painting of her, and the inscription states that the ship was built for Cropper, Benson & Co of Liverpool and was the first vessel built at Greenock for the East India trade. The painting reproduced here in figure 152 shows her in four different positions.

This large broadside view of the *Bengal* with the sails on the main aback, yields very good detail. The old-fashioned mizen is brailed in and the driver or, as it was beginning to be called then, the spanker is set. Whereas the mizen was a small, boomless sail, the clew of the larger spanker was hauled out to a boom. No sail was bent on the crossjack yard. There being no jackstays, the square sails are attached to the yards with rope bands (later corrupted to 'robands') passing around the yard. The standing jib is a huge sail, hoisting almost to the head of the stay. There are no signs of trysail gaffs on the fore and main masts and the topmast staysail, which have been taken in but not furled, look large sails. The stern view on the right of the picture shows that the royal masts are separately fidded spars with their own crosstrees. A spritsail yard is carried, but the rigging is so close around it that it would be difficult to set a sail. A broadside of nine guns is shown and the ship appears to be flush-decked.

Regrettably, the records of Robert Steele's ships do not coincide in kind with those of Alexander Hall's apart from the existence of the yard list. No costs or spar dimensions exist for Steele's ships, but there is a specification of the *Albion* (1818), which is set out on pages 45–46 of *Merchant Sailing Ships 1815–1850*.

Alexander Hall opened his own shipyard at Aberdeen in 1811, at the age of 51, and by 1815 had launched 15 vessels which comprised 3 ships, 5 brigs, 1 schooner, 3 smacks, 1 sloop, and 2 of rigs not stated. A sail plan of the schooner, the *Plough*, appears in figure 174. Two of the full-rigged ships, the *Don* and *Brilliant*, were sisters of 332 tons apiece, built in 1814 for the whaling trade at a cost of £15 10s per ton.

Fig 151. Brilliant. *Lines plan. The* Brilliant *was built in 1800 at Greenock by Steele & Carswell. The lines were taken off the builder's half-model by the Author, and the plan derived from this was traced by Paul A Roberts. Dimensions: 96ft 4in (keel and fore rake) × 27ft 6in × 17ft 0in and 321½ tons. Length of hull on plan scales 97ft 4in for keel and fore rake.*

Fig 152. This fine painting by Robert Salmon (1775–c1884) depicts the Bengal *under easy sail off Greenock, where she was built in 1814.* (Science Museum)

152

BRIGS AND BRIGANTINES

By 1800, the rigs of brig and snow were beginning to coalesce, until the only difference was the presence or absence of a main trysail mast, a main trysail boom, or a square mainsail.

After the declaration of peace in 1815 more economical crews had to be carried, which brought the brigantine with a fore-and-aft mainmast increasingly into favour. Yet the word 'brigantine' seems to have slipped out of general usage at the beginning of the century; even *Lloyd's Register* did not list it prior to 1834 amongst their rigs. The name most commonly applied to the brigantine after 1800 was that of 'schooner', and also 'brig-schooner' or 'hermaphrodite brig'. The word 'schooner' is certainly the maid of all work and covers a multiplicity of rig variations. In his published engravings, Jean Baugean has recorded both brigantines and main-topsail brigantines, but the terminology was very slack. Although the former was called a brig-schooner (*brick-géolette*)[28] the latter was termed both schooner-brig[29] and also just plain brig.[30] A vessel from northern waters with masts fidded in four lengths, perhaps with the royal masts fidded abaft, provides a striking contrast to a Mediterranean polacca with pole masts in one length and three yards furled together.

There were some examples of brigantines with square main topsails built in America and France during the first decades of the nineteenth century and similar sail plans were designed by William Symonds for some of his small slave-chasers, such as the *Dolphin* in figure 88 of *Fast Sailing Ships*. But there was still confusion over nomenclature: Symonds's main-topsail brigantine *Bonetta*, on a sail plan dated 1835, is called 'hermaphrodite';[31] the brigantines *Griffon* and *Forester* with a fore-and-aft mainmast, on a sail plan dated 1832, are also referred to as 'hermaphrodite'.[32] Slavers and opium clippers used the main-topsail brigantine rig and Dr E A Dingley recorded having seen and photographed a Norwegian vessel so rigged at Weymouth in 1890.[33]

Two early nineteenth century examples of brigantines with fore-and-aft mainmast are illustrated on page 58 of

Fig 153. This photograph, taken on 25 June 1857, is entitled 'Snow at Wisbech'. She is not large but looks old, having been built probably before 1820. The photographer was Samuel Smith. (Wisbech Museum)

153

155

Fig 155. Another Baugean engraving in Recueil de Petites Marines *(1817) calls this vessel a 'brig-schooner', a term that has persisted on the Continent of Europe for what the British call a 'brigantine'.*

*Fig 154. A lively engraving by Baugean, published in 1814, of two vessels in a stiff breeze under reduced canvas: on the left, a British brigantine with her fore topgallant and square main topsail furled, has the wind on the quarter; on the right, a Genoese pink is closed hauled under square sails, having lowered her lateen yards. This pink does not have the 'pink' stern described in the last chapter, but has a wing transom. (*Collection de . . . Bâtiments de Guerre et Marchands *plate 58)*

Dessiné et Gravé par Baugean.

Brick allant vent de quartier.

Pinque Génois, courant au plus près sous son quarré.

154

156

Fig 156. *A lithograph, probably by J R Jobbins, of a brig drying her sails. There is no evidence of a dolphin striker.* (MacGregor Collection)

Fig 157. *The conventional choppy water to be seen in many of Robert Salmon's paintings is here exchanged for a calm setting with a snow hove-to off Greenock. She still sets four-sided staysails from the mainmast, but there are a large standing jib, a flying jib, and royals on each mast. The broadside of nine guns suggests a date of about 1810 – 1815. Strictly speaking, there should be no boom to the trysail or spanker for her to qualify as a snow.* (Transport Museum, Glasgow Museums and Art Galleries)

Fast Sailing Ships: one is the East India Company's packet *St Helena* built in 1814, and she is described as a 'schooner'; the other is a drawing by Copley Fielding[34] in a sketchbook covering the years 1809-20, and he has called her 'A Barque'.

Henry Moses drew a lofty brigantine lying in the Regent's Canal, London, and from his engraving, dated 1826, the following points emerge: she has a square-rigged foremast crossing four yards, together with a standing gaff; the fore lower mast is much shorter than the main lower mast; the main gaff has been lowered; the masts have a fair rake and there are six ports in the bulwarks.[35] In Fincham's first edition of *The Masting of Ships* (1829), proportions are given for three kinds of schooners: 'common', 'Bermuda', 'brig forward'. This last term endured until the middle of the century, the word 'brigantine' being adopted but slowly.

The terms 'hermaphrodite' or 'hermaphrodite brig', meaning a vessel with square-rigged foremast and fore-and-aft rigged mainmast, are so clumsy that they have been abandoned here in favour of 'brigantine', which is accordingly employed throughout the text, but with any necessary qualifications in doubtful cases. (In America the term 'hemaphrodite brig' is sometimes employed as the equivalent to the British true brigantine.) The snow's rig had meanwhile remained unaltered, although by 1815 any two-masted vessel that was square-rigged on both masts tended to be described as a brig, regardless of whether she had a trysail mast or masts, a square mainsail or a main boom. In his *Rigging and Seamanship*, David Steel wrote that a '"hermaphrodite" is a vessel so constructed as to be, occasionally, a snow, and sometimes a brig.'[36] Baugean drew a Swedish snow with a large boomless mainsail, but with a lug sail set on a raking mizen stepped near to the taffrail, the clew being sheeted to an outrigger. A square sail was furled on the main yard, there was no dolphin striker, and a spritsail was set below the bowsprit.[37] Anomalies can be quoted throughout the nineteenth century.

Among the first twenty-six vessels launched by Alexander Hall & Sons at Aberdeen in the years 1811-18, six are described as brigs and six as brigantines, and the dimensions of their spars and costs show two important points: first, that all the brigantines had the same number of yards on the main as on the fore; secondly, that every example of each type, with the exception of a single brig, had a trysail mast. After careful consideration of each ship's particulars, one is forced to the conclusion that the words 'brig' and 'brigantine' were used interchangeably and that the latter term was used in its early eighteenth century meaning. The main lower yard is never referred to as a crossjack yard nor is the word 'snow' ever mentioned.[38] Wide variations in the nomenclature of ship rigs existed then as today: for example, in a Glasgow shipping register of 1828 'Sw' stands for 'snow', 'Bg' for 'brigantine', and 'brig' is not listed.[39] Scottish practice seems to have been ultra conservative.

Alexander Hall's first brigantine was the *Matilda*, launched in 1829, and described in the builder's certificate as a 'square-sterned schooner or hermaphrodite having one deck, two masts and a trysail mast.'[40] Other brigantines built by Hall are sometimes referred to in the builder's certificate as 'hermaphrodite schooner', 'hermaphrodite rigged vessel', and 'hermaphrodite rig', but never 'hermaphrodite brig'.

157

COLLIERS

Many of the three-masted barks and cats which carried coal were not being replaced by the end of the century and, instead, there were more two-masted vessels in use, with the brig or snow the most popular rig. Writing in his *Treatise on Naval Architecture*, published in 1794, William Hutchinson describes the 'Making of passages in the coal trade' (page 134). He does not hide his admiration for the men who manned the colliers, either in this passage or in others in his book:

> Blowing weather and contrary winds often collect a great many of these colliers together, so that they sail in great fleets, striving with the utmost dexterity, diligence and care, against each other, to get first to market with their coals, or for their turn to load at Newcastle, where at the first of a westerly wind, after a long easterly one, there are sometimes 200 or 300 ships turning to windward in, and sailing out of that harbour in one side.

A typical brig constructed at the end of the eighteenth century is represented by the collier brig of 170 tons which appears as plate XXII in David Steel's *Naval Architecture* (1805) and has been redrawn here as figure 158. The measurements are 75ft 9in tonnage length, 22ft 11in extreme breadth, and 10ft 0in depth of hold. The proportion of beams to length is slightly less than 3½ to 1 as specified in the Smuggling Acts. In calculating a ship's tonnage, the depth was not measured prior to 1836, but for the purpose of the tonnage calculation it was assumed to be half the breadth. Both these proportions are exemplified in this collier brig, which is therefore a good example of what officialdom considered a fair-proportioned vessel. In addition, she has quite pleasing lines for a bulk carrier and almost as much deadrise as Hedderwick's Leith smack of about the same tonnage. Bilges for cargo ships were generally more rounded at this date than later in the century, yet all coasting vessels and many sea-going ships had to take the ground in a moderately upright position, a factor which discouraged deadrise. Numerous photographs of ships dried out in harbour or on the beach, reveal the need for flat bottoms.

Steel's collier brig has a full, convex entrance but a fine run for a bulk carrier, and some hollow is worked into the run near the sternpost. The floors are flat with slack bilges and rounded sides which curve back to give a fair degree of tumblehome, and the whole forebody is noticeable for its convex shape and lack of hollows. The knee supporting the cathead is run into a moulding taken to the stem, which was a typically attractive and neat detail of the eighteenth century.

In a comprehensive table of scantlings, Steel specified the keel as 12in square and in two lengths scarfed together; twenty-nine floor timbers were specified with 24in room and space, and the keelson was 11in square. The construction at bow and stern was particularly solid and a great deal of heavy timber was bolted together to form the counter. The outer bottom planking was 2½in thick and the wales 3½in. The lower deck beams were sided 11in and moulded 8in, with 6in round of beam. Along the lower deck, no planking was laid between the fore end of the fore hatch and the after end of the main hatch. The height amidships between decks (top of lower deck to underside of main deck) was 4ft 6in, but at the stern there was an average height of 6ft 0in, which would give just sufficient headroom for the after accommodation. At the forward end, the maximum height was 4ft 9in for the crew. The main deck beams were sided 8½in and moulded 7in, with 7in round of beam.[41] Steel's plate shows a few deck fittings, but in plan only: the windlass barrel is 14ft 10in long and 15½in thick at the centre; no capstan is shown; two 5-inch copper pumps are placed each side of the mainmast; and a cargo winch is specified abaft it, although the normal place would be at the foreside, in which position it is drawn on the reconstructed deck plan.

The deck layout has been reconstructed in the perspective view of the collier, drawn by William Ward in figure 159. The deck fittings are taken from contemporary models and illustrations, but it is always hard to assemble complete details in the case of merchant vessels, although

158

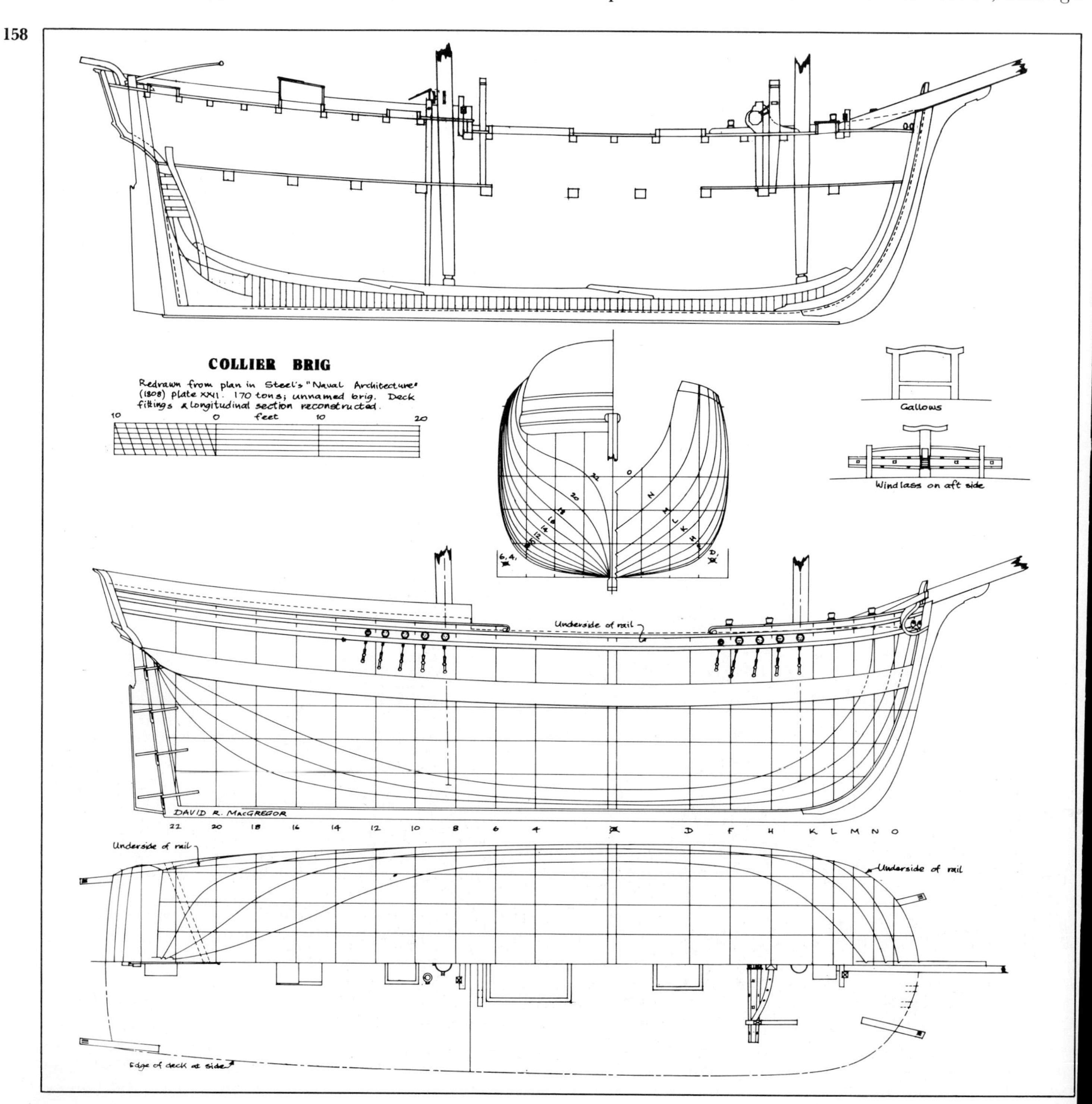

the result here looks reasonably convincing. It is not known if the collier is an actual vessel nor whether she represents a London-built brig but, for the reasons given earlier in this chapter, David Steel might have obtained a design from the Blackwall Yard. In the twenty years before his book appeared, this shipyard built only one collier, namely the *Crowley*, of 183 tons and built in 1789 at a cost of £13 12s per ton, but as the London Custom House register assigns three masts to this vessel the correct identification of this plan has still to be determined.[42]

The photograph of the brig *Favourite* in figure 160 shows a craft very similar to Steel's collier. The *Favourite* was built at Liverpool in 1785 with dimensions of 74.3ft × 23.5ft × 14.5ft and a tonnage of 164. A comparison of the dimensions shows that the length and breadth of the two brigs are virtually similar, but that the *Favourite* is 45 per cent deeper, the latter's ratio of L/D being 5.12 and B/D 1.62. This unique photograph was taken prior to 1858.

As no sail plan existed for Steel's collier brig, a sail and rigging plan has been reconstructed from the given spar dimensions.[43] These dimensions are for brigs of 150 tons – twenty tons less than Steel's collier – but although the only alteration here has been to increase the length of the gaff and boom by 5ft in each case, the resultant spar plan looks

Fig 158. Collier Brig. *Lines, section and decks, unidentified, and redrawn from David Steel's* Naval Architecture *(1805) plate XXII. Reconstruction: longitudinal section, deck fittings (Steel's plan only gave hatchways on plan, windlass and mast positions.) Dimensions on the plan: 75ft 9in (length for tonnage) × 22ft 11in (extreme) × 10ft 0in and 170 tons.*

Fig 159. This drawing by T W Ward, of a collier brig of 170 tons is based on figures 158 and 163, but some additional reconstruction has been made. Extra detail has been given to the deck fittings and new items have been added: a boat on the stern davits, anchors and anchor cables, stove pipe on quarter deck, bulwark stanchions, external planking, and a man beside the mainmast. It was decided not to include deck planking as it might confuse the other detail. As regards the gear aloft, all the necessary running rigging has been added to work the yards and sails, and the cloths of the sails are now drawn. Running rigging is either coiled up on deck or belayed as appropriate. As drawn, the brig is drying her sails at low water, sitting upright on the bottom of an estuary or tidal harbour.

160

Fig 160. A scene in Whitehaven Harbour showing (on the left) the brig Bee, *built in 1830 at Workington of 89 tons. On the right is the much older* Favourite, *built at Liverpool in 1785 of 164 tons, with dimensions given of 74.3ft × 23.5ft × 14.5ft. Still afloat in 1866, she was broad and deep.*

Fig 161. Breeze. *Sail plan of an English brig, dated 'Carls Krona [Sweden] 23 August 1806'. She was built at Hull in 1805 of 112 tons with 11ft draft. Dimensions on the plan:* $66\frac{1}{4}$*ft (between perpendiculars) ×* $21\frac{2}{3}$*ft (moulded) ×* $12\frac{1}{3}$*ft. The yards look short but this would permit a small crew; stunsails would undoubtedly have been set in fine weather.* (Maritime Museum, Stockholm)

Fig 162. Pencil drawings by E W Cooke (1811–80) of collier brigs, dated 20 December 1827. In the brig in the centre of the top line, a ringtail and fore-and-aft topsail and topgallant are faintly drawn.

161

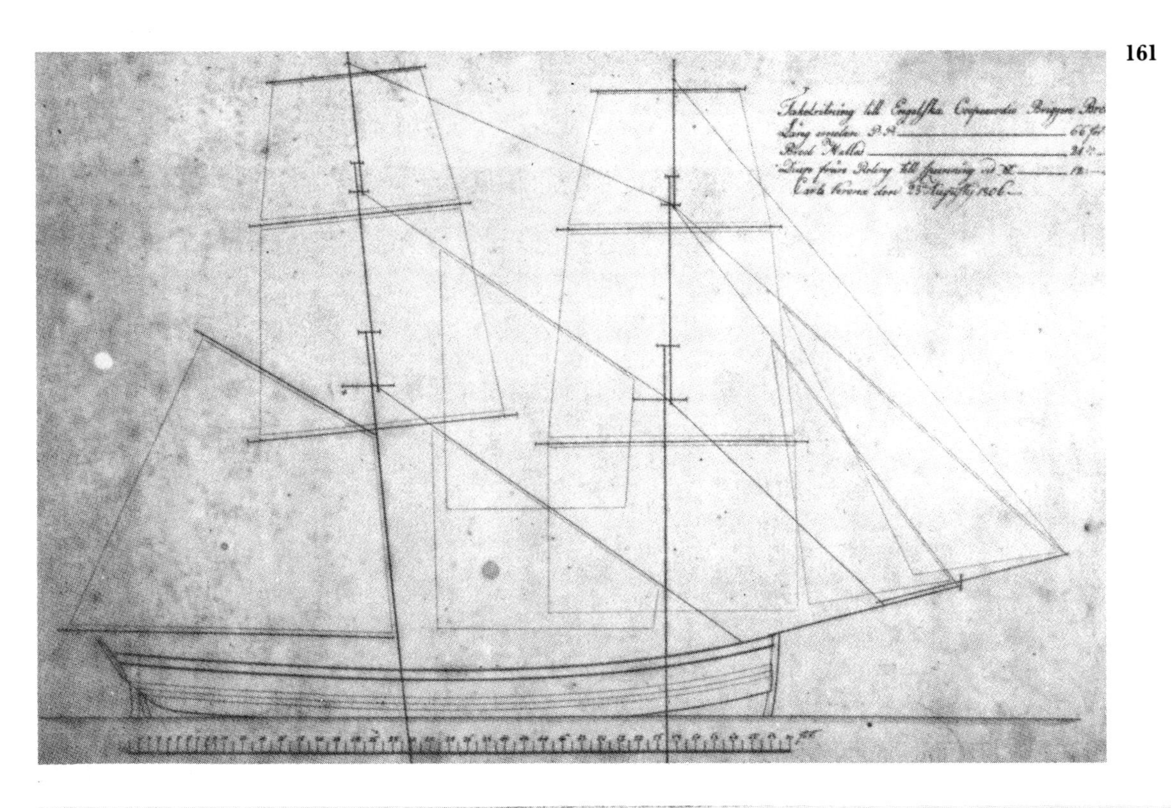

162

163

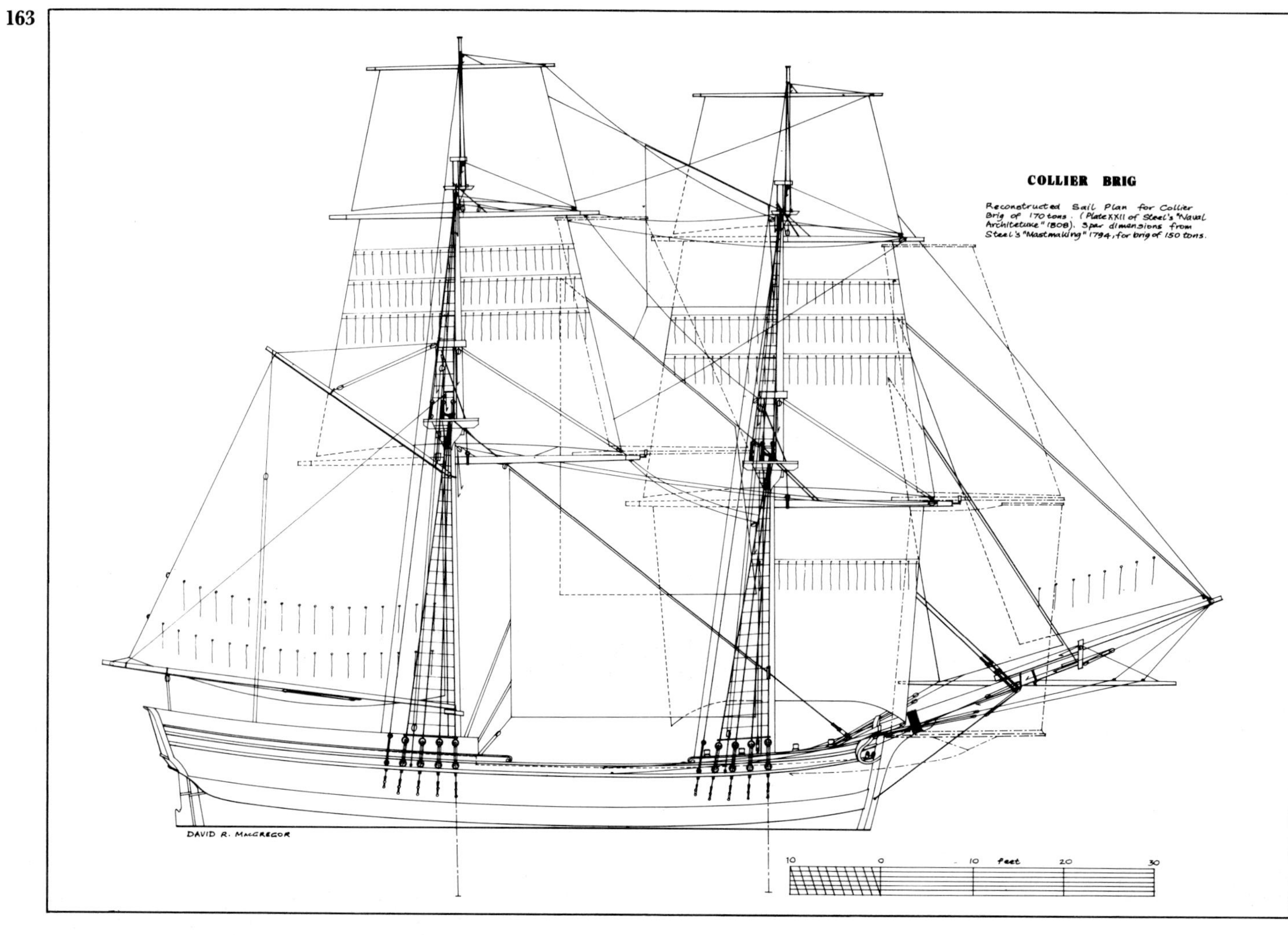

164

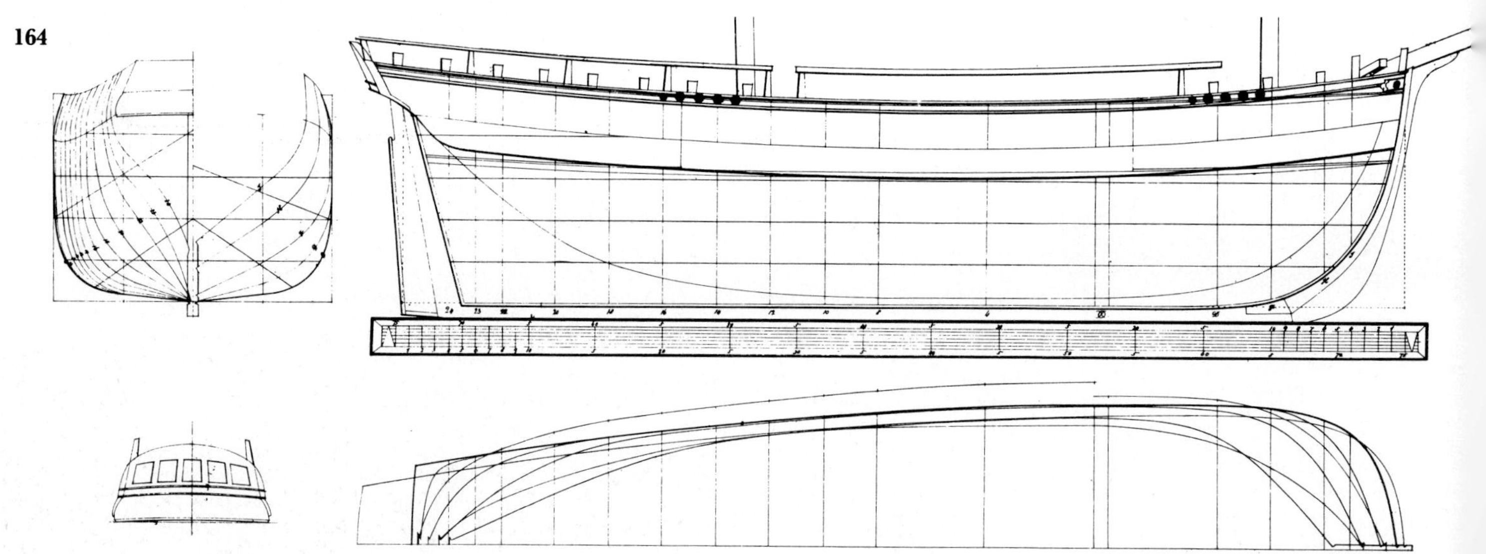

Fig 163. Collier Brig. *Sail plan. Entirely reconstructed from the following sources: sheer elevation from the lines plan in figure 158; spar dimensions from Steel's* Rigging and Seamanship *(1794) vol I, for brigs of 150 tons; sails and rigging from the same work and from Darcy Lever's* Sheet Anchor *(1808); contemporary paintings and plans. Stunsails are drawn dotted, but no square mainsail is drawn.*

Fig 164. Brig or Schooner. *Lines plan, unidentified, and dated c1800. The plan is reproduced from an original, drawn to ¼in scale. Dimensions scaled off the plan: 74ft 6in (between perpendiculars) × 20ft 9in (moulded) × 13ft 0in (approx).* (MacGregor Collection)

amply large enough for the bigger hull. The rule given for men-of-war was to make the length of the mainmast equal to half the sum of the lower-deck length, extreme beam and depth of hold. For the collier, this would result in a mainmast of 56ft 0in, whereas the table for merchant brigs gives 60ft 0in. Darcy Lever's *Sheet Anchor* has been closely followed for rigging details,[44] and a useful corroborative sail plan has been the outline plan of the English brig *Breeze*, dated 1806, preserved in the Chapman Collection at Stockholm.[45] Copley Fielding's sketch of a collier at Folkestone[46] (figure 166) and some plates in Cooke's *Shipping and Craft*[47] have proved very helpful. One of Cooke's original drawings is reproduced in figure 162 and shows colliers under way in several positions.

The resultant sail plan of Steel's collier, reproduced in figure 163, shows a true brig, with her fore-and-aft mainsail hooped to the mast and no square mainsail carried. A spritsail yard is listed in the spar dimensions, but by 1805 it was probably used only for spreading the bowsprit rigging; another point to watch is that the main topmast is two feet shorter than the fore topmast. In carrying out the reconstruction, it was decided not to show a dolphin striker,

166

Fig 166. A pencil drawing by Copley Fielding (1787–1855) entitled 'Collier at Folkestone', probably done in 1820 or shortly before. The rigging and spars are drawn in more detail than the hull. The absence of a dolphin striker suggests a brig built prior to 1815. (National Maritime Museum)

Fig 165. Thomas. *Sail plan dated January 1875. The* Thomas *was built in 1800 at Whitehaven with a tonnage of 211, and termed a brig in* Lloyd's Register *of 1822, but this plan shows her to be a snow with a main trysail mast and no boom to her spanker. Of course, by 1875, her original single topsails had been changed to double ones, and her fore royal mast and yard removed as a measure of economy. The cut of the three headsails was quite different from the style at the beginning of the century. The diagram on the left shows the yards on the mainmast with the sails furled. The original, which I traced in the Whitehaven Museum and Central Library, was drawn in indian ink on cartridge paper, the sheet measuring 26in × 16¼in.*

165

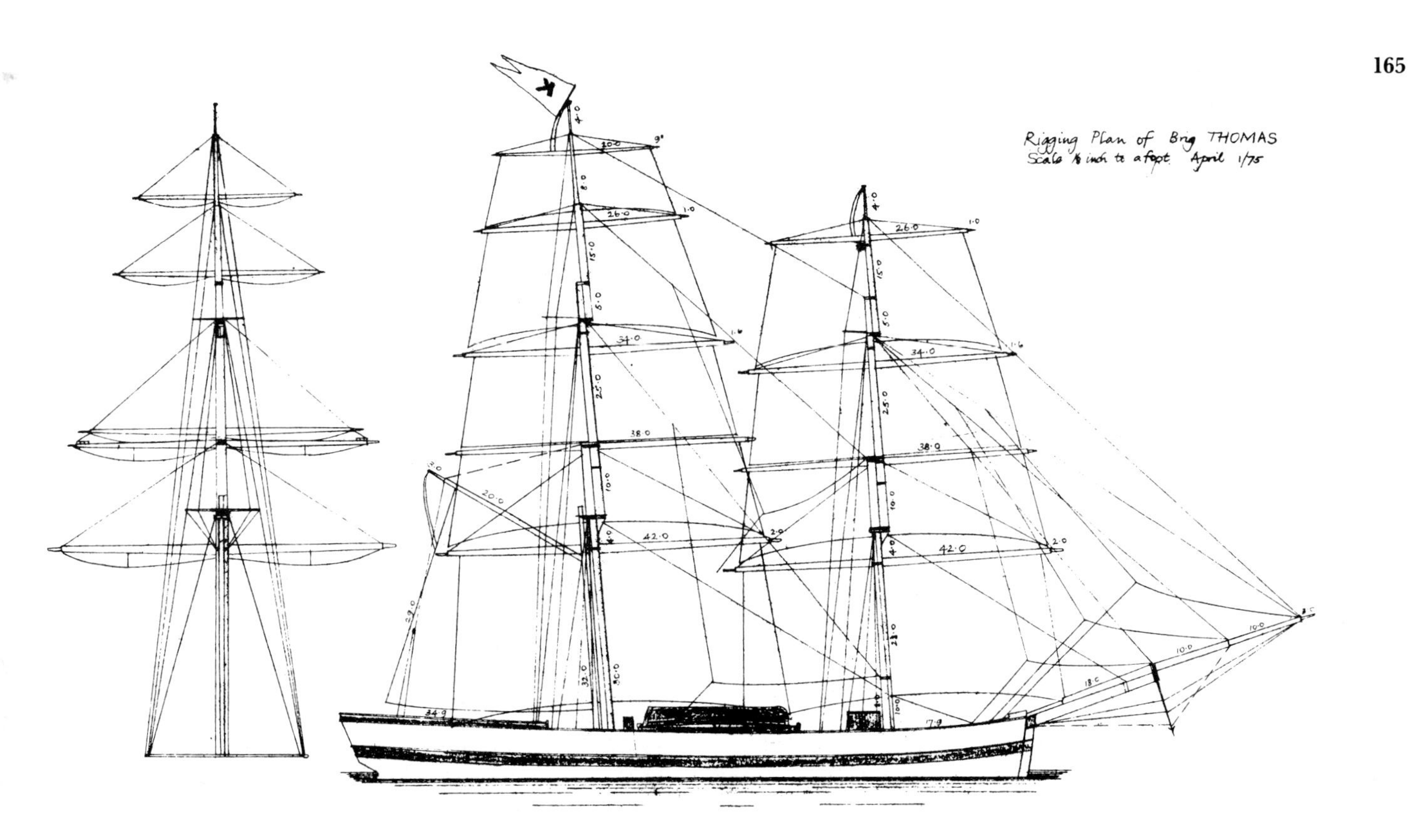

as illustrations suggest that colliers were slow to adopt them. Darcy Lever stated that the main staysail was seldom used except by brigs,[48] which gives sufficient licence to include it here, and the square nock follows the pattern of the *Breeze*. The shape of the main topmast staysail is also based on this brig and hoists on its own stay, not on a spring stay set up below the top as drawn on the sail plan of the brig *Neilson* in figure 64 of *Fast Sailing Ships*. In the *Breeze* the foot of the topsails and topgallants is shown straight without any roach, as in David Steel's *Rigging and Seamanship*, where the beautifully engraved plates illustrate each individual sail according to naval practice.[49] Steel remarked that in the merchant service the foot of these two sails was slightly gored near the clew, although the curve in 1800 was still fairly flat. As the nineteenth century wore on, the amount of roach increased in the foot, so that the sail received less chafe from stays and braces. Ward's drawing of the collier indicates the heaviness of the gear and illustrates the relation of the two masts to each other and to the hull.

This general arrangement of hull and sails continued for the next half-century in the sailing collier, although a main royal was set on a longer topgallant mast in some examples. The snow's trysail was useful because it obviated the need to provide such large mast hoops, thus saving costs and giving easier sail control, but the general adoption of the spanker with its boom and longer gaff was gradually adopted in the snow, in preference to the older boom-less gaff sail. The *Neilson's* sail plan shows the combined results.

Eighteenth century design methods, in which the sections of the body-plan were normally built up with arcs of circles, still influenced the shape of Steel's collier, because the floors are slightly curved, although no centres for radii are shown. It is probable that brigs and smaller craft, built in shipyards accustomed to constructing naval vessels and ship-rigged merchantmen, may have been designed on the older methods as described in books by such writers as William Sutherland, Mungo Murray and David Steel, although such methods were fast dying out after 1800. An Admiralty design drawing, dated 1802, of the lines of a sloop for use at Port Jackson shows centres of radii for the bilge sweep.[50] Steel's *Shipwright's Vade-Mecum* shows all the centres on the body plan for the 74-gun ship but none on the body plan of the Merchantman of 330 tons.[51] Over twenty years later, when commenting on the discontinuation of drawing curved lines by a series of arcs of circles, the naval architect, William M Rice, wrote, 'This barbarous practice of trammelling the ideas of the constructor has been wisely exploded at the Navy Office School of Naval Architecture and no doubt by most private ship-builders of any celebrity...'[52] Rice had left the School in 1819.

SOME BRIGS COMPARED

A lines plan in the Whitby Museum shows the 118-ton brig *Orient* which was built in the port in 1810 by John Barry, who also built the ship *Hyperion*. She has a broad shallow-draft hull suitable for carrying cargoes into small harbours or on to open beaches, and the shape of her sheer elevation and hull-form is almost identical with that of the Whitby sloop *Clio* (figure 196). The *Orient* has the same depth of hold, but there is an increase in length and breadth, the proportion of beams to length being three to one. Her deck is surrounded by an open rail as far forward as the foremast, the fitting of which was common practice in many merchant ships at the beginning of the nineteenth century although it was soon replaced with solid bulwarks. Steel's collier brig had no rail whatsoever in the waist but merely a low wash strake, just as many estuary spritsail barges have today. Rather than have a forward rail that could be

Fig 167. An example of a large brig is the Congress, *photographed at low water in harbour, perhaps at Maryport, where she was owned. Built at Maryport in 1818, she began life with a tonnage of 299, but she was lengthened in 1853 and the tonnage increased to 391, with measurements of 104.8ft × 27.8ft × 17.0ft. She was regularly in the transatlantic trade and was still afloat in 1868. No date is given for this photograph, but single topsail yards are still crossed, and she has royal yards on each mast, although they have almost faded away in the picture. There is a topgallant yard schooner between her and the quay, whose hull looks quite diminutive.* (Nautical Photo Agency)

168

Fig 168. *Watercolour drawing of the* Hoffnunge, *ex* Junge Janus, *which was built in 1780 and renamed in 1800 when bought by Hamburg owners. She was a whaler; the bentinck booms to both main and fore courses and other features of interest are described more fully in the text.* (Museum für Hamburgische Geschichte)

unshipped when lifting the anchor on deck, this rail was often omitted altogether. With her foremast right up in the bows, the *Orient* would have looked very much like the 'Yarmouth brig' of c1780 or the tiny snow photographed at Wisbech in June 1857 (figure 153). The *Orient* has similarities to Brocklebank's *Ceres*, because both have a broad, shallow-draft hull, but the *Ceres* is longer in relation to depth. The *Orient's* masts are placed in similar positions to those of the Hilhouse schooner *John*, with the mainmast a long way aft.

These full-bodied brigs were sound, comfortable vessels like the old Workington-built snow, *Edward*, that was launched in 1797. 'As might be supposed from the general appearance of her lines,' commented one who had served in her, 'the *Edward* went along like an old shoe and as dry as a bone, five knots being, ordinarily, about the best she could do.'[53] She could occasionally make a spurt of six knots but would then require two hands at the wheel. In the 1870s her total complement numbered six, including the master. She closely resembled the typical merchant brig of the early nineteenth century, but by the seventies it was common practice to fit these old brigs with double topsails and dock their fore royal, and many were thus photographed.

An example of a larger brig is given by the *Balfour*, owned by T & J Brocklebank and built by them at Whitehaven in 1809, as already described. Her tonnage of 310 equates her with many ship-rigged vessels of her day in respect of size. She had a crew of eighteen and in 1819 was valued at £4200 or £13 10s per ton.[54]

There was a large variety of rigs on the Continent of Europe and artists have recorded many of them. A watercolour drawing in the Museum of Hamburg History (Museum für Hamburgische Geschichte) depicts the whaling brig *Hoffnung* ex *De Junge Janus* which was built at Sonderburg in 1780 but sold to Hamburg owners in 1800 and renamed (figure 168). Like Steel's collier brig, she carries nothing above her topgallants, but in other ways her rig combines many interesting features. The trysail masts on both fore and main were nothing unusual, although that on the fore was stepped on an iron gooseneck, and that on the main stepped on the spanker boom. But abaft the main topmast was another sort of trysail or gunter mast running from the main cap to the crosstrees, to which was laced a big fore-and-aft topsail with a long head yard. The setting of the fore course on a bentinck boom was quite normal, but here the main course was also set on a bentinck boom. It was only in whaling ships that it was found fitted to the mainsail, the idea being that the few hands left aboard when all the whaling boats were away could still sail the ship.

169

170

Fig 171. An engraving by Jean Baugean, published 1814, of an American brig drying her sails; she has a large spanker and carries a flying jibboom, but nothing above her topgallants. (Collection de ... Bâtimens de Guerre et Marchands plate 41)

171

Green was a popular colour for painting ships inboard, and the *Hoffnung* has two green whale boats on each side, another on the stern davits, a green spanker boom, and bases of the lower masts. Also in green are the tops of the carrick bitts and the gallows over the ship's bell. Doubtless many of the fittings were in the same colour as well as the inboard side of the bulwarks.

The round-sterned hulls described in Chapter 2 continued to be built in large numbers, particularly in northern Europe.

Fig 169. This photograph of the Harmonien *shows a brig which has the same sort of hull and cut-down rig as the* Thomas *in figure 165. The* Harmonien *was built in 1815, (according to a date on the back of the photograph,) but I have been unable to trace her. The* Bureau Veritas Repertoire General *of 1886 has a barque of this name, built at Flensburg in 1810 of 234 tons and under Norwegian ownership. The hull photographed here looks hogged. The* Harmonien *has a bentinck boom and an anchor with a wooden stock, and the jibboom has been hauled in-board and triced up.* (Nautical Photo Agency)

Fig 170. The brig in the left foreground, sailing out to sea past a lighthouse, bears the name Resolute *on a flag, and the brig on the right closely resembles her and might be supposed to show her in a different position; but curiously she is taking in sail – her main topgallant and flying jib – and is inward-bound, presumably on an earlier occasion. Nevertheless, the artist, Robert Willoughby (1768–1843), has created a fresh and lively atmosphere here and clearly depicted the deck fittings of the brig. It is interesting to note that she has made-masts and bowsprit, and carries a flying jibboom, while no sail is bent to her spritsail yard. The sloop on the left, bearing the figure 5 on her mainsail and flying a blue flag, is presumably a pilot cutter, and ahead is a naval cutter with her guns run out. The scene is probably off Hull where the artist lived, and the date c1805–20.* (Courtesy of Henry S Streeter)

APPRAISAL OF AMERICAN DESIGN

During the period covered in this chapter, which starts with the French Revolution and ends with the fall of Napoleon, American shipowners engaged in overseas trade were faced with having to send their ships into seas patrolled by the navies of warring countries, where private warships exacted their toll and where strict neutrality was essential for self-preservation. Since escape by means of fast sailing was usually easier than a running battle, many American vessels were built on fine lines during these long periods of war, and such schooners and brigantines tend to get most of the attention. The hull-form of such craft has been well researched and illustrated by Howard I Chapelle in *Search for Speed under Sail 1700–1855*, but these fine lined vessels do not really fall within the scope of this book. I have given plans of the snow, *Duchess of Manchester*, which was built in America (figure 85) and also of the ship *Cupid* built in Newfoundland (figure 76), but neither was built on really fine lines. On the other hand, the *Cupid* had finer ends and more deadrise than the ship designed by Christian Bergh in 1804, whose lines and sail plan Chapelle reproduces as plates 48 and 49 in *Search for Speed under Sail*. This ship has not been identified and Chapelle wrote that she 'was designed to obtain a fair turn of speed and to be an economical carrier'.[55] She had dimensions of 83ft 0in length on deck, 24ft 0in extreme breadth and 13ft 5in depth of hold. Thanks to her large sail plan, she probably had a reasonable turn of speed in moderate weather.

Perhaps the ship *Lucy*, built at Kingston, Massachusetts, in 1806, was of this latter type. She was named after the wife of her builder and owner, Joseph Holmes Jr, and cost $7366 complete; her tonnage was 208. Not many full-rigged ships were built at Kingston, as a published list shows. Lysander

172 Goelette venant d'appareiller d'un port de marée. 56

Bartlett was the foreman carpenter, and Samuel Skillin of Boston carved the figurehead, brackets and trailboards at a cost of $47.50. The figurehead was of a woman and stood 6½ft high – a large size for such a small ship. Her first two voyages took her safely across to Liverpool and back to Boston, but on her third voyage in 1807, bound from London to Hamburg with sugar, she was seized by French customs officials and accused of smuggling because her papers were not in order. The ship was valued at $12,000 and the cargo at $10,000. Although insured, Holmes was unable to collect.[56]

An inventory was drawn up for the *Lucy* a few months before her capture:[57]

INVENTORY. SHIP *LUCY*. 12 MONTHS OLD JUNE 1807

Mast, Yards and Booms Complete

SAILS

Four Top Sails
One Main Sail
Two Royals
One Spanker
One Fore Top Mast Stay Sail
One Middle Top Mast Stay Sail
One Main Stay Sail
Two Top Gallant do-do-do
One Fore Sail
Three Top Gallant Sails
One Mizzen
One Jib
One Main Top Mast Stay Sail
One Mizzen Stay Sail
Two Top Mast Studding Sails
One Lower do-do-do

Two Bower Anchors
One Kedge
One Stream Cable
One Camboose & House
One Hand Lead & Line
One Half Hour Glass
Ten Water Casks
Three Marling Spikes
One Runner & Tackle
Two Cat Blocks
Hatch Bars Locks & Keys
Three Setts Pump Gear
Two Hammers
One Ships Axe
Four Paint Brushes
Two Draw Buckets
One Pair Can Hooks
Four Chairs
One Dozen Plates
One Case Knives & Forks
One Tea Pot
One Turene
Six Wine Glasses
Two Table Cloths
One Cabin Bell
One Castor
Four Table Spoons
One Per Grains
One Stream Anchor
Two Bower Cables
One Hawser
One Deep Sea Lead & Line
One Log Reel & Line
Two Second Glasses
Nine Hand Spikes
One Long Boat & 4 Oars
Three Burton Blocks
One Fish Hook
Two Lanthorns
Two Scrubbing Brushes
One Cooks Axe
Three Scrapers
Six Paint Pots & Bucket
One Pair Hnd. Slings
One Boat Hook
One Side Ladder
Two Wood Compasses
One Hand Trumpet
A Quantity Spare Hooks & Thimbles
One Table
Two Dishes
Two Pitchers
One Coffee Pot
Four Small Mugs
One Crobar
One Spare Top Mast
One Spare Top Sail Yard
One Shovel
One Tea Kettle
One Sauce Pan
One Pendant
One Coffee Mill
Three Serving Mallets
A Quantity of Bolts, Spikes & Nails
Two Spare Top Gall Masts
One Grind Stone
One Frying Pan
One Ensign
Three Covered Buckets
Two Mops
A Quantity Blocks, Sheaves and Pins
One Brush
Two Tea Cannisters
One Looking Glass
Six Cups & Saucers
Six Tea Spoons
One Pr. Man Ropes
One Brass Compass
One Speaking Trumpet
One Medicine Chest

Fig 172. Another of Baugean's engravings which capture the mood of ships and sea so imaginatively. Here a schooner and a cutter are making sail out of a tidal harbour and, judging by the rocks along the base of the harbour wall on the left, they are not a moment too soon. The cutter has a deeply roached topsail set, but her topgallant is still furled. The schooner has topsails and topgallants on each mast, and has loosed her fore topgallant sail ready for hoisting it. There is a man standing on the boom at the base of her foremast, on which a square sail is furled; this sail is capable of being set between this boom and the fore yard. (Reproduced from plate 56 in Recueil de Petites Marines, *1817)*

From the list of sails carried, it can be assumed that she set royals on the foremast and the mainmast but not on the mizen; that one of the four topsails was a spare sail; that the 'mizen' was set on a gaff like the old mizen course and that the 'spanker' acted like a driver. The middle topmast staysail was set from the main topmast hounds, above the main topmast staysail.

In plate 74 of *Search for Speed under Sail*, Howard Chapelle gives the lines of the brigantine *James Munroe* which was built in 1815 from a design by William Doughty, the Naval Constructor at Washington. She was 66ft 7½in on deck, 21ft 0in moulded beam and 10ft 1in depth of hold. She has a full convex entrance, a finer hollow run, and marked deadrise with slack bilges. She was reported to be a fast sailer with good cargo capacity, which was a popular combination.

On the matter of buildings costs in America, there was a curious contribution to the *European Magazine*, in the form of an extract from the *Pennsylvanian Packet* of May 1790:[58]

> Ship-building is an Art for which the United States are peculiarly qualified, by their skill in the construction, and by the materials with which their country abounds; and they are strongly tempted to pursue by their commercial spirit, by the capital fisheries in their bays and on their coasts, and by the productions of a great and rapidly-increasing agriculture. They build their Oak vessels on lower terms than the cheapest European vessels of Fir, Pine and Larch. The cost of an Oak Ship in New England is about 24 Mexican dollars per Ton fitted for Sea; a Fir vessel costs in the ports of the Baltic 35 Mexican dollars, and the American Ship will be much the most durable. The cost of a vessel of American live Oak and Cedar, which will last, if salted in her timbers, 30 years, is only 36 to 38 dollars in our different ports; and an Oak Ship in the cheapest part of England, Holland, or France, fitted in the same manner, will cost 55 to 60 dollars. In such a country the fisheries and commerce, with due care and attention on the part of the Government, must be profitable.

Comments on American schooners can be found in the next two sections, where they are compared with their British and European counterparts.

TWO-MASTED SCHOONERS

By the end of the eighteenth century there were two classes of schooner: those rigged with square sails on fidded topmasts, and those with pole masts and a purely fore-and-aft rig. As the nineteenth century advanced, the schooner rig was generally applied to decked vessels, open boats being rigged as sloops or ketches, but there were so many local differences that it is impossible to lay down any hard and fast rules.

For convenience of handling, the relatively smaller sail units of a schooner scored an advantage over the fewer and larger sails of a sloop or cutter of similar size, and it is interesting to note that the design of a sloop for use at Port Jackson, whose plans were prepared by the Admiralty in 1802, had her rig amended to that of a schooner the next year.[59] Nevertheless it was the single-masted rig which remained in use in Great Britain for many years as the most popular rig for coastal craft, and J A Atkinson's etching of a 'Coasting Schooner' published in 1808 shows the rig of a main-topsail schooner on a sloop's hull, with a plain bow

173

Fig 173. Entitled 'Coasting Schooner', this was drawn and etched by J A Atkinson. It was published in 1808 and is one of a series that he did of coastal scenes; two others appear in figs 189 and 199. This small schooner has a cutter's running bowsprit to starboard of the stem head; there is a lower yard on each mast for setting square sails. (Parker Gallery)

174

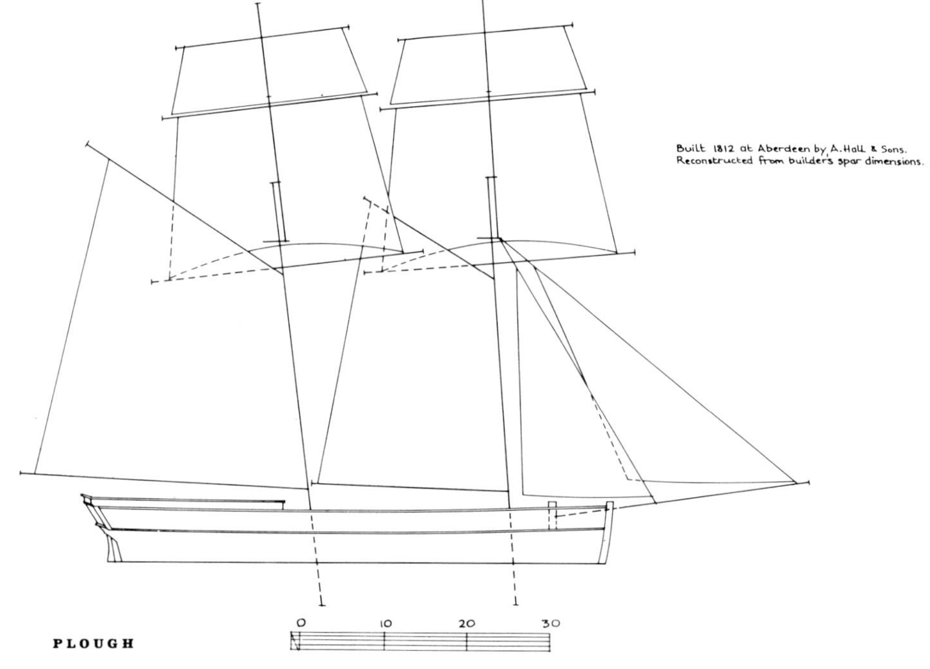

PLOUGH

175

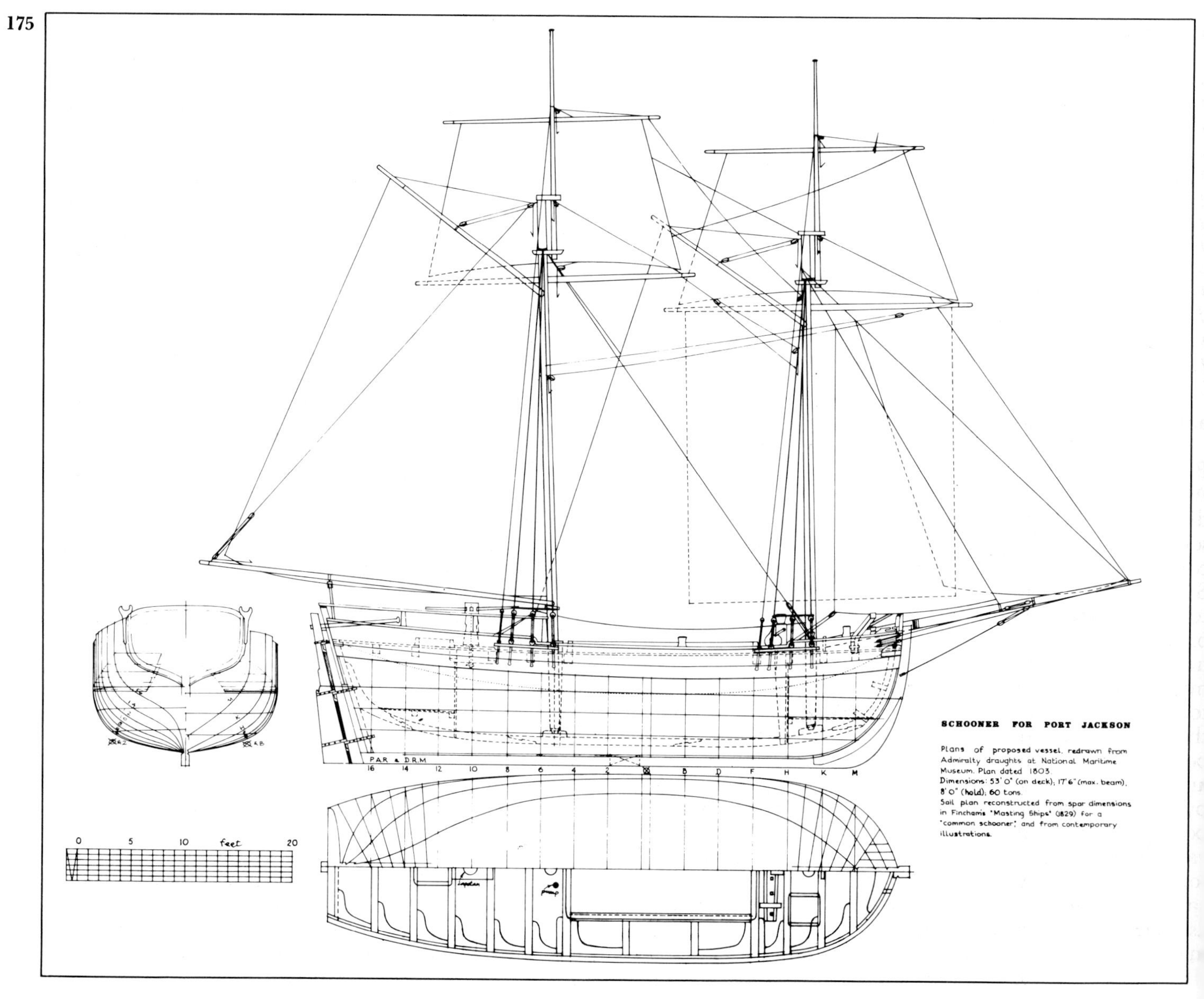

SCHOONER FOR PORT JACKSON

Plans of proposed vessel, redrawn from Admiralty draughts at National Maritime Museum. Plan dated 1803.
Dimensions: 53' 0" (on deck); 17' 6" (max. beam), 8' 0" (hold); 60 tons.
Sail plan reconstructed from spar dimensions in Fincham's 'Masting Ships' (1829) for a 'common schooner' and from contemporary illustrations.

176

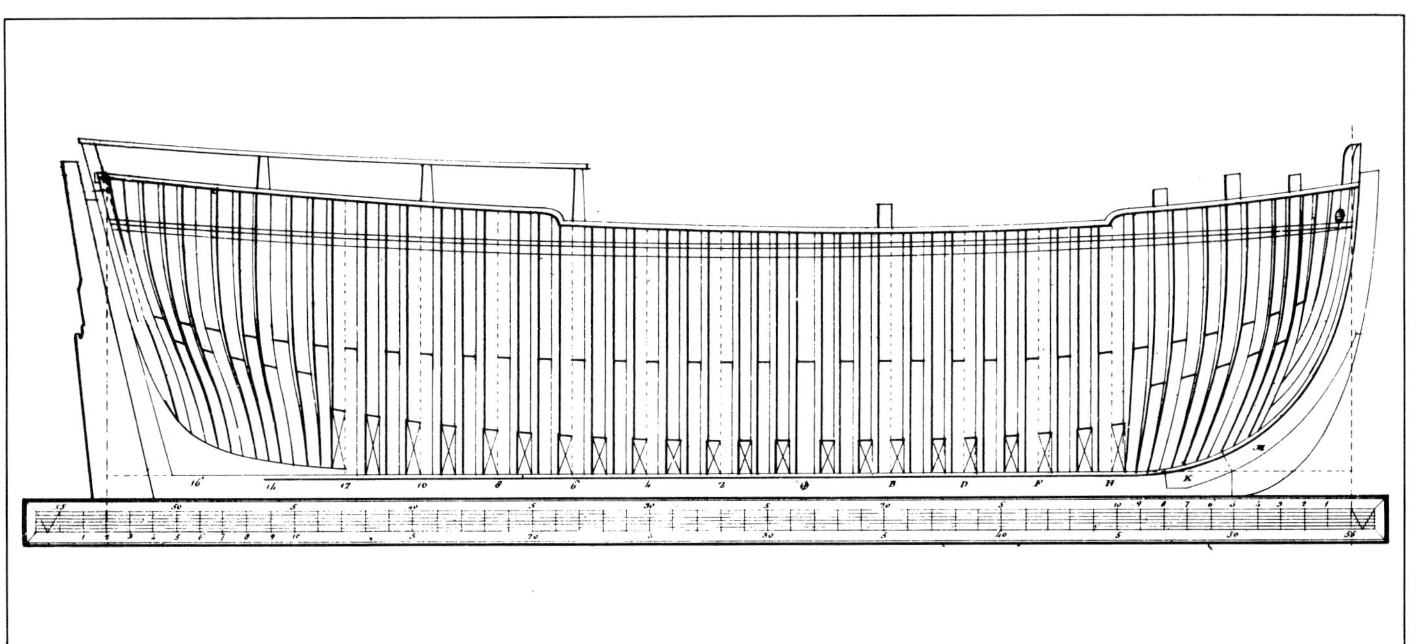

Fig 174. Plough. *Outline sail plan. She was built at Aberdeen in 1811 of 86 tons. The plan has been reconstructed from spar dimensions in the yard book of A Hall & Sons, supplied by James Henderson. The* Plough *has been drawn with a plain bow and no head.*

Fig 175. Schooner for Port Jackson. *Designed by the Admiralty as a sloop in December 1802, she was re-masted as a schooner by January 1803. Hull lines, deck beams and fittings have been redrawn from Admiralty draughts 4533 and 4534 at the National Maritime Museum, Greenwich. The mast, sail and rigging plan has been reconstructed from spar dimensions in John Fincham,* Masting Ships *(1829), as for a 'common schooner'. Dimensions on the plan: 53ft 0in (on deck) × 17ft 6in (extreme) × 8ft 0in and 68 tons. The lengths of bowsprit and jibboom are combined in a single spar here.*

Fig 176. Schooner for Port Jackson. *Frame elevation, redrawn by Paul A Roberts from part of an Admiralty draught. This completes the plan in figure 175.*

and a running bowsprit hauled inboard (figure 173).

Lack of authentic data concerning the schooner in Great Britain is very noticeable at this date, but the sail plan of the Aberdeen-built *Plough*, reconstructed from the spar dimensions and shown in figure 174, gives an idea of a schooner of this period which Atkinson's etching corroborates. The *Plough* was built by Alexander Hall & Son in 1811 for owners in Newburgh and measured 60ft 6in tonnage length, 2ft 7in rake of sternpost, 18ft 8in extreme breadth, 18ft 3in moulded breadth, $86\frac{53}{94}$ tons custom house measurement and $88\frac{12}{94}$ tons carpenter's measurement. She cost £10 per ton, being charged at $86\frac{1}{2}$ tons. Positions of the masts are not given, nor the lengths of the fore boom and gaff, but the yard book states: 'Fore boom and gaff to fit between masts'. Had the masts been arranged closer, there would have been excessive overlap by the topsails. In deciphering the entry for the *Plough*, it has been impossible to determine whether the word 'topgallant yard' is singular or plural. If it is singular, there would be no topgallant sail on the mainmast. The main lower yard is called, in the account books, a 'crossjack yard', a term often assigned to this yard in the case of main-topsail schooners or main-topsail brigantines.[60]

As there was evidence from the illustrations given here that schooners with square topsails on both masts were in regular use in Great Britain, I decided to reconstruct a sail plan of one and place this on an Admiralty draught of a schooner designed for use at Port Jackson – now re-named Sydney. The lines plan of this vessel was dated December 1802, and she was given one mast, but this was amended in January 1803 when two masts were drawn in. The frame elevation and deck layout are dated January 1803, and she is described in the title as 'a sailing vessel schooner-rigged to be built at Port Jackson, New South Wales, for the service of that port'. On this plan was a note stating that a copy had been sent to Chatham to be forwarded to the *Calcutta* which was bound for Port Jackson, so presumably the port authorities received it, but whether they built a schooner and what her name might be, I have yet to discover.

The schooner on this plan (figure 175) measures 53ft 0in length on deck, 17ft 6in extreme breadth, 8ft 0in depth in hold, and 68 tons. She has a plain bow without a gammon knee, a square tuck stern and outside rudder steered with a tiller; on deck she has a large hatchway between the masts, a capstan aft, a windlass abaft the foremast, and the only rail to her flush deck is abaft the mainmast. She has easy lines with rounded bilges and does not draw too much. Having decided to reconstruct her sail plan, I used the dimensions in the 1829 edition of Fincham's *Masting Ships*,[61] employing the measurements and proportions listed as for a 'Common Schooner'. The tables of spar lengths were arranged according to the breadth for the masts, and the vessel's length for the yards and gaffs. Fincham lists the following types of yard for a 'common schooner': square sail yard, topsail yard, and royal yard, but the latter has been omitted here. According to the table it was 13.9ft. He gives the main yard as 2.9ft shorter than the fore yard, but the topsail yards are virtually similar. I have combined the lengths of bowsprit and jibboom into a single spar. No boom is placed at the foot of the foresail, nor are any stunsails drawn, although they might well have been carried. The topmasts are fairly lengthy above the topsail yards, and on reflection I wonder why I did not draw the topsails with more drop or indeed cross a topgallant yard on each, rather as in the

Plough. But this sail plan shows the basic square and fore-and-aft sails that would have been set.

An American schooner with topsails on each mast is the *Fame* of Salem which was built at Ipswich, Massachusetts, in 1795. As can be seen from her portrait in figure 177, the lower yards or 'spread yards' are set some distance below the hounds, thereby giving the topsails a greater depth. The fore topgallant has a short yard but there is no equivalent sail on the main; there is a fore-and-aft topsail hoisted above the mainsail, and it was probably found that it would blanket any topgallant sail set on the main topmast. As sails and sky are almost the same tone in the photograph of the painting, it may be difficult to make out the sail outlines. The method of setting the topsails below the cap is reminiscent of some cutters, and was coming into fairly widespread use after 1800 for one, two and even three masted vessels. Most examples come from countries bordering the Baltic and the North Sea. Peter Hedderwick's schooner *Glasgow* was so rigged, as can be seen in the sail plan reproduced in figure 53 of *Merchant Sailing Ships 1815–1850*. There are further illustrations in the same chapter. In Hans Szymanski's book on German

Fig 177. The American schooner Fame *of Salem, built in 1795, had square sails on both masts and the setting of these is described in the text. The rigging is well-detailed on the original although less easy to pick out in the reproduction. The braces from the main yard lead aft to the stern, but the main topsail brace goes forward to the foremast; the topping lift for the fore boom is taken up to the hounds of the mainmast; the hoisting of topsail yards on the doubling as pictured here, was less common in America than in western Europe.* (Peabody Museum, Salem)

Fig 178. HMS Sea Lark, *ex* Fly. *Lines, deck plan and longitudinal section, redrawn by Paul A Roberts from Admiralty draughts in the National Maritime Museum, Greenwich. Dimensions on plan: 81ft 3in (length on deck), 22ft 8in (extreme breadth), 9ft 10in (depth of hold), and 178 tons. Reconstruction: particulars on longitudinal section were obtained from the original lines plan, where they were over-drawn in a different coloured ink; deck plan from a separate drawing.*

Fig 179. HMS Sea Lark, *ex* Fly. *Sail plan, reconstructed from spar dimensions on the original lines plan, and from a reconstructed sail plan of this schooner kindly supplied by Howard I Chapelle.*

177

179

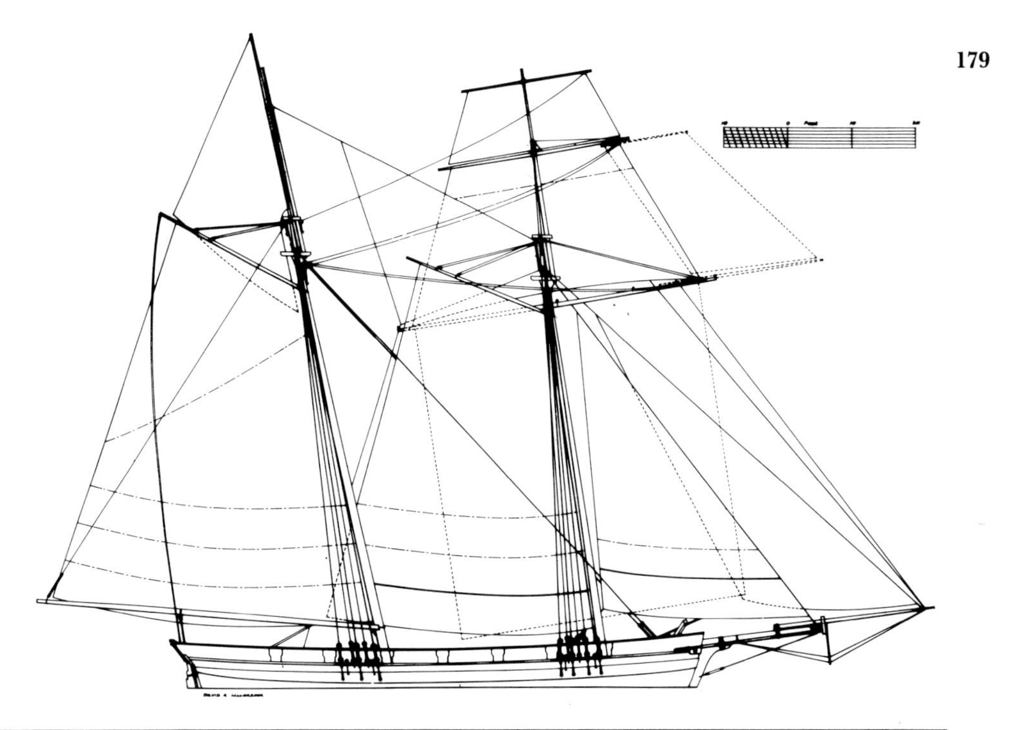

178

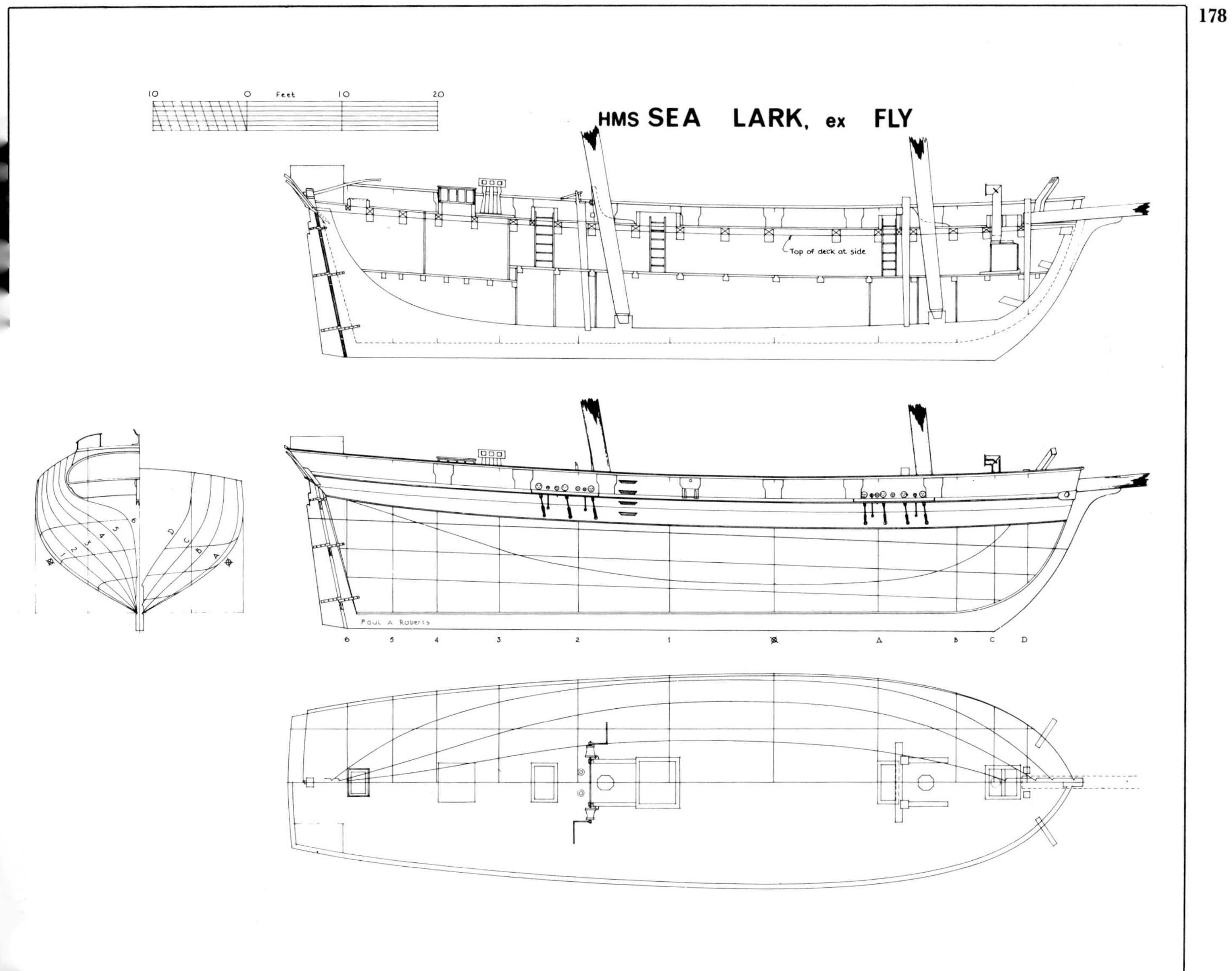

10 0 Feet 10 20
HMS SEA LARK, ex FLY
Top of deck at side
Paul A Roberts
6 5 4 3 2 1 ⊠ A B C D

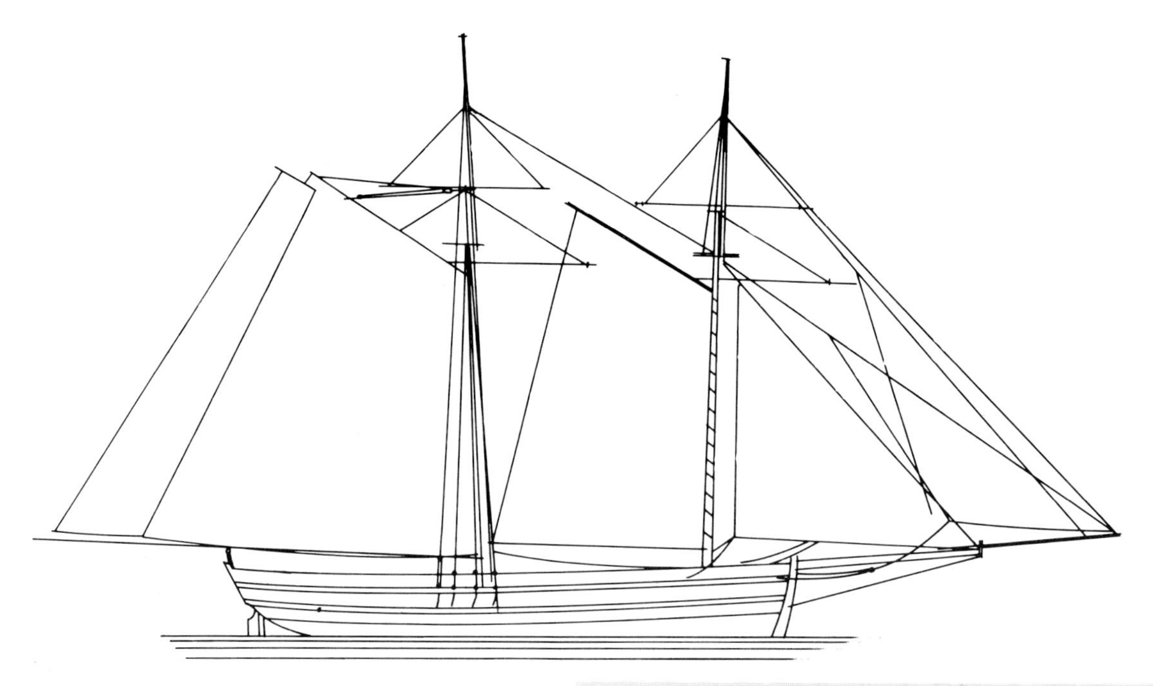

180

Fig 180. Schooner. *Sail plan, traced from a Brocklebank plan in the Liverpool County Museums of an unidentified schooner, possibly the* Experiment, *built in 1802. There is no reconstruction, so two positions for the jib are left as on the original; also the topsail yards are drawn lowered, without any sails set.*

shipping, almost half the sloops, galleasses and schooners are fitted with this type of topsail in the years 1800–20.[62]

David Steel gave no plan of a British schooner in his *Naval Architecture*, but he did give plans of three American schooners and the offsets of a fourth. Plans of schooners prior to about 1815 would have been comparatively rare had it not been for the zeal of the Admiralty draughtsmen in recording their lines. A wide selection of extremely fine-ended schooners having big deadrise and large spreads of canvas is presented by Howard I Chapelle in *Search for Speed under Sail*, but all these vessels are of the clipper category.

However, it is instructive to compare one such schooner, not built on extreme lines, with British and European vessels, and accordingly the lines and sail plan of the American schooner *Fly* are offered here. Her place of build and date are unknown but she was captured off the Scillies in 1811 and taken into the Royal Navy the following year under the name of *Sea Lark*. Her lines were taken off by Admiralty surveyors, and a plan drawn on which the spar dimensions were tabulated. This plan shows that she was not of extreme form, even though she had fairly steep deadrise, because the waterlines are convex and the entrances not particularly sharp. Measurements inscribed on the plan give 81ft 3in length on deck, 22ft 8in extreme breadth, 9ft 10in depth of hold, and 178 tons. The Admiralty drawings have been re-drawn here in figure 178, and a sail plan has been reconstructed from the spar dimensions (figure 179). The lofty masts of this Baltimore clipper make the square topsail and topgallant that much smaller on the foremast. Howard I Chapelle kindly provided a copy of his reconstructed sail plan to assist me.

At Whitehaven, Brocklebank's only schooner prior to 1823 other than the shallops was the *Experiment*, built in 1802 with dimensions of 62ft 3in on deck, 18ft 3in extreme breadth, 9ft 10in depth of hold and 89¼ tons. The mainmast was 41ft from deck to hounds and the topmast

181

182

Goelettes Balaou, au mouillage.

Fig 182. Two schooners at anchor. The one further away has what must be a red ensign at her stern; she is crossing a topgallant yard, has a fore stay too close to the mast to set sail on, and there are vangs from her fore gaff. The nearer one has her topgallant yard stowed on top of the topsail yard and has cock-billed her fore yard. Both schooners have a boom hanging just above the bulwarks to set the foot of a narrow square sail. The engraving is by Jean Baugean and is entitled 'Goelettes Balaou, au mouillage'. My thanks to Elizabeth Wiggans who researched the word 'balaou' and revealed its meaning as 'needlefish'. Pâris refers to the yacht America *as 'Yacht* America *Balaou' presumably because of her long sharp entrance, which was probably a feature of these French schooners.* (Recueil de Petites Marines,).

had a 'hoist' of 20ft; dimensions on the foremast were 2ft shorter in each case. Lower and topsail yards in the plural are listed, so that square topsails were carried on each mast; the fore sail was boomless; and no jibboom is listed. Schooners cannot have been popular on that north-west coast as Brocklebank's yard book records in February 1811: 'Schooner *Defiance* built at Maryport altered into a brig'.

Found amongst the Brocklebank plans was a sheet of paper, size 12in × 9½in, with a small sail plan drawn in pencil of an unnamed main-topsail schooner, reproduced here as figure 180. Perhaps it was a preliminary design for *Experiment*; no scale is given, and at ⅒in the main boom, the yards and the bowsprit are approximately correct, but the lower masts and topmasts are too short. The hull length is also too short – it should be 55ft register length. Noted on the same sheet of paper are the sizes of three sails: main sail 189 yards, fore sail 130 yards, 'Jibb' 55 yards, total 374.

On the north-east coast of England, that home of the brig, schooners in the 65 to 120 tons range were occasionally being built at Whitby, but single-masted craft were still preferred in England. Eslewhere in Europe the ketch-rigged galliot was popular and provided some fore-and-aft canvas on a second mast.

Fig 181. The schooner Alert, *photographed at Whitby in 1880, was built in 1802 at Whitby with a tonnage of 43 and has the bluff bows of a cargo carrier. The topsail yard is hanging on its lifts from the lower mast cap, above which it could not be hoisted; the topgallant sail has been lowered below the mast cap, so its yard could not have a parral.* (Nautical Photo Agency)

THREE-MASTED SCHOONERS

There were a few schooners built before 1815 with three masts, and fresh names are constantly cropping up. An early example is the *Jenny*, which sailed from Bristol in June 1791 for Hawaii via Cape Horn; she was of 78 tons and was built in Bristol, probably by Sydenham Teast. In October 1793 she was convered into a full-rigged ship.[63] The *Curlew* of 54 tons was built at Teignmouth in 1794. In 1800 the American privateer *Experiment* was chased by two French privateers in the West Indies, of which one was a three-masted schooner.[64] In 1801 the American three-masted schooner *Success* was at Jamaica, and this rig was popular for fast vessels in West Indian waters at that date.[65] From then on, named vessels are more common.

The Baltimore-built three-masted schooner *Revenge* of 150 tons was captured in the West Indies and taken into the Royal Navy under the name of *Flying Fish*. She was a shallow-draft design with a ratio of L/D of 10.04, based on the dimensions recorded on her plan. Sent to England, she had her lines taken off at Portsmouth in September 1806 and these plans were employed to build six three-masted schooners of the '*Shamrock* class' at Bermuda.[66] This class was in commission from 1807 until about 1820, and probably inspired the building of other three-masters. The Admiralty surveyors must have been very intrigued with her sail plan because they took the unusual step of actually drawing it out, not merely of recording the spar dimensions.[67] Howard Chapelle has redrawn it and added standing and running rigging, but he has omitted the four-sided main topmast staysail and added a boom to the fore square sail.[68] The narrow fore topgallant is very curious.

In 1807, John Brockbank contracted to build a schooner at Lancaster of 153 tons. The dimensions from her builder's contract give 81ft 6in length aloft, 65ft 0in length of keel for tonnage, 21ft 0in extreme breadth above the bends, 10ft 3in depth of hold. As regards her masts and spars, the contract book entry was typically ambiguous: 'the builders to make and find three masts, bowsprit boom and gaffs and other poles suitable for such a vessel. Masts to be coated with rozin and oil or tar varnish'. The contract price was £10 10s

Fig 183. This rakish three-masted schooner is of the type used for privateering between 1790 and 1815. Small square topsails were carried on fore and main above long lower masts. Lithograph by J Rogers dated 1820. (Parker Gallery)

Fig 184. Transit. *Sail plan. The* Transit *was built in 1800 at Itchenor, Sussex, of 195 tons. The plan shows the rig with the masts reduced from five to four. It is probably the earliest known barquentine rig, reproduced from* A Narrative of a Mode Pursued by the British Government to Effect Improvements in Naval Architecture *by Richard Hall Gower (1811) plate 1 (following page 108).*

Fig 185. Transit. *Mast and rigging plan. This is the vessel shown in figure 184; unfortunately the yards are drawn end-on, but the run of their braces can be followed to give their positions. Reproduced from the same work as figure 184; plate 2.*

per ton. Her builder described her rig as 'schooner'.[69] In 1808 she made a passage to Barbados.

As the *Flying Fish* carried five square sails on two of her masts, it would hardly be surprising if other so-called 'schooners' with three masts were found to set sufficient square sails to be classed by modern parlance as 'barquentines'. The earliest known example of this rig was to be seen in the *Transit*, as described fully in *Fast Sailing Ships*. Between 1800 and 1801 her rig was in the form of a five-masted barquentine, but was later reduced to four masts. Figure 184 shows the rig with sails set and figure 185 gives her appearance with them furled, although the yards on the foremast are unfortunately drawn end-on and so might seem to have been removed.[70]

It was Captain Richard Gower, a master mariner in the East India Company's service, who designed the *Transit*, but how he reached this form of hull and rig was not divulged in his books. He formed the bottom half of the body plan with arcs of circles which must have proved easy to someone who was not a naval architect, and above that the sides flared outwards in a straight line. The lines plan in figure 186 is from Fincham's *History of Naval Architecture*[71] and shows the short sharp ends and some 55ft of parallel middle body which is quite straight and was a feature of the design. It is though that Gower's published plan does not accurately show the vessel as built.[72] She was a long narrow vessel for her day with a proportion of 4.6 beams to length, given by dimensions of 102ft 6in length for tonnage, 22ft 0in

183

184

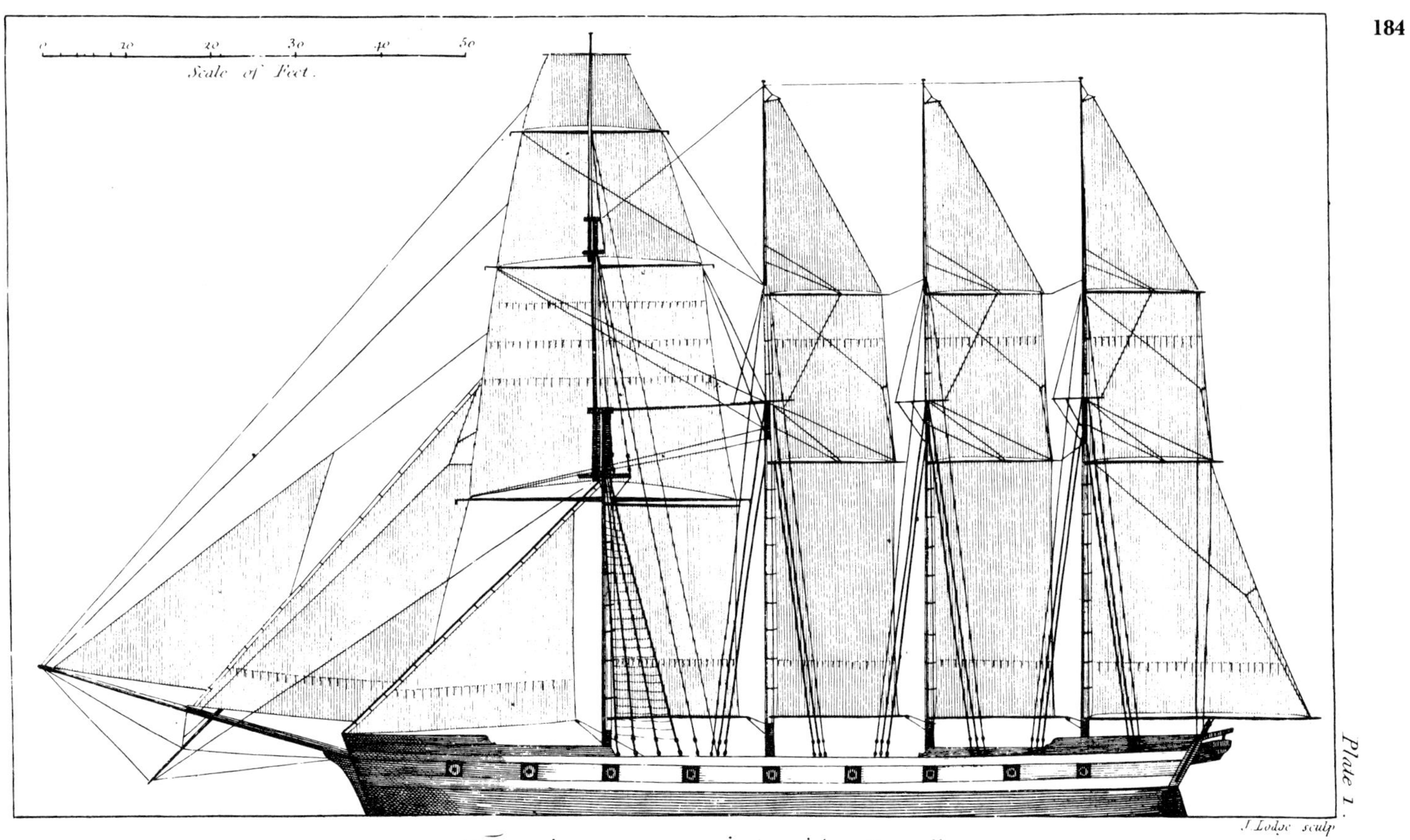

Transit, upon a wind, with all sail set.

185

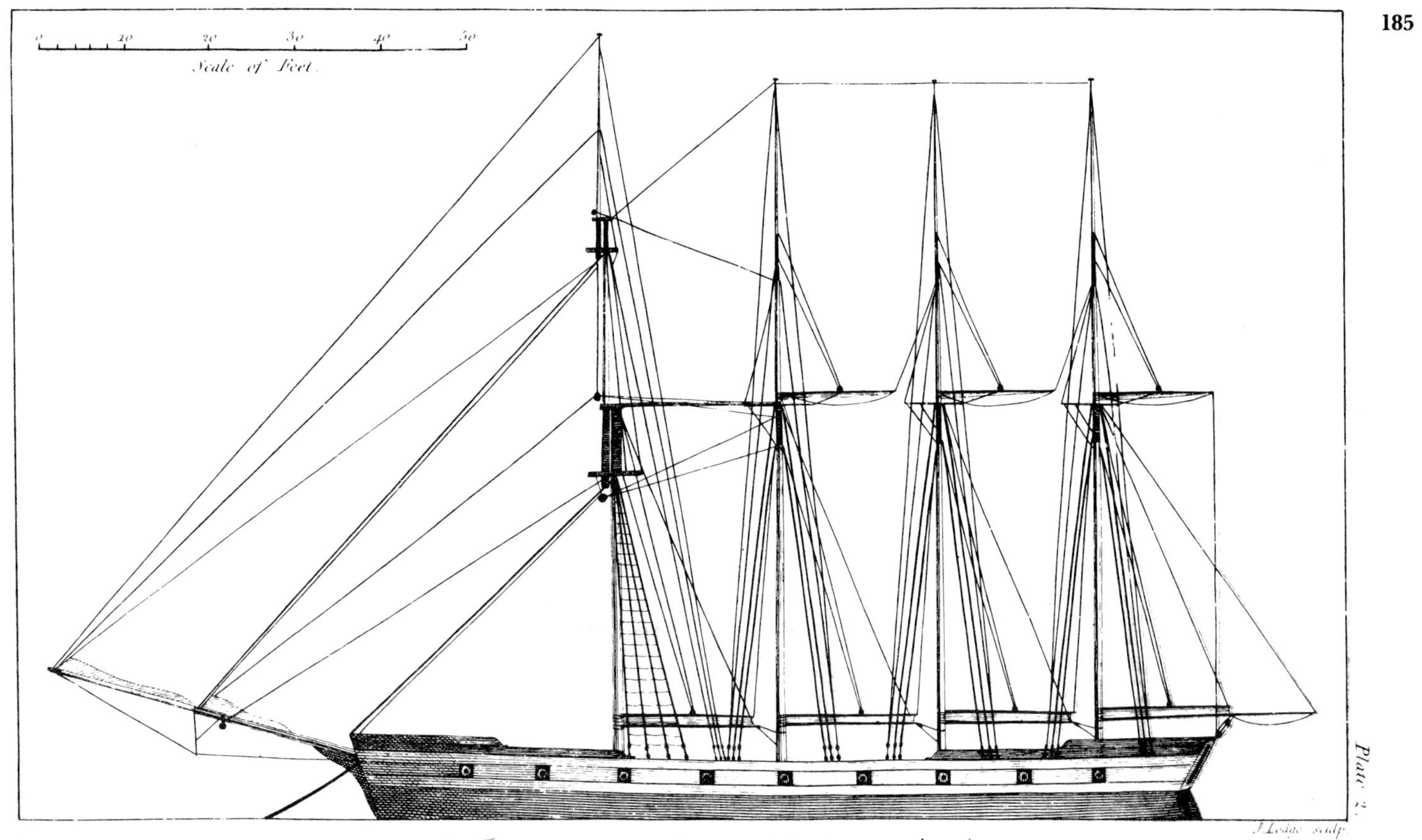

Transit at anchor, with her sails furled.

186

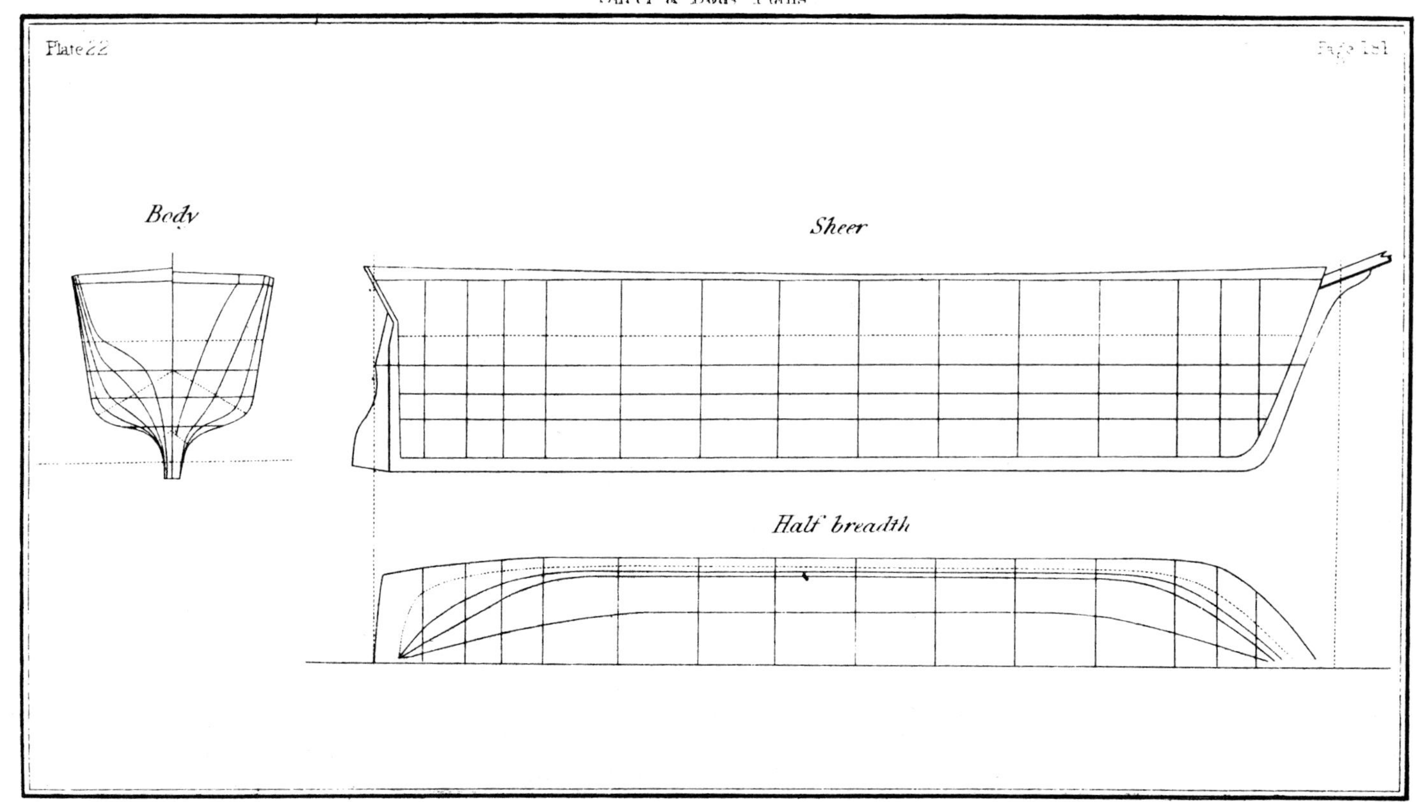

Fig 186. Transit. *Lines plan, reproduced from a plan in* A History of Naval Architecture *by John Fincham (1851) plate 22 (facing page 181). Dimensions: 102ft 6in (length for tonnage), 22ft 0in (extreme breadth), 12ft 6in (approx depth in hold), and 195 tons.*

extreme breadth, 12ft 6in depth in hold (approx) and 195 tons. She was constructed at Itchenor in 1800 at a cost of £6900 which had been subscribed by people who had seen the model exhibited by Gower in the previous year.[73]

In 1801 the number of masts was reduced to four but she consistently performed well at sea, especially when close-hauled, although she was never hired or bought by the Post Office, the Admiralty or the East India Company. The first *Transit* was wrecked in 1810, but was replaced by a second, longer version ordered by the Admiralty and built upon similar lines, although the entrance and run were longer and finer. The four-masted barquentine rig was repeated. With the same breadth and a length of 134ft 0in, the proportion of beams to length rises to 5.9. A three-masted barquentine version was built at Ipswich in 1819 as a yacht for the Hon G Vernon. Although I have used the word 'barquentine' when describing the rig, it should be noted that the term was not employed until the 1860s. A more likely expression was 'cutter-rigged on four masts'.

KETCH OR GALLEAS AND GALLIOT

The Swedish, English and French equivalents of five varieties of ketch-rigged craft whose sail plans appeared in Chapman's work on naval architecture[74] were listed on page 101, where it was pointed out that no hard-and-fast rule could be drawn to identify a vessel positively as a ketch, dogger, hoy, galliot or hooker. Perhaps hull-form was a better guide in this respect than rig, because in the rest of Europe hoys, galliots and hookers usually had round sterns. In 1768, the only equivalent term to be similar in Chapman's three languages was 'galleas', and the English confined it to the Baltic and the French to Germany. As Alan Moore and Morton Nance insisted, 'the species of the round-sterned genus are closely allied, and sometimes scarcely to be distinguished one from another, either by us, or by the men who knew them, and it is certain that the resemblance was often very close'.[75]

Some twentieth century writers have found it convenient to classify round-sterned ketches as 'galliots' and square-sterned ones as 'galleases'. Many of those illustrated under these two headings in Szymanski's *Deutsche Segelschiffe* carry three yards on the foremast, and in many cases the topsail yard hoists to the lower mast cap. Sometimes the mizen is a pole mast longer than the main lower mast, at other times there is a short fidded topmast, but the mizen is always a narrower sail than the mainsail. The *Themis* (1806) of Bremen, described as a *hukergaliot*, is the only one to have a three-piece mainmast with a mizen pole mast slightly higher than the head of the main topmast;[76] and in the galleas *Catharina Maria* (1810) of Rostock, the mizen is

Fig 187. A Belgian galliot close-hauled in a fresh breeze. The big mainsail is a low-peaked sail, presumably to avoid fouling the braces from yards on the foremast; here there is a fidded topmast, but the topgallant mast is stepped abaft the topmast. The full-bodied hull with its rounded stern is barely heeling over in the wind, and the leeboard on this windward side is hauled clear of the water. (Engraving No 66 by Jean Baugean published, 1817, in Recueil de Petites Marines)

Fig 188. Another of Baugean's engravings from the same work (plate 42). In the foreground is a square-sterned galleas with fidded topmasts on both main and mizen. The topsail yard on the main hoists to the lower mast cap which is why the doubling is unusually long; the topgallant yard appears to have been sent down. Beyond her is a brig undergoing repairs to her mainmast, from which all her rigging has been removed. Both are probably from northern Europe but lying in a southern port.

187

188

189

Dock at Bristol with a Trader
London Published Jan.y 1 1808 by W. Miller 49 Albemarle Street, and W. Walker 8 Conway Street, Fitzroy Square

Fig 189. An etching by J A Atkinson, published 1808, entitled 'Dock at Bristol with a Trader'. The 'trader' is a ketch-rigged trow outside the lock gates of the floating harbour at low water. Her mainsail is lowered and can be made out swung outboard to starboard. The seams of the hull planking are rather predominant. (MacGregor Collection)

190

Fig 190. Some of Thomas Luny's sketches of a small ketch near Teignmouth re-drawn from a sketchbook dated 1799 at the National Maritime Museum, Greenwich. No rigging is drawn in the sketch of the craft under sail.

almost as large as the mainsail and the mizen truck almost level with the main truck.[77]

Baugean published drawings in 1817 of Dutch, Belgian and Swedish galliots. A fourth galliot wearing a plain flag has a three-piece mizen carrying three shortish yards as well as a hoisting gaff and boom mizen; on the main are four yards, a gaff and boom mainsail, and a long head yard of a fore-and-aft topsail which is brailed into yard and mast.[78]

Of the five types of ketch rig depicted by Chapman, Nos 8 and 9 are most nearly followed by the galliot and galleas in the first half of the nineteenth century, although the main topmast is kept straight and three yards are usually crossed. Baugean's galliot, square-rigged on each mast, was less common and combined parts of Nos 3 and 11. No 7, with a pole mainmast, is not illustrated by Szymanski, but Baugean drew one and called it a 'Tartane', giving it a square stern.[79]

In Great Britain, the Severn trows provide a form of ketch development. During the eighteenth century some contemporary illustrations show them with two masts on which are two square sails on the mainmast and a lateen yard on the mizen. A drawing done in 1782 by Nicholas Pocock of the 'Floating Harbour' at Bristol shows such a vessel with a foresail set on a short bowsprit, a square mainsail and topsail, and a gaff mizen.[80] There seem to be several variations to this rig which in essence is that of the dogger.[81] Soon after 1800 the trows are illustrated with both one and two masts: the single-masted ones have one or two yards for square sails, with or without a gaff; the two-masted ones have similar arrangements on the mainmast with the addition of a gaff mizen, as can be seen by examining Atkinson's etching, figure 189, in which the fore-and-aft rig predominates. Peter de Wint sketched a similar ketch at Gloucester when he was painting there in 1825 or 1828.[82] By the middle of the century the yards had gone and the trows were rigged as fore-and-aft ketches or sloops.

The English employed the term 'galliot' and probably their own version of the Dutch rig. A perusal of part of the 1815 *Lloyd's Register* (Shipowners' edition) revealed a limited number of galliots; of these the majority were built in north Europe and only a few in the British Isles. Under the letter M, thirty-two galliots were listed as built in north Europe, one in America, one in Scotland, and five on the north-west coast of England and Wales. As galliots were round-sterned vessels with the rudder mounted abaft the stern, and since a stern of this type in the British Isles is today considered to be indigenous to the Irish Sea and the north-west coast, it is possible that *Lloyd's Register* employed the term 'galliot' to indicate a hull type rather than a rig. In its broadest sense comprising both hull and rig, it may be inferred that a form of ketch in which the fore-and-aft sails predominated was under construction in at least one area.

In view of the established use of the term 'ketch' as applied to a 'full-rigged ship without a foremast', the mere employment of the term raises grave doubts as to the type of rig that is implied, and the extent to which square canvas was superseded by fore-and-aft. From his exhaustive research among the Custom House registers of the West of England, Grahame Farr was able to say that the first mention of the term 'ketch' in the Bridgwater registers was in 1792, at Gloucester in 1797, at Chepstow in 1806, and at Bristol in 1814 (where the registers are incomplete), while at the complex of ports behind Bideford Bar, the first mention was at Barnstaple in 1859.[83] One can obviously accept the date of 1859 as referring to the modern style of ketch; perhaps 1814 also indicates the predominately fore-and-aft ketch, but can the same be said of 1806 at Chepstow or earlier at Gloucester and Bridgwater?

Some contemporary illustrations depict ketches under sail and at anchor along various parts of the coastline. An engraving by Hall after Nicholas Pocock, published in September 1806 and entitled 'South Sea Castle', depicts as

Fig 191. Rigged model of a Dutch kof, with round stern, outside rudder, and balance of square and fore-and-aft canvas. (Nederlandsch Historisch Scheepvaart Museum, Amsterdam)

Fig 192. A typical sale notice with an interesting brief inventory. The Harmony *advertised here could have looked like the galliot in figure 193.* (MacGregor Collection)

191

192

To be Sold by Auction,

On SATURDAY, September 13th, 1800.

BY MR. HANSELL,

In the EXCHANGE, Hull, between the hours of one and two o'clock in the afternoon,

THE GOOD SHIP

HARMONY,

(Now lying in Hull Dock,) Captain PANNELL,

Meafuring 84 feet, 3 inches Length,
22 ditto Breadth, } Extreme.
10 ditto 4 inches in the Hold,
And 170 Tons Regifter.

N. B. This Veffel is Dutch built, with two Mafts, called a Galliot Hoy, with round Houfe and Quarter Deck, a faft failer, and particularly well found.

As per Inventory.

All her ftanding and running rigging.

SAILS.

Two main fails
Two main top fails
One top gallant fail
One lower ftun fail
Two fquare fails
Two top maft ftun fails
Two top gallant fails
Two fore-fails
Six jibs
Two mizen fails
Two mizen top fails
Two long boat fails
Two yaul fails

Two boats

ANCHORS.

Two bower anchors
Two kedge ditto

CABLES.

Two 11 inch cables (one new and the other as good) 120 fathom each
One 11 inch ditto, fixty fathom
A piece of ditto, twelve fathom
A hawfer in two lengths

ROPES.

One fea buoy rope
One river ditto
Two 4½ inch towlines, 120 fathom each
Two half coils of rope for Lanyards
A fufficient quantity of rope, to rig a brig; of feveral hundred weight
A quantity of feizing line
A long boat, rigging, maft and boom complete
A dip fea and hand line, with two leads

CABIN.

A fhip ftove
A looking glafs
Five compaffes
Two half minute glaffes
A quarter minute ditto
A log and line
Two fifhing lines

SUNDRIES.

A copper tea kettle
A frying pan and Grid-iron
Black jack
A horn
Crockery and glafs
A chair
Two iron crows
Three pair of fcrews
A carpenter's cheft of tools, complete
Three lanthorns
Bell
Three cannifters
A fett of colours, &c.
Pump gears
Hand fpikes
A large quantity of fpare blocks
Points and gafkins
Four beef tubs
Seven water and beer cafks
Tarpauling, &c.
A quantity of firewood
And every other neceffary article to fit her immediately for fea

HULL, September 9, 1800.

ROBERT PECK, Printer of the HULL PACKET, Scale-Lane, HULL.

193

the central object a fore-and-aft ketch with square topsail and topgallant and a full-bodied hull having pronounced sheer. It is assumed that she is not an English-built craft, and although it is a bow view, the big tumblehome at the quarter suggests a round stern.

There is a definite emphasis on fore-and-aft rig amongst small harbour craft and local barges. One such ketch is shown on the right of the engraving picturing divers working on the wreck of the East Indiaman *Abergavenny* in 1805[84], and Thomas Luny drew some in 1799 in the region of Teignmouth and Topsham.[85] The craft in Luny's sketches are shown under sail or about to anchor, and are managed by a crew of two. Some of his sketches are redrawn in figure 190. One shows one of the crew at the tiller and the other forward throwing out the anchor, after lowering the mainsail and dropping the foresail. Such craft may have been very similar to the open-decked shallops which were schooner rigged. After describing the various sails carried by barges and lighters in 1826, C F Partington wrote, 'some large barges have a ship's Mizen', an obvious description of a ketch rig in its modern form.[86]

The continual interchange of small trading vessels between Dutch and British ports cannot fail to have left its mark and the appearance of the Dutch kofs and galliots by the turn of the century, represented in painting after painting of British sea scenes, suggests that the British may have been influenced by this source. With the reservation that the hull-form of certain British east coast craft possibly stemmed from the English herring buss, it must be observed that it was the rig of these Dutch craft rather than their hull-form which is likely to have been adopted. A typical Dutchman, with leeboards, high stern, mizen topmast, and bluff bow, was painted by F L T Francia (1772–1839), the teacher of Bonington, as illustrated in figure 193.

Fig 193. A Dutch kof at anchor painted by F L T Francia (1772–1839). There is an indication of a leeboard just abaft the main rigging and there is no dolphin striker. As the topsail is not deep, it may not have hoisted higher than the lower mast cap. (Private Collection)

Fig 194. Two sloops under sail: one has a square topsail set; the other a big square sail below the yard. The artist is Baugean and the engraving was published 1817 in Recueil de Petites Marines.

SINGLE-MASTED CRAFT

Goods carried to the London markets from north Kent ports were taken by hoys, some of which in the first quarter of the nineteenth century were large vessels, like the *Thomas and Stephen* of 120 tons.[87] David Steel in his *Elements and Practice of Naval Architecture* (1805) gives a plan of a Southampton fishing hoy of 13 tons (plate XXVIII), and of a sloop trading to London of 60 tons (plate XXVII). Steel's 60-ton sloop measures 50ft 5in tonnage length, 16ft 8in extreme breadth, 9ft 8in depth of hold, and bears a close family likeness to his collier brig, especially in the shape of the body-plan. She has a fine run and draws two feet more water aft than forward, but her high counter stern and big sheer suggest a late eighteenth century design. Sloops sometimes had a pole mast or a short fidded topmast above a lower mast, a long bowsprit, square topsail and large gaff mainsail. This 60-ton sloop represents a craft employed along the coast and for short sea routes, rather than for estuary work alone.

The lines plan of a general purpose sloop in the Hilhouse Collection, folio 47, is surely not to their design, as there are

195

Dimensions

	Feet Inches
Length of the Keel for Tonnage	[illegible]
Breadth Extream	17.0
Depth in Hold	9.0
Height in the waste	[illegible]
Burthen in Tons	No 70 63/94

NB. The scale is [illegible]

196

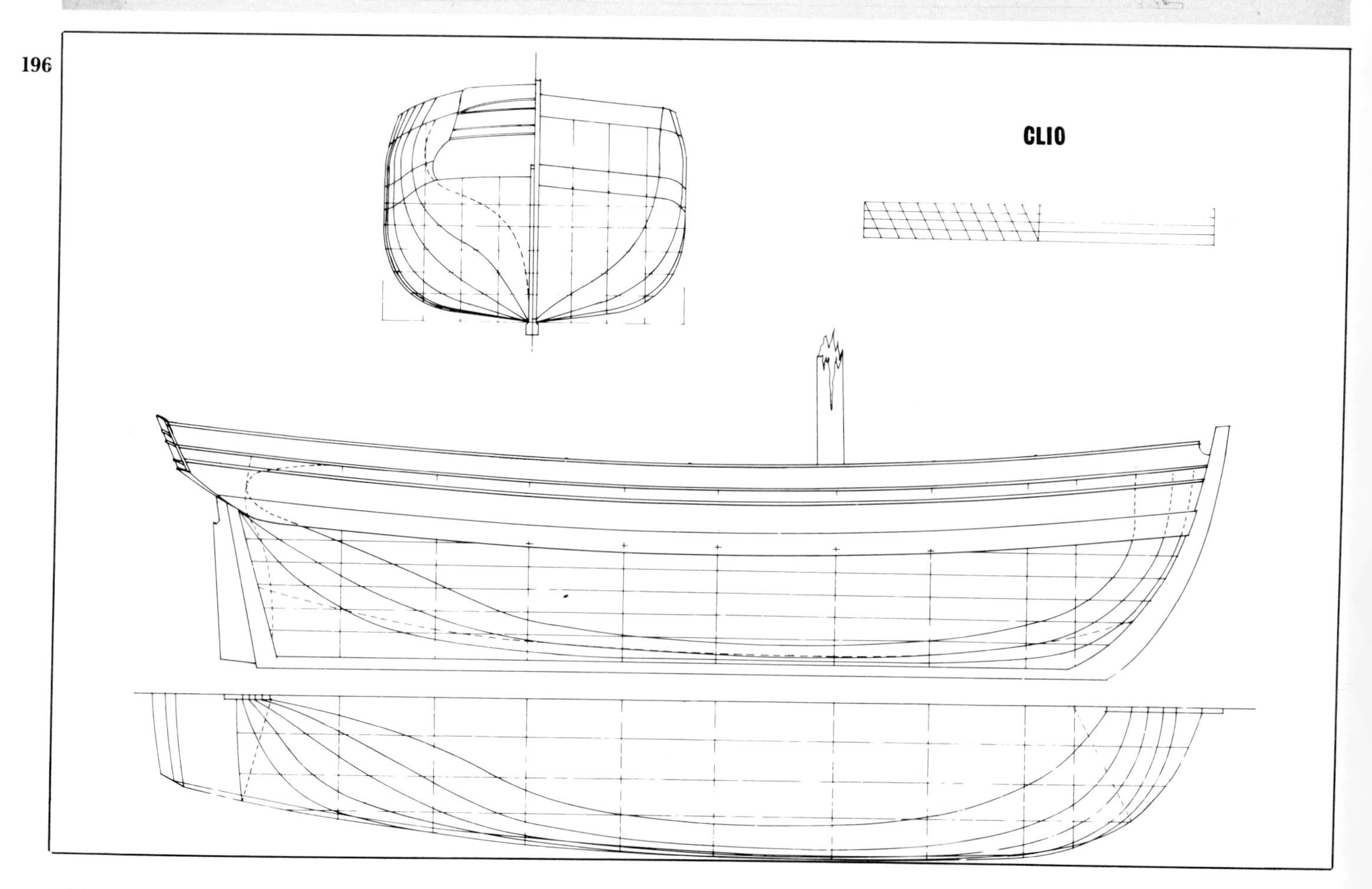

Fig 195. 'Packet by Mr Constable'. *Lines plan of an unidentified sloop, reproduced from a plan in the Hilhouse Collection at Charles Hill & Sons, folio no 47. Dimensions on plan: 46ft (keel for tonnage) × 17ft (extreme) × 9ft and 71 tons.*

Fig 196. Clio. *Lines plan of a sloop built at Whitby in either 1813 (82 tons) or in 1816 (86 tons). The plan has been redrawn from one in Whitby Museum. Dimensions scaled off the plan: 57ft 6in × 17ft 4in × 8ft 6in (approx). Reconstruction: bulwarks, rudder, stern elevation.*

Fig 197. Clio. *Sail plan, reconstructed from the following sources: the sheer elevation from the lines plan in figure 196; and spar dimensions from Peter Hedderwick,* Treatise on Marine Architecture *(1830), p 363. This is a typical sloop's rig, but a ringtail and stunsails would also have been set.*

several points which do not agree with the usual features embodied in their small vessels. For instance, she has a head, the forefoot is rounded not angular, the draught is complete not unfinished, and there is a note about the wale which states: 'NB The wale is fitted as wrought on the Vessel'. They would hardly have written this if she had emanated from their yard. In addition, the following is written in ink on the back of the plan, in an old hand: 'Packet by Mr Constable'. This suggests that the lines were taken off a hull which they approved. It is undated but must be from the period 1790–1815. Dimensions on the plan give 46ft length of keel for tonnage, 17ft breadth extreme, 9ft depth in hold, 1ft 'height in the waste' and $70\frac{63}{94}$ tons.

This sloop had a large after cabin. The heavy head was not common in sloops and the hull might equally well have passed for that of a schooner or brig if no mast position had been shown. The full sections would permit her to take the ground without heeling unduly and the fullness in the bottom is repeated in the entrance and run. The sail plan of this sloop would probably have been similar to that of the *Clio* (figure 197) with a gaff and boom mainsail, jib-headed topsail set on a fidded topmast, a bowsprit with two or three headsails, and a crossjack yard – as it was called – setting a square sail below it and a square topsail with a fairly short head above.

The plans of *Clio* are also given in *Merchant Sailing Ships 1815–1850* because plans of named sloops of this date are hard to come by. As already stated in this chapter, her hull-form is a scaled-down version of a brig. Dimensions measured on the plan give 55ft 8in tonnage length, 17ft 4in extreme breadth and 8ft 6in approximate depth of hold; her tonnage is 86. As no sail plan is known, I reconstructed one using Hedderwick's rules which are, like many at this date, a curious mixture of proportions and suggest that, having found a set of spars which suited a hull, the architect then tried to propound rules to fit them. Although his *Treatise on Marine Architecture* is dated 1830, Hedderwick had been practising for quite thirty years and his rules can usefully be followed for the years 1800–1845.[88]

SPAR DIMENSIONS OF SLOOP *CLIO* BASED ON HEDDERWICK'S RULES

	Length	**Diameter**
Mainmast	56ft 0in	16in
Main topmast	38ft 0in	7½in
Bowsprit	36ft 8in	12⅘ (at stem)
Main boom	50ft 6in	11¼in (at sheet)
Main gaff	33ft 8in	8in (at cheeks)
Crossjack yard	40ft 6in	—
Rake of mast	½in to every 1ft of length	

Note: the length of the load waterline in 55ft and the breadth is 17¾ft for these calulations.

197

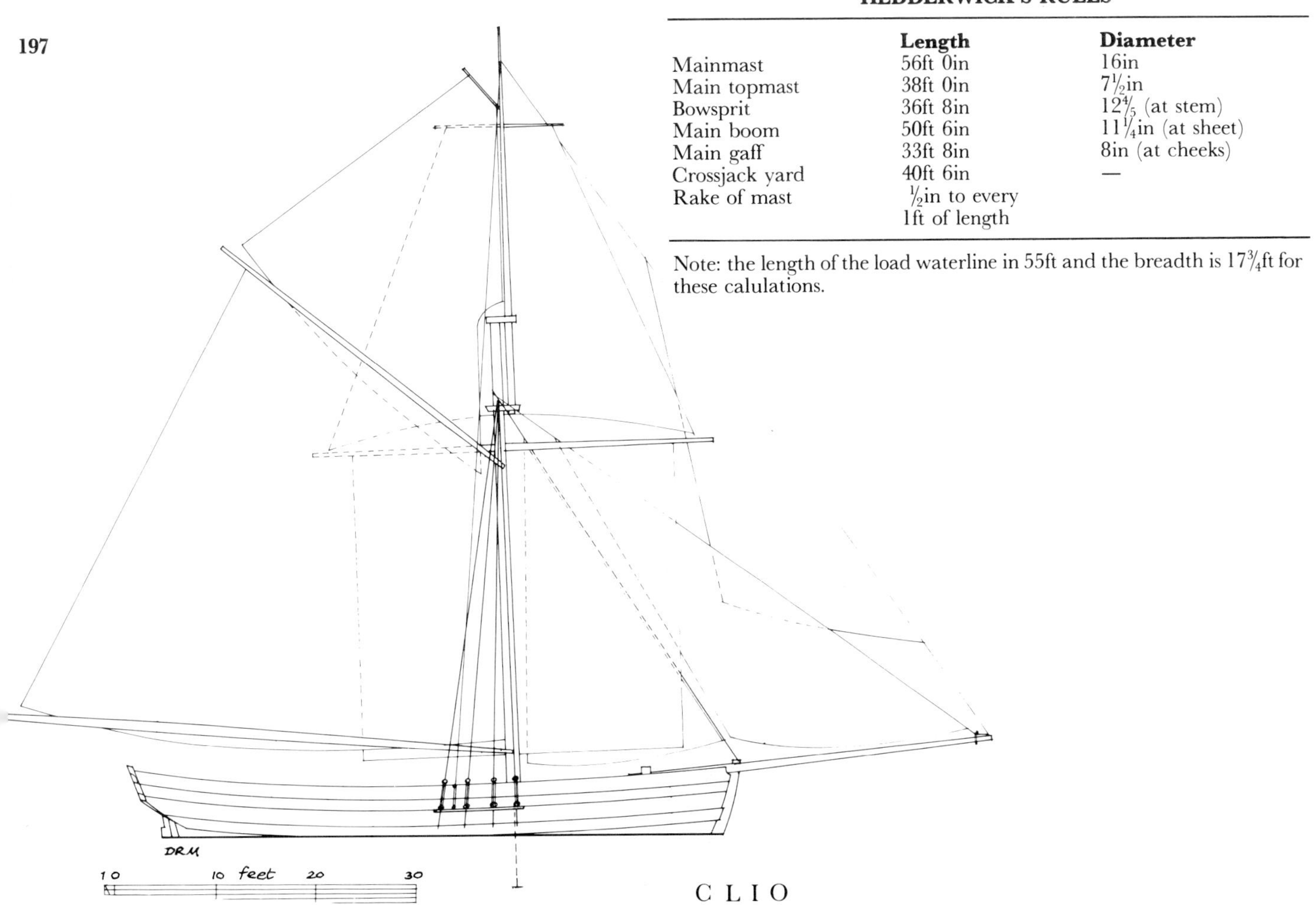

CLIO

Sloops of similar type were in use in Continental Europe, and a few, such as *Die Frau Marica*, set four square sails like a heavily-rigged cutter. This sloop had a full-bodied hull, according to an old painting reproduced in figure 198, with a bluff bow, square tuck stern and outside rudder. Since the lower yard does not hoist up to the crosstrees, the topsail is deeply roached to ride over the stays. She was built at Flensburg in 1802. Some sloops had their topsails set on the doubling.

Thus by 1815 all the principal rigs and their variations had been established: the remainder of the century concentrated on the elimination of superfluous and uneconomical rigs, the improvement of construction, and the alteration of hull-form and general proportions.

Fig 198. Die Frau Marica *of St Jörgen was built at Flensburg in 1802. The deeply-roached topsail with a yard hoisting up to the lower mast cap, and a square sail yard a long way below the hounds, were features of this rig.* (Städtisches Museum, Flensburg)

Fig 199. Entitled 'Rigged Lighter', this is another in J A Atkinson's series of English coastal views done about 1806. The flat-bottomed, swim-head barge sits upright while a steep-floored cutter lies on her side. The barge has leeboards, gaff sail and yard for a square sail. (Parker Gallery)

SLIDING-KEELS AND CENTREBOARDS

Peter Hedderwick submitted particulars of drop-keels in his work on naval architecture and referred to having met their inventor, Captain Schank, when the latter was a Commissioner of the Navy. This must have been early in the nineteenth century. Captain Schank, a naval officer, first thought of sliding keels in 1775, when stationed at Boston, Massachusetts, where he built a small boat to embody his idea.[89] In 1790 he induced the Admiralty to put his plan to the test on the Thames by installing three keels in a small flat-bottomed sloop which outsailed a boat of standard type that had lee-boards but no keels. The sloop with the sliding keels so out-distanced the other that a bigger vessel was ordered. This was the 120-ton cutter, *Trial*, built at Plymouth in 1791. Her success with sliding keels induced the Admiralty to fit them in the new ship-sloop *Cynthia* in 1796 and in two classes of brigs built the following year.[90]

The article 'Shipbuilding' in *Encyclopaedia Britannica* for 1797 states that Captain Schank's sliding keel was a development of a proposal made by Thomas Gordon in 1784 in his *Principles of Naval Architecture*[91] to place a series of

198

fixed keels on the flat bottom of a shallow-draft vessel. This sounds like an attempt to discredit the originality of Schank's proposals. At the National Maritime Museum there are six models of projected designs of vessels fitted with Captain Schank's keels and covering the years 1790–99; one is of a merchant brig, one is of a yacht, and the remainder are warships.

An early example of the drop keels in use may be found in the shallop *Peggy* which was built in 1791 by George Quayle at Castletown, Isle of Man, and was fitted with three such keels. Quayle evidently wrote to Captain Schank early in 1791 concerning the principle of the drop keels, which shows that there was widespread interest in Schank's project. The *Peggy* has been referred to earlier in this Chapter in the section on 'Shallops'.

Samuel Bentham also experimented with sliding keels at the end of the century, but the difficulties attendant on making the drop-keel cases watertight resulted in the Admiralty's abandoning the whole project. In 1809 the British naval officer, Molyneux Shuldham, made a model of a 'revolving keel' similar to a centreboard, and two years later three Americans took out a patent for one which they described as a 'lee-board through the bottom'.[92] Other Americans were quick to see its advantages for the coastal trade. The rise and fall of the tide was so slight on the American coastline south of Maine that vessels rarely took the ground and thus avoided the damage to centreboards which could not be prevented in the British Isles. In addition, the stigma of the leaking cases lasted long enough to prevent the style becoming popular in Great Britain, apart from isolated examples, whereas they were successfully employed in America and later fitted in three, four and five-masted schooners. It has not been established whether Hedderwick's published drawings actually resulted in the building of craft fitted with drop-keels, although there are occasional examples throughout the nineteenth century.

199

Fig 200. The East Indiaman Princess Royal *off Sheerness painted by John Cleveley (1723–77) in 1771, after her return from China in July of that year. This was her first voyage, and her tonnage was 499.* (Rutland Gallery)

200

4
EAST INDIAMEN

SHIPS OF THE HONOURABLE EAST INDIA COMPANY

East Indiamen were generally larger than other merchantmen and their size continued to increase during this century. From 1755 it became the practice to enter the tonnage of ships as 499 tons, because of a regulation that ships over 500 tons must carry a chaplain, even though the real size was usually in excess of 500 tons. This regulation was eased in 1773 and accordingly the tonnage of ships on the list began to increase markedly, so that forty of them were then rated at between 657 and 750 tons, and a further twenty at over 750 tons. By 1780, a tonnage of 758 had become standard. In 1786, the size was again raised by the building of the *Hartwell* of 938 tons at Itchenor, near Chichester, but later in the same year came the first ship of over 1000 tons, namely the *Nottingham* of 1152 tons. On her maiden voyage she returned from China with 1570 tons of tea, which was considered a very successful operation as she carried a crew hardly larger than for a ship of the 800-ton class and yet twice as much cargo. More and more of the larger ships came to be built, and in 1793 it was decided by the Company that thirty-six of the 1200-ton class would be required in future, together with forty of the 800 and 500 ton classes. The smallest class was restricted to the India trade, the others voyaged to both India and China. All these were 'regular' ships, but there were also 'extra' ships which, although built specially for the trade, were chartered for one voyage at a time, and they were usually of the smallest class.[1]

Eventually some ships of 1300 and 1500 tons were constructed, although the Company never increased this class above the nominal 1200-ton rating. It appears that ships were chartered to load goods equivalent in capacity to the tonnage of their class, and that any cargo loaded in excess of this was at half-freight. Thus the class referred not to the actual tonnage of the ships but to their burthen or capacity.[2]

It is worth pointing out that the Company did not own the ships, but chartered them at high freight rates, nor did the Company deal directly with the owners but with the

201

The East India House in its former State.

managing owners or ships' husbands, who had usually been commanders of East Indiamen and now represented the owners. They had complete freedom to handle all the affairs concerning a ship, from signing a contract with a builder, arranging payment, fitting the ship out, chartering her to the Company, organizing her voyage out to India or China and then home, and finally declaring a dividend to the owners after the ship's return. But a husband had another important role, that of owning a 'bottom' which was the right to replace a lost or worn-out ship with a new one and with subsequent ones.[3] This so-called 'right' had arisen in 1730 when 'on the request of Captain Micklefield of the ship *Marlborough*, which had been burnt, he was permitted to build a new vessel in her place for the Company's service. Similar applications made in 1731 and 1732 were also complied with, and thence arose the practice of owners being permitted to build new vessels on the bottoms of old ships, a custom which tended to keep the supply of ships to the Company in the hands of an exclusive set'.[4] From this developed the term 'hereditary bottom' and those claiming this right of ownership joined forces to keep the freight rate at a high level. However, their power was somewhat curtailed after 1796 when the rights pertaining to hereditary bottoms were abolished.

The ship's husband was not appointed by the owners; on the contrary, it was he who applied to the Court of Directors of the East India Company for permission to build a new ship on the bottom of the old one. He would then seek owners to support this investment by putting up capital in proportion to the number of shares held. Often they were the owners of the worn-out ship being replaced and the husband would hold some shares himself.[5]

By the beginning of the nineteenth century, ships' husbands still applied to the Court of Directors for leave to build a new ship, as is indicated by extracts from the minutes of the Committee of Shipping:[6]

On Wednesday, the 6th April 1808.

The Committee again resuming the consideration of the several tenders to build ships in the room of those lost or taken;

Letter from Robert Williams, Esq, dated the 31st ultimo, and referred by the Court the 1st instant, offering to build a ship of 1200 tons, in the room of *Hindostan*, on the terms proposed in the letter written him by the Secretary in consequence of the Court's resolution of the 23d ultimo, was read; as were also

Letter from John Pascal Larkins, Esq dated the 30th ultimo, and referred by the Court the same day, offering to build a ship in the room of the late ship *Warren Hastings*; and...

The terms 'bottom' or 'in the space of' were also sometimes employed when applying to the Court of Directors.

Costs of building on the Thames were always high for this class of ship, as the following table indicates:

COST OF BUILDING A SHIP IN THE 800-TON CLASS ON THE RIVER THAMES FOR THE EAST INDIA SERVICE[7]

Season	Per ton	
1781	£14 14 0	War
1782	14 14 0	
1783	13 0 0	Peace
1784	12 12 0	
1785	11 17 6	
1786	12 10 0	
1787	12 10 0	
1788	12 16 0	
1789	12 16 0	
1790	12 10 0	
1791	12 10 0	
1792	12 10 0	
1793	14 0 0	War
1794	15 0 0	
1795	16 13 0	
1796	17 6 6	
1797	16 16 0	
1798	17 10 0	
1799	15 15 0	
1800	19 10 0	
1801	21 15 6	

The list of ships built at the Blackwall Yard is given in Appendix 1 and includes the prices of individual vessels, from which it will be seen how prices had soared by the end of the Napoleonic War. For instance, in 1813 the *Lady Melville* of 1257 tons cost £28 per ton. A year after the long war with France ended, the Ipswich shipbuilder, Jabez Bayley, was fortunate to secure a contract for the Indiaman *Orwell* in 1816 at £22 10s, the ship being built entirely of

Fig 201. Entitled 'The East India House in its Former State', this engraving dated 1813 depicts the building erected in 1726 on the site of the old India House. In turn, the building illustrated here was replaced in 1815 with a larger and grander edifice. (MacGregor Collection)

Fig 202. A photograph said to have been taken in 1850 at the Bluff, Durban, of the wreck of the Minerva. *If this is correct, then she is probably the East Indiaman built in 1812 at Bombay of 987 tons, according to* Lloyd's Register *1850.* (Local History Museum, Durban)

Suffolk oak.[8] These prices must be for hull, or hull and spars only.

Prompted by additional shipbuilding costs in wartime, the Company gave a form of grant to the owners to cover the extra, as mentioned in the last paragraph of this letter:[9]

HONORABLE SIRS. London, 30th March 1808.

I beg leave to tender to your Honorable Court a ship of 980 tons, now nearly built, at Messrs Wells, Perry, and Green's, Blackwall, to complete the term of the contract of the late ship the *Warren Hastings*, and to be commanded by Captain Thomas Larkins, on the following terms, and to have included in her tonnage one hundred tons of kintledge:

For 800 tons, at £19 10s
For all surplus tonnage £9 15s

The Company to pay £6 per ton for the high price of war building, and in every other respect as according to the original tender of the ship *Warren Hastings*.

I remain, Honorable Sirs, most respectfully,
Your most obedient servant,
The Honorable Court of Directors. J P LARKINS

202

203

AN INDIAMAN SHORTENING SAILS.
Published by Charles Tilt, Fleet Street, London

PROGRESS OF SHIPS BUILDING FOR THE HONORABLE EAST-INDIA COMPANY, 1808

Leave to build	To be launched	Bottoms	Husbands	Commanders	Tonnage	Keels laid	Works performed	Builders expect to launch	Builders
1808 Ap 12	July 1	*Hindostan*	Robert Williams, Esq	Edward Balston	1200	1807 April	Lower, middle, and upper decks nearly laid, and round-house in hand	1808 October	Barnard & Co
May 11	July 1	*Warren Hastings*	John Pascal Larkins, Esq	Thomas Larkins	980	1806 Nov	Launched the 6th instant	Sept	Wells & Co
May 11	July 1	*Lady Burges*	William Agnew, Esq	A F W Swinton	800		Coppering the bottom and the ship nearly furnished	Sept	Wells & Co

East-India House, 14th September, 1808

James Coggan, Esq

John Hillman

Fig 203. A lithograph published by Charles Tilt c1810 and drawn in the style of J R Jobbins. (See figures 156 and 220.) The sails are full of wind, but there is no crew to be seen aboard. This is strange, as the title is 'An Indiaman Shortening Sail'! No royal yards are crossed, nor topgallant yards on fore and mizen; the mainsail and main topgallant are being clewed up, and the sheets of the foresail have been started prior to manning the clew lines. No headsails are set. (MacGregor Collection)

Sometimes, during the course of construction, a progress report such as the above would be submitted to the Committee of Shipping at East India House:[10]

Fig 204. The Earl of Balcarres *of 1417 tons was built in 1815 at Bombay, and could set skysails on each mast, although neither these yards nor those of the royals are crossed here. This painting by W J Huggins shows the ship off the China coast.* (Parker Gallery)

204

206

This progress report was signed by John Hillman, who was 'Surveyor of Shipping' to the Company.

The ships' husbands received unwritten guarantees that ships built for the service would be employed for a specified number of voyages, because they could obtain employment nowhere else. These were the 'regular' ships. In 1773, a ship was considered worn out after four voyages, but by 1790, after the introduction of copper sheathing, it was considered that she could make six voyages if properly repaired after the third voyage. Later, eight voyages were allowed.

Fitting-out costs added considerably to the price of an Indiaman, and the Master Attendant of the Company, who was in 1809 Captain Joseph Boulderson, compiled estimates of expenses for a ship of 1200 tons with a crew of 135 men over a period of six voyages, calculating the fourth voyage as a 'repairing' voyage. These expenses included not only the cost of the hull, spars and rigging, but a full inventory of the ship's fittings as well as all the food for the outward passage. Inflation or rising costs were ignored, so that the butcher's bill of £378 remained constant for each voyage, but many of the costs to fit out the ship when new were not repeated, although an estimate for maintenance or repair was included. Boulderson also made similar calculations for a ship of 800 tons with a crew of 120 men. The totals are as follows:

Fig 206. An unidentified Indiaman of the largest class *(c1820) drawn in pencil with a sepia wash. No royal yards are crossed and there are no stays from the topgallant masts.* (MacGregor Collection)

	Ship of 1200 tons[11]	**Ship of 800 tons**[12]
First voyage	£64,580	£45,931
Second voyage	£16,737	£12,828
Third voyage	£19,508	£14,777
Fourth voyage	£29,071	£20,944
Fifth voyage	£19,663	£14,609
Sixth voyage	£20,353	£15,111

Costs worked out in favour of the bigger ship which could carry more cargo and earn more. After six voyages, a further two could be undertaken after considerable repairs and maintenance had been carried out. This work included doubling the hull with 3in planking from the lower port cills to 2ft below the floor heads; stripping off the copper sheathing, rebolting the chain plates, adding new iron riders to the floors and futtock timbers; inserting new beams in the lower hold fitted with iron knees; and various other work to strengthen the ship.

At the end of the terms and conditions dated January 1809 for building a ship of 1200 tons at Prince of Wales Island (now called Penang) there is a list of scantlings which probably applied generally to all vessels of this class:[13]

Fig 205. The titles on the original explain the relevant midship sectons, comparing standard naval practice (left) with that recommended by Snodgrass (right). The 38-gun frigate was about the size of a large East Indiaman and so is relevant here. (Collection of Papers on Naval Architecture ... communicated through ... the European Magazine, *vol II, part 2, 1798, facing page 56*)

205

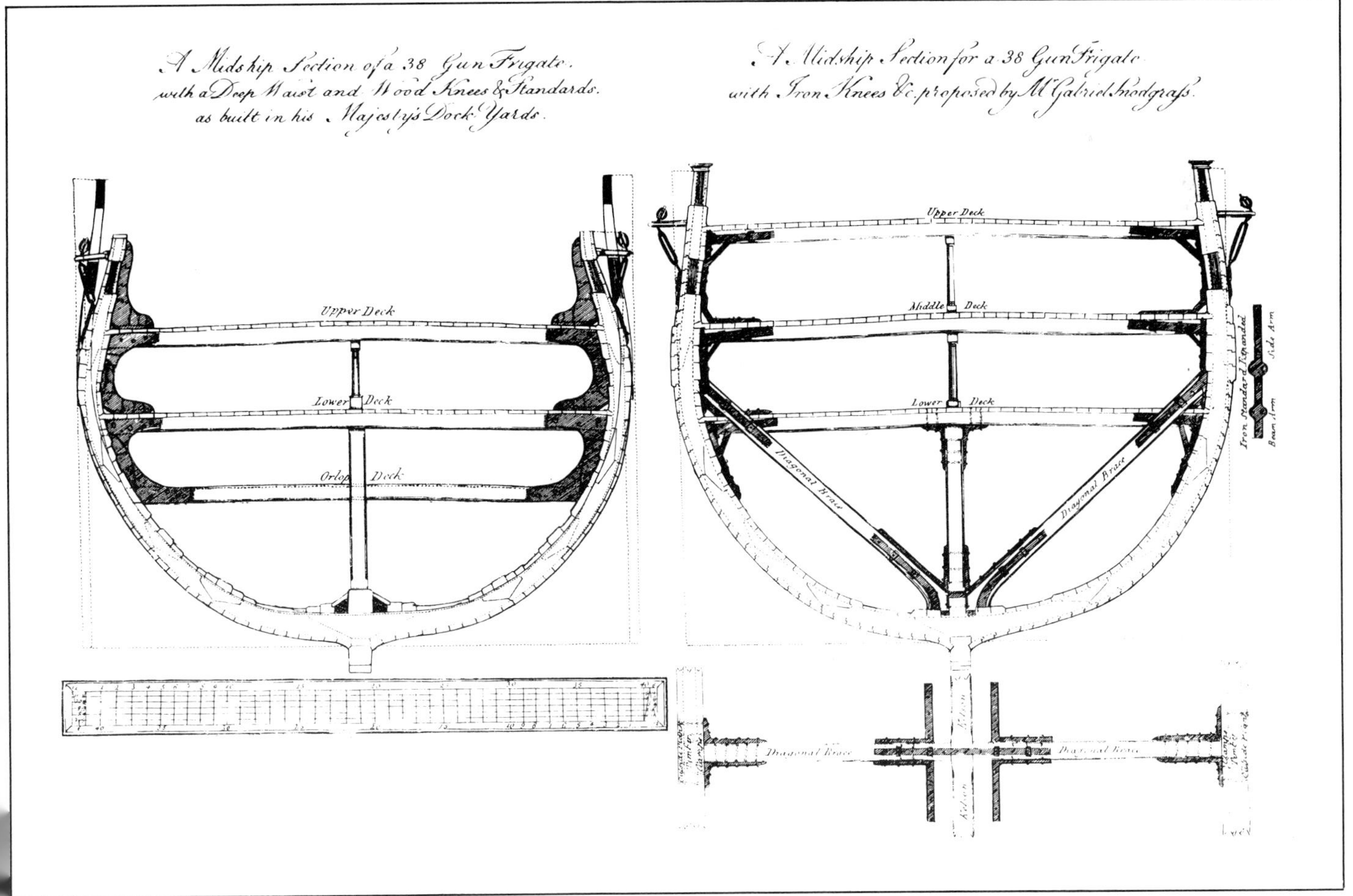

PRINCIPAL DIMENSIONS AND SCANTLINGS, AND WEIGHT OF IRON KNEES AND STANDARDS, FOR SHIPS OF ABOUT 1200 TONS BURTHEN

Principal Dimensions

Length of keel for tonnage	134ft 0in
Breadth extreme to a 4-inch plank	42ft 0in
Burthen, in tons, 1257 30/94 Depth in hold	17ft 0in
Height between the lower and middle decks	6ft 6in
Height between the middle and upper decks	6ft 6in
Height between the upper deck and round house forwards	6ft 4in
abaft	6ft 6in
Depth of the waist	1ft 6in

Scantlings

	Sided	Moulded
Main Keel	15½in	16½in
Keelson	15½in	15½in
Stem at the head	15½in	16½in
Stern-post at the wing transom	16½in	16½in
Wing transon	15½in	19½in

	Sided	Moulded On the Keel	Moulded at the Head
Floor timbers	15in	15in	13½in
Lower futtocks	14in		12⅞in
Middle futtocks	13½in		12½in
		At Middle Deck	
Upper futtocks	13in	11in	
		At Port Cells	
Top timbers	12½in	10½in	6½in

Main wales, 6 strakes, 6 inches thick.
Thick stuff under do., 1 stake, 5¼ inches thick.
Bottom, 4 inch plank, and 1 stake next the keel to be rabbitted.
Topside from the main wales to the sheer stake, to be 4-inch thick.
Sheer strake, 5 inches thick and 11 inches broad.
Plank above the sheer strake, 3 inches thick.
Gunwales, 5 inches thick.
Room and space, 2 feet 7½ inches.

Inside Plank

To have a piece of oak on each side the keelson, from the sleeper under the main-mast to 8 feet before the fore-mast, 13 inches by 14 inches, and from the after end of the sleeper under the main-mast to the mizen mast, bolted through every floor and lower futtock, with bolts of 1⅝ inches diameter.
To have 4 iron floor riders on every other timber under the main-mast, and 3 iron floor riders under the fore mast, to weigh 6 cwt. each, to be 16 feet long, and bolted with 12 bolts of 1⅞ inches diameter.
To have two eakings on each side the bow, one of each between the lower and middle decks, the other in the hold, to be in length from the stemson to the foremost square frame, to have a bolt in every timber of 1⅜ inches diameter.
At the lower futtock heels, 2 strakes 5 inches thick.
Do floor heads, 6 strakes 5 inches thick.
To shut in between the floor heads and lower futtock heels with 3-inch plank, except 2 strakes which are to be 4 inches thick; one to be worked next the 5-inch stuff at the floor heads, the other next the thick stuff at the lower futtock heels.
Lower deck clamps, 2 strakes 6 inches thick, and two strakes under, 1 of 5½ inches and 1 of 5 inches thick.
To shut in between the lower deck clamps and the floor heads, with 4-inch English plank.
To bolt the frame lower futtocks to the floor timbers, with 4 bolts in each, of 1¼ inch diameter.
Lower deck spirketting, 2 stakes 4 inch plank.
Middle deck clamps, 2 strakes 5 inch plank.
To shut in between the lower deck spirketting and middle deck clamps with 4-inch plank.
Middle deck spirketting, 2 strakes of 4-inch plank.
Upper deck clamps, 2 strakes of 4-inch plank.
Short stuff between the middle deck ports, 3-inch plank.
Upper deck spirketting, 2 strakes 3-inch plank.
Round-house clamps, 1 strake 4-inch plank.
Short stuff between the upper deck ports, 2½ inch plank.
Lower, upper and middle decks to be 3inches thick.

	Sided	Moulded
Lower deck beams	14½in	13½in
Middle deck beams	13in	11in
Upper deck beams	10½in	8½in
Round house beams	7in	5in

The cook-rooms, sheep-pens, and hog-sties, to be built upon the upper deck, in the manner which has lately been practised in ships built for the Company's service.

Now follows a description of the guns to be carried on a ship of 1200 tons and on another of 800 tons:[14]

AT A COURT OF DIRECTORS
Held on Wednesday, the 3rd August 1808

On reading a report from the Committee of Shipping, dated the 27th July 1808;

Resolved. That agreeably to the resolutions of Court of the 23d September 1801, and the 18th May 1803, prescribing the mode in which ships of 1200 tons and 800 tons in the Company's service should be armed, the ships building in the room of the late ships Hindostan and Lady Burges be armed as follows; *viz.*

Hindostan (1200 Tons)

On the Gun Deck, Twenty-four cannonades, eighteen-pounders, with a proper chamber and lock, to be six feet and a half long, to weigh not less than twenty-eight hundred weight and a half each, and the proper charge of powder to be marked on each gun.- Two cannonades, eighteen pounders, with chambers, to be not less than eight feet long, nor to weight less than thirty-three hundred weight, to be fitted with locks, &c. to be used occasionally as stern chasers.

On the Upper Deck. Twelve carronades, eighteen-pounders, four feet long, and not to weigh less than fourteen hundred weight, to be fitted with locks &c as before-mentioned.

Lady Burgess (800 Tons)

On the Gun Deck. Twenty cannonades, eighteen pounders with chambers, &c., to be furnished with locks, &c., to be six feet long, and not to weigh less than twenty-six hundred weight.- Two cannonades, eighteen pounders, for stern-chasers, to be eight feet long, and not to weigh less than thirty hundred weight.

On the Upper Deck. Ten carronades, eighteen pounders, three feet and a half long, and not to weigh less than eleven hundred weight.

That the new ship in the room of the *Warren Hastings*, of about 980 tons burthen, do carry:

On the Gun Deck. Twenty-two cannonades, eighteen pounders with chambers, &c., as before-mentioned, six feet and a half long, and to weigh not less than twenty-eight hundred weight and a half. Two cannonades eighteen-pounders, for stern-chasers, eight feet long, and not to weigh less than thirty-three hundred weight.

On the Upper Deck. Ten carronades, eighteen-pounders, four feet long, and not to weigh less than fourteen hundred weight, to be fitted with locks, &c as above.

That the ships be manned agreeably to the resolution of Court of the 19th October 1791, and that they do carry the quantity of kintledge prescribed for ships of their respective chartered tonnage.

As the cost of the increased armament of the *Hindostan* was slightly double that of the previous armament of the ship she was replacing, the ship's husband, Robert Williams, sent a note of the new cost to the Court of Directors in September 1808:[15]

It is difficult to establish the actual builder's

EXPENCE OF ARMING ACCORDING TO THE HONORABLE COURT'S DIRECTIONS

To 24 carronades,	28½ cwt.	each is	684 cwt.,	at	22*s*. per cwt.	£752 8 0
2 do.	33 do.		66 do.		22*s*. do	72 12 0
12 carronades,	14 do.		168 do.		26*s*. do.	218 8 0
38 locks					20*s* each	38 0 0
Drilling guns to receive locks					5*s* each	9 10 0
38 Carriages					105*s*. each	199 10 0
						£1290 8 0

measurement tonnage of the largest ships are in the the way in which figures were altered on various occasions, and because length and breadth dimensions are known in only a few cases, but the largest Indiamen appear to have been those shown in the table at the bottom of the page.

The *Earl of Balcarras* is included because she is popularly regarded as being one of the largest East Indiamen constructed, which may partly stem from the fine engraving of her as a two-decker under full sail, and partly from the fact that her builder's measurement tonnage was always given while the other ships were normally assigned to the 1200-ton class.

Ships of 1400 tons differed little in size from small two-decked ships of the line, except that they did not mount guns on the lower deck, and those of 1200 tons could be compared with large frigates. Some dimensions are compared below:

HMS *Vanguard* is a small example of a seventy-four. The *Hope* would have been able to carry more guns than this if required, but her length between perpendiculars seems excessive when compared with her length of keel. Ships of the 1200-ton class often carried thirty-eight 18-pounders, some of which were carronades as listed previously, so Steel's plan gives the official number. No gun ports were cut in the lower deck but ports were sometimes painted at this level to deceive the enemy; this would make an Indiaman look like a two-decker, and if the bulwarks were high on the upper deck, then she resembled a three-decker. It is probably this matter of external appearance which is responsible for comparisons of Indiamen with seventy-fours, because such men-of-war were usually of 1600 to 1750 tons, and therefore so much larger in bulk than an Indiaman. Ships of the 1200-ton class were fitted as 64-gun ships when in the Navy.

Gabriel Snodgrass introduced many improvements in shipbuilding during his tenure of the post of ship surveyor to the East India Company, a position which he held for 37 years, during which he surveyed 989 vessels both new and old. After he had served his apprenticeship to Mr Snell, 'a builder's measurer in one of the King's dock yards', he became a working shipwright there himself. He was then recommended to the East India Company by Benjamin Slade and was sent as a shipwright to Bengal, where he superintended the Company's shipping. He became the

COMPARISON OF EAST INDIAMEN AND TWO-DECKERS

Date	Name	Tons	Length on Keel	Length between perps	Length gun deck	Max Beam	Depth in hold	Guns
1783	HMS *Culloden*	1638	138ft 11in		170ft 0in	47ft 8in	20ft 1in	74
1797	*Hope*	1471	144ft 0in	194ft 0in[18]		43ft 6in	17ft 5in	34ft
	HMS *Vanguard*	1609	137ft 8in		168ft 0in	46ft 10in	19ft 9in	74
1796	HMS *Lancaster* ex East Indiaman *Pigot*	1430	144ft 0in		173ft 6in	43ft 3in	19ft 9in	64
1805	Steel's *Naval Architecture* Plate XX	1257	134ft 0in	165ft 6in		42ft 0in	17ft 0in	38
1814	*HMS Glasgow*	1247	132ft 1in		159ft 2in	42ft 1in	12ft 4in	50

LIST OF LARGEST EAST INDIAMEN

Name	Tons (Hardy's List)[16]	Date of build	Length of keel (Hardy's List)	Breadth	Builder	Tons (from Cotton)[17]
Lowther Castle	1507	1811	176ft 4in*	43ft 2in	Pitcher	
Ganges	1502	1796	149ft	43ft 6in	Wells	
Hope	1471	1797	144ft	43ft 6in	Pitcher	
Neptune	1468	1796	144ft	43ft 6in	Wells	
Hindostan	1463	1796	144ft	43ft 6in	Barnard	
Royal Charlotte	1460	1796	144ft	43ft 6in	Pitcher	1518
Walmer Castle	1460	1796	144ft	43ft 6in	Barnard	1518
Earl of Abergavenny	1460	1796	144ft	43ft 6in	Pitcher	
Warley	1460	1796	144ft	43ft 6in	Perry	
Earl of Balcarras	1417	1815	176ft 8in*	43ft 3in	at Bombay	

Note: Hardy's list probably gives BM tons.
*length aloft; not in Hardy's list

Company's surveyor in England in 1757 and took particular interest in the breaking up of men-of-war, both British and foreign.[19]

In a famous letter addressed to the Rt Hon Henry Dundas, one of the principal Secretaries of State, and also to the Chairman and Directors of the East India Company, concerning ways of improving the Navy, he included comments on the improvements which he had introduced into the East India Company's ships. This quotation begins in the middle of his letter:[20]

It is upwards of twenty-four years since I first introduced in the East India Company's shipping the mode of fastening on the outside and inside plank with bolts, and leaving the tree-nail holes open for air until the ships were nearly finished and ready for caulking, which has been, and is now universally acknowledged to be the best method of seasoning the timbers and plank of any yet adopted. But although this is a matter of so much importance to the preservation of the ships of the Navy, it has not been practised in his Majesty's dock yards, nor have I ever heard of its being introduced into any contract for building ships of war in the Merchants' yards.

It is more than seventeen years since I brought into use, for the East India ships, round-headed rudders, requiring no rudder-coats. Experience taught me how dangerous the old fashioned rudder-coats were, particularly in small ships of the Navy, many of which, I cannot doubt, were lost from the sea having carried away their rudder-coat.

The round-headed rudders are now universally

Fig 207. An engraving which illustrates the steering of a ship with a jury rudder, as practised aboard the Indiaman Neptune *of 499 tons when she was under the command of Gabriel Steward. His last voyage in command ended in 1767, but I do not know the precise year when the vessel was damaged. She crosses a mizen yard and is under jury rig.* (Parker Gallery)

207

acknowledged to be much superior, in every respect, to the square-headed rudders of the ships of the Navy; and I am very anxious that these should be introduced into all ships to be built in the King's yards, and provided for in the contracts made, in future, for ships of war to be built in Merchants' yards.

About twenty-seven years ago I also introduced four-inch bottoms to ships for the East-India Company's Service, instead of three-inch bottoms; and there are ships of less than six hundred tons burthen, built for that service, with four-inch bottoms, also with sheathing of three-fourths of an inch thick, and coppered as usual; whilst, on the contrary, there have been frigates of a thousand tons burthen, lately built for Government in Merchant's yards, with three-inch bottoms, and a ship of eight hundred tons with a fir bottom only three inches thick; and there are ships of seventy-four guns, now building in those yards, of eighteen hundred tons burthen, with not more than four-inch bottoms; which ships, I presume are intended to go to sea, as usual, without any wood sheathing.

It appears to me that continuing the practice of *thin* bottoms tends to risk the loss of the ships and the lives of his Majesty's subjects, more especially if fir be taken instead of English, Quebec, or East-country oak-plank, which may always be procured. In my opinion; no ships of four hundred tons and upwards should have less than a bottom of four inch oak plank;- all ships of the Navy, of eight hundred tons and upwards, should have not less than five-inch plank;- line-of-battle ships should have bottoms at least six inches thick;- and all ships should have the addition of wood sheathing. The thickness of the inside plank of those ships may then generally be reduced in proportion.

It is many years since the keels of all the East-India ships have been rabbitted in the middle, which is certainly safer and better than having the rabbit on the upper edge, as is the practice in the ships of his Majesty's Navy at this time.

About twenty-six years since, I had the capstands to the ships in the Company's service fitted with an iron spindle, paul-head, and catch-pauls. This has ever since been allowed effectually to prevent the people from being thrown from the bars, which, is well-known, has frequently happened on board of his Majesty's ships, and whereby many lives have been lost, and great numbers crippled.

Every old capstand in the King's ships should be fitted with an iron spindle and catch-pauls, which may be done in a short time, and at a very moderate expence, compared with the great safety and other advantages that must attend this improvement.

I have made it a practice, for many years, to add iron knees under the beams to all old ships in the Company's service; and, of late years, to such ships as have made three voyages, I have frequently added an iron knee under every beam of the lower and middle decks, from the fore-mast to the mizen-mast, where there has not been a standard. If his Majesty's ship the *Centaur* (although French-built) and others that have foundered at sea, had been fitted in this manner, it would have prevented their sides from separating from the ends of their beams, and consequently might, in all probability, have prevented those ships from foundering.

Indeed, I am persuaded that the loss of most of the ships of war and even merchant ships that have foundered at sea, has been occasioned by their having been insufficient in point of strength.

After having stated, in my answers to the questions put to me by the Commissioners of the Land Revenue in the year 1791, every alteration I then thought necessary to be made in future, so as to prevent accidents of that kind, even in the worst weather, I cannot but sincerely regret that my remarks have not been attended to. I feel this the more when I consider the frequent losses of the King's ships, particularly the very recent catastrophe of his Majesty's ship *Leda*, when (as it is said) only seven of the whole crew were saved.

Amongst the various reports and comments which followed this letter in the pages of the *European Magazine*, is a list of ships fitted with iron knees:[21]

A LIST OF SHIPS IN THE EAST-INDIA COMPANY'S SERVICE, BUILT WITH ALL IRON KNEES, STANDARDS, &C.

Built	Name	Bottoms thick	Builder's Measurement	Total Tonnage
1794	*Arniston*	5in	1433	
	Cirencester	5in	1439	
1795	*Thames*	5in	1432	
	Royal Charlotte	5in	1453	
	Henry Addington	5in	1432	
	Glatton	5in	1432	
	Walmer Castle	5in	1460	
	Cuffnells	5in	1429	
1796	*Warley*	5in	1460	
	Hindostan	5in	1463	
	Earl Talbot	5in	1428	
	Ceres	5in	1430	
	Earl of Abergavenny	5in	1460	
	Neptune	5in	1468	
	Coutts	5in	1451	
	Ganges	5in	1502	
	Hope	5in	1471	
				24643
1794	*Earl Howe*	4in	876	
1795	*Tellicherry*	4in	465	
1795	*Sir Stephen Lushington*	4in	608	
1796	*Admiral Gardner*	4in	813	
1797	Five ships building about 800 tons each	4in	4000	
				6762
In all, 26 ships built and building			Total	31,405 Tons

East-India House,
Nov 2, 1797.

By 1810 the East India Company required all its ships to be fitted with iron knees and standards as well as iron hold pillars and hooks.

In a journal he kept on the maiden voyage of the 820-ton *Walthamstow*, owned by Sir Robert Wigram, the Revd William Money, the commander's brother, describes the start of the passage in measured tones:[22]

Thursday March 20 1800. This morning we were clear of the Channel with a fine fresh breeze from the Nor. East. The increase of motion was now very sensibly felt on all sides, and the decrease of our party at morning muster plainly evinced the effect of the same on many of the unseasoned passengers. To me the scene afforded a most magnificent picture: the Bay of Biscay, a fine open sea rolling with a majestic motion, and each ship in her respective station sailing briskly before the wind, which seemed in real earnest determined to hurry us from our native soil.

Friday March 21 1800. After the continuance of a fine breeze all night, early this morning a noble sight appeared in view. A West India fleet consisting of sixty-two sail bearing away for the Channel. I could not but watch them with an anxious eye, till no other appearance remained than one or two topsails; on these I gazed to the last, thinking perhaps the hearts of some were then exulting in the prospect of soon meeting again the dearest friends, after many a rough day on the boistorous ocean. With reluctance I then turned away, and looked on the wide expanse we were then measuring over. The remainder of this day afforded no further particular occurrence.

In times of war the outward-bound East India fleet sailed in convoy when in hostile waters and on this occasion the 48-gun frigate *Anson* gave protection as far as the Canaries. In his book, *A Ship of the Line*, C S Forester aptly describes the tribulations encountered by a naval officer when convoying a group of Indiamen.

The total fleet of regular East Indiamen and extra ships numbered about 100 in 1810 with a total tonnage of about 90,000.[23] In 1811, thirty-seven ships arrived home and fifty-three sailed. The sizes of the ships which sailed were distributed fairly evenly amongst the three main classes. In 1825, twenty-six regular and eleven extra ships sailed for India and the East, and in the same year twenty-five regular and five extra ships arrived arrived home. Of the regular ships, four-fifths of those sailing or returning were of the 1200-ton class.[24]

The East India Company's monopoly of trade with the East was severly curtailed in 1813 when free trade with India was permitted. This resulted in a surge of exports to Asia. In 1823, trade to anywhere in the East, with the exception of China, was opened to all.

Other European countries were terminating trading monopolies in the decades after 1815, as the desire for free trade swept across the mercantile communities. In Denmark, the Asiatic Company received a charter in 1732 and a trading monopoly to the East for forty years; on its expiry in 1772, monopoly with China was retained but that with the East Indies was lost, although the Company received duties on goods carried. The Charter was renewed in 1792 and was not finally repealed until 1843.[25] In France, the East India Company was founded in 1696 but its privileges were abolished in 1770. The Swedish East India Company started in 1731 but was dissolved in 1813; during its existence it owned thirty-eight ships.

Fig 208. It was in 1791 that John Perry & Co erected a tall 'mast house' at Blackwall on the western side of Brunswick Basin – known as 'Perry's Dock' – to shorten the time taken for stepping masts. It was reported that the first ship to use the new device, the Lord Macartney, *had her masts and bowsprit stepped in 3 hours 40 minutes. This probably applied only to the lower masts, as the topmasts would hardly have been erected before the lower rigging was put over the lower mast heads and the lower stays set up. The mast house was demolished in 1862.* (MacGregor Collection)

Fig 209. Launch of the East Indiaman Edinburgh *at the Blackwall Yard on 9 November 1825, with the* Abercrombie Robinson *on the stocks to the left, almost ready for launching. This was a very festive occasion.* (Parker Gallery)

208

View of Mr. Perry's Dock at Blackwall.

209

Most long established shipyards were subject to continuous changes of name as old partners left and new ones were brought in, and quite abrupt changes occurred when the controlling interest was sold to an outsider. A typical example is the Blackwall Yard, which is well-documented. The Perry family were in control of the yard from the 1730s for most of that century and built many Indiamen and warships. John Perry succeeded his father at the business in 1772 and ten years later took as his apprentice George Green (1767–1849), who married his second daughter in 1796. Prior to 1797, the firm was called John Perry & Co, but in that year it became, Perry, Sons & Green when George Green became a partner. In 1798 the name was changed to Perry, Wells & Green, when Perry sold part of his holding to John & William Wells of Deptford; in 1803 he sold his remaining half share to the Wells brothers, but the firm's name remained as before. The brothers sold some of the yard to Sir Robert Wigram in 1805 and when William Wells retired in 1812 the whole was vested in Wigram, the firm's name then changing to Wigram, Wells & Green. A year later John Wells retired and some of Wigram's sons were brought in, so that the firm became Wigrams & Green. The firm owned shares in nineteen vessels in 1814. In 1819 Sir Robert Wigram retired and the shares were so divided that George Green held half and Wigram's two sons, Money and Henry Loftus, held one-quarter each. The yard was then called Green & Wigram and after 1829, when Green's eldest son Richard became a partner, the name was again altered to Green, Wigrams & Green. George Green retired in 1838, and, when the partnership expired in 1843, the yard was divided between the two families, to universal regret.[26]

Other builders of note on the Thames were Randall at Rotherhithe, Barnard at Deptford, Pitcher at Northfleet, John & William Wells at Rotherhithe up to 1798, and Dudman at Deptford.

With the probability that the Honourable Company's trading charter was to be terminated, there was not the same inducement to build large, costly ships after the middle of the twenties. The *Abercrombie Robinson*, *Edinburgh*, *George the Fourth*, and *Lord Lowther* were all launched in 1825 but had probably been contracted for three years earlier. The *Duke of Sussex* was launched in 1826 and the *Reliance* in 1827. The *Reliance* was the last Indiaman to be built of the 1200-ton class. In 1833 the Company's charter was entirely changed, with effect from April 1834: it was to lose its exclusive privilege of trade with China but was to continue with the government of its eastern possessions, retaining control of the Indian Navy.[27] Most of the East Indiamen were sold by the end of 1834, and *Hardy's Register* has a list showing how forty-nine ships were disposed of: nineteen were sold for breaking up, an average price being £5000–£6000. Some were bought by their commanders, others sold to Parsee firms, and a few were fitted out for further trade. The *Earl of Balcarras* was sold for £10,700 for further trade, and likewise the *Buckinghamshire*, but for £220 less. The *Scaleby Castle*, which was thirty-six years old, fetched £6900 in 1834 and was re-sold a month later, with fresh stores aboard and ready for sea, for no less than £13,500.[28]

Fig 210. English East Indiaman. *Reproduced from plate LI in* Architectura Navalis Mercatoria *(1768) by Fredrik of Chapman. Dimensions in the English index to the plans: 129ft 9in (length between perpendiculars), 33ft 4in (moulded breadth), 19ft 4in (draft of water); 314 Swedish heavy lasts, which equals 753.6 long tons. She is roughly the same size as the* Bridgewater *in figure 215.*

DESIGN APPRAISAL OF EAST INDIAMEN

It is a curious fact that although models exist for both men-of-war and merchant ships, they are scarce in the case of East Indiamen. This seems all the more strange because big fortunes were made through these ships, and it would have been normal to commission a model to commemorate such an event. Our knowledge of these ships is restricted to a few models and plans, to numerous oil paintings and prints, and to the voluminous collection of log-books in the India Office Library.

A lines plan in the Charnock Collection at the National Maritime Museum shows an Indiaman of about 1750 with a length on keel of 114ft 0in, length on lower deck of 124ft 0in, and moulded breadth of 32ft 6in. She has great tumblehome, a fair amount of deadrise and rounded bilges, double quarter galleries, eleven ports on her middle deck and two aft on her lower deck. There is a short poop, a long

210

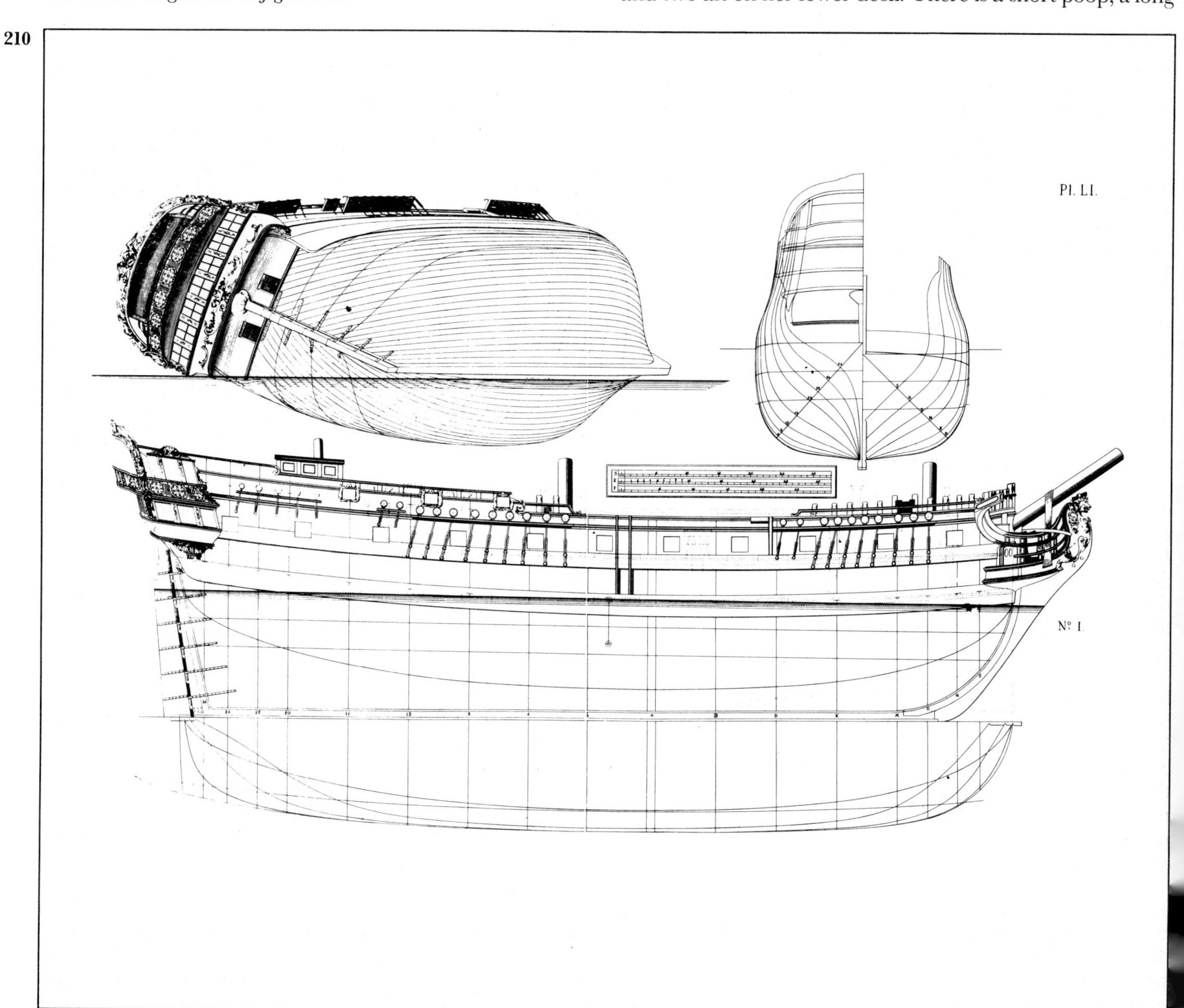

211

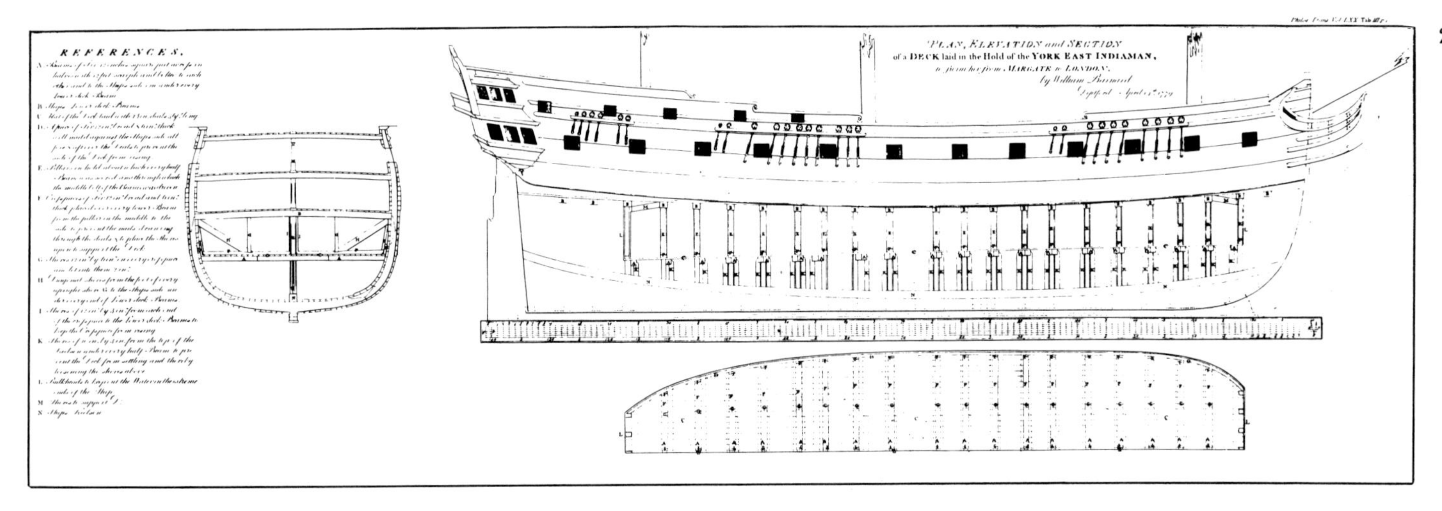

Fig 211. York. *Sheer elevation, section and deck. The* York *was built in 1772 and of 758 tons; she had gone ashore at Margate and these plans show the proposals of the shipbuilder, William Barnard, to float her back to the Thames for repair. A completely watertight deck was laid at level* C-C *and braced against the water pressure; it extended fore and aft and was contained by transverse bulkheads* L. *The deck plan is of the watertight deck. The holes in the bottom were not filled, but the ship was floated back to London in this manner. The plans are dated April 1779. (*Philosophic Transactions, *vol LXX, Table III, p 108)*

quarter deck reaching to the mainmast, a waist and a forecastle. The tonnage was about 650.

A longitudinal section and half deck plan of the *Falmouth* are in the National Maritime Museum, drawn to a scale of $3/20$in to 1ft. This ship was built at the Blackwall Yard and took two years to build, being completed in 1752. A companion drawing to the above is reproduced in *Chronicles of the Blackwall Yard* and depicts a port broadside view under sail, with stern and bow views of her also under sail.[29] On this drawing her measurements were inscribed as 108ft 9in length of keel, 34ft 0in breadth, and $668^{65}/_{94}$ tons burthen. She was officially rated as of 499 tons and was wrecked in 1766 on her sixth voyage off the coast of Arakan. Like the ship in the Charnock Collection, the *Falmouth* had eleven ports cut in her middle deck with two at the after end of her lower deck; three ports in her quarter deck bulwark where there was an open rail supported on stanchions as far as the poop; a double quarter gallery, and a projecting stern gallery to the upper tier of stern windows; wide gangways along the sides connecting the forecastle and quarter deck which had the makings of a flush deck; a flat bow bulkhead meeting the side at an angle; and a fairly angular forefoot. In the *Falmouth's* plan, there appears to be a cabin on the quarter deck, the front of which is open and covers the wheel, but the after part is enclosed and butts against the fore end of the poop. This is drawn on the longitudinal section but omitted on the deck plan.

Another plan of this date shows the *London* of 630 tons, first taken up by the Company in 1750. William Salisbury has drawn out her lines from offsets in Mungo Murray's *Treatise on Shipbuilding*, first published in 1754.[30] There is considerable tumblehome, but she is less full in the bottom than later ships. Length on the lower deck is 124ft and the moulded breath is 32ft. This ship, the *Falmouth*, and the plan in the Charnock Collection all represent the same type and size of vessel.

A detailed lines plan of an unnamed East Indiaman appears in Chapman's book on naval architecture and it bears strong similarities to the three ships already described. The measurements are 129ft 3in between perpendiculars (lower deck length), 33ft 6in moulded breadth, about 15ft depth of hold, and 753 tons. She must represent a ship built about 1760. She has a cabin abutting the poop similar to that aboard the *Falmouth*; also eleven ports on the middle deck, but none on the lower deck. She has a full-bodied hull with little deadrise but slack bilges that round up into the sides; above the waterline there is considerable tumblehome; the waterlines are full but there are no deadflats. Above the sheer elevation, a starboard quarter view has been drawn showing the ship heeled to port so that the keel is clear of the water; by this means, the run of the external planking up to the lower counter is clearly indicated, as are the stern elevation and ornamentation.[31]

In the National Maritime Museum is a sheer elevation and cross-section of an unnamed Indiaman inscribed 'John & William Wells November 24th 1779'. Dimensions listed on the plan give:[32]

Length of the keel for measurement	116ft 0in
[plan scales 131ft 6in cut keel]	
Breadth to a 4inch plank	35ft 0in
Depth in the hold	14ft 3in
Between lower and middle deck	6ft 0in
Between middle and upper deck	6ft 2in
Roundhouse { fore part	6ft 4in
Roundhouse { aft part	6ft 6in
No of tons	$755^{80}/_{94}$

All the written dimensions except the length stand up to being checked on the plan, and the length discrepancy is inexplicable. The term 'keel for measurement [of tonnage]' included the extent of fore rake, and this scales about 146ft

212

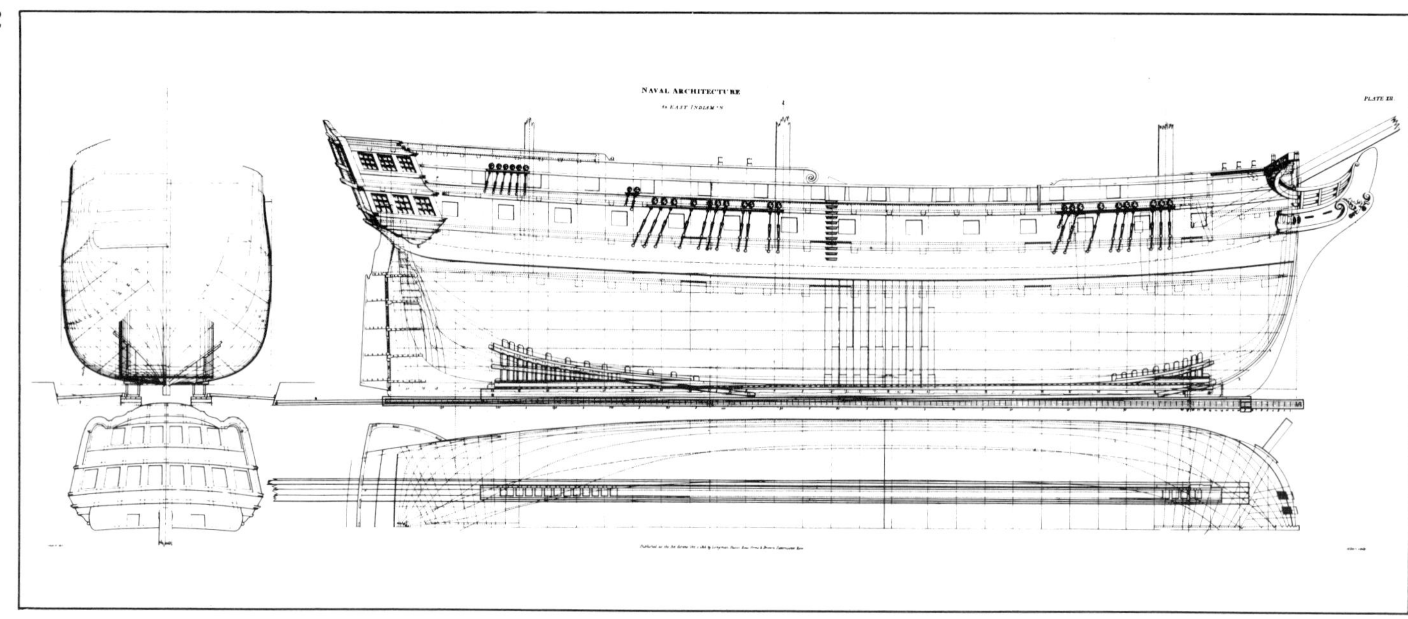

on the plan. Perhaps 116 ft represents an error by the draughtsman. Length of the lower deck scales 146ft as well. This was presumably intended as a design drawing and although the stations and centre line are ruled off in the half-breadth plan, nothing is plotted here. The sheer elevation is well drawn to show thirteen ports on the middle deck and six on the quarter deck; amidships there is a rough tree rail and on the poop is an open rail; there is a full-length female figurehead supported by a carved trailboard. The cross-section indicates that the tumblehome is much reduced and there is less deadrise with slack bilges and a filling-out of the bottom. This was altogether more of the shape which Gabriel Snodgrass was attempting to achieve as illustrated by the pairs of cross-sections he compared in published engravings. The plan of this Indiaman contains eleven small ports which are 9in square and spaced out between the gunports; they were presumably intended for ventilation rather than as ports for sweeps.

In 1786 came the *Nottingham* of 1152 tons, the first English Indiaman of over 1000 tons. Professor Parkinson writes that 'she was copied, to some extent, from some of the Swedish ships which traded to China. Her tonnage was almost the same as that of the *Gustavus III*...'[33] Nathaniel Smith, chairman of the Court of Directors of the East India Company, had particulars of this Swedish ship, which he presumably referred to in his pamphlet published in 1778. If this is so, then the *Gustav III*, to use the Swedish spelling, was not newly off the stocks in 1786. This Swedish influence, if correct, makes one think immediately of Chapman's great work; the ship was indeed designed by him and built in 1778 of some 1230 tons for the East Indies trade. But as was shown more than once in *Fast Sailing Ships*, it is easy to attribute a new design to a certain influence but hard to prove it.

In Steel's *Naval Architecture*, first published in 1805, is the lines plan of an East Indiaman of 1257 tons with dimensions of 165ft 6in length between perpendiculars, 42ft 0in maximum breadth, and 17ft 0in depth of hold. Although she is unnamed, a number of ships of this tonnage had been launched at the Blackwall Yard, such as *Alnwick Castle* and *Marquis of Ely* in 1801, *Royal George* in 1802, and *Essex* in 1803, and this plan may represent one of them. There is a little deadrise and the floors round up into slack bilges with almost vertical sides and a small amount of tumblehome; the entrance and run are full but there are no dead flats. Fourteen ports are cut in her side on the middle deck and a further thirteen on the upper deck, and amidships the solid bulwarks are 3ft high; there is also a round-headed rudder.[34]

A somewhat similar plan to David Steel's Indiaman was published in 1816 as plate XII in Abraham Rees' *Cyclopædia*. This illustrates a ship measuring 159ft 0in between perpendiculars and 37ft 3in extreme breadth (dimensions scaled off the plan), making her 6ft 6in shorter and 5ft 0in narrower than Steel's ship.[35] This plan by Rees is undoubtedly the plan used by Admiral Pâris in *Souvenirs de Marine* figure 279, volume 5. For the sake of comparison, Paris has added the outline sail plan of a 52-gun ship, as he considered the spars of suitable length.

Some useful pointers towards observing the differences between an East Indiaman and a man-of-war at the turn of the century were that the former had a round-headed rudder; less tumblehome and more vertical sides; forecastle and poop joined by a solid deck without gangways or gratings; less sheer; and the futtock shrouds secured to the mast instead of to the lower shrouds.

There now follows the memorandum sent by George Millett, a former captain in the East India service but now a director, and addressed to Charles Grant, chairman of the East India Company. It is an interesting document for its appraisal of the design of Indiamen during the period under review, and must have been compiled at the request of the chairman or the Board of Directors:[36]

Sir, Wallwood-House, Leytonstone, 9th May 1809.

In consequence of our late conversation upon the subject of advertising for ships to be built for the season 1810, I have attentively considered the class of ships which, in my opinion, is the one best calculated for the general service of the East-India Company, and with the aid of long experience, and such inquiries as I have been able to make, now beg leave to submit the result to your consideration. But before I endeavour to impress upon your mind the necessity which has long been obvious to every experienced commander, of abandoning, in future, the scale and plan of the 800 ton ships now in use, it will be necessary for me to enter into something like an historical detail of the progressive imperfections in the construction of those ships, and which have, at last, grown to such an height, as to render them extremely expensive to the Company, inconvenient to manage, and not profitable to the owners.

I entered into the service in the year 1769, and, as far as I can recollect, the ships were then generally fitted with gratings, for the purpose of stowing the long boats below, the upper decks were laid with two-inch deal only, and every attention was paid to make the upper part of the ship as light as possible. But about that time, or in the year 1767, the *Granby* and *Queen* were built with flush decks, and the scantlings increased, to carry the long boat aloft. Those ships were still unencumbered with cook-rooms, hog-sties, sheep-pens, or birthing up in the waist; the increased scantlings, however, of that deck, and the long boat carried between the booms, made a very material change in the weight above.

Before I proceed any further, I wish to examine the dimensions of the above description of ships, and to make some

Fig 212. Unnamed East Indiaman. *Lines plan, reproduced from* Cyclopaedia *(1816) by Abraham Rees, plate XII, in the section on 'Naval Architecture'. Dimensions scaled off the plan: 159ft 0in (length between perpendiculars) and 37ft 3in (extreme breadth).*

Fig 213. Painting by an Indian artist of the East Indiaman Carnatic *which was built on the Thames in 1787 with a tonnage of 1169 and made her first voyage in 1788. The foremast and mainmast look too lofty for her length, and she still crosses a long mizen yard; but of especial interest is the dolphin striker. As this ship made her sixth and final voyage in 1801–02, the painting could represent either an early example of a dolphin striker or have been painted on one of her last voyages, when the mizen yard would have been rather old-fashioned* (Parker Gallery)

213

remarks thereon; for which purpose I shall take the *Speaker*, built in 1762, and the *Granby*, which was launched about five or six years afterwards.

Dimensions of the *Speaker*.	**Dimensions of the *Granby*.**
112ft 0in Keel for tonnage	110ft 0in Keel for tonnage
35ft 0in Broad	36ft 8in Broad
14ft 4in Depth in hold	14ft 6ins Depth in hold
702 Tons burthen	786 Tons burthen

Here the builder has very sensibly added to the breadth and diminished the length, to compensate for the great additional weight upon the upper part of the ship: I wish subsequent builders had been permitted to do the same. The *Granby* was in her time a favorite ship, and performed well to the last.

About the year 1776, the *Royal Admiral* was built, and we now find, for the first time I believe, the introduction of hog-sties raised two feet above the upper deck, the bottom being a platform over the cables and manger. Her dimensions were as follows:

120ft 0in Keel for tonnage
37ft 7in Breadth
16ft 0in Depth in hold
903 Tons burthen

Here the builder adds to the weight above, to the length of keel and depth of hold, without a proportionate increase of breadth, consequently the ship must have required more ballast.

In 1787, the *Boddam*, of 1001 tons burthen, was built, with precisely the same scantlings with the 800 ton ships. And now we come to the material alteration, of having the forecastle raised four feet above the upper deck, the bows raised fifteen inches, the ship's hearth rose, with the forecastle, the hogsties. and sheep-pens, brought on the upper deck, and the side birthed up a midships. Her dimensions are as follows:

128ft 1in Keel for tonnage
38ft 9in Breadth
15ft 6in Depth in Hold

Here is a ship eight feet longer than the *Royal Admiral*, with a great increase of weight aloft, and only one foot more breadth, to compensate for the length and elevation of the additional weight, and the consequences are too obvious to mention: but she never was a good ship, either for the Company or the owners.

The foregoing instances are adduced, to shew how the weight has been constantly augmented upon the upper part of our ships, the length of the keel and depth of the hold increased

214

215

Fig 214. The True Briton *running up Channel with a single reef taken in her topsails. She was built in 1790 by Wells at Deptford and was of 1198 tons. She is shown carrying guns on two decks which would deceive an enemy into thinking she was a two-decked ship-of-the line.* (Parker Gallery)

Fig 215. Oil painting, attributed to Thomas Luny (1759–1837), of the Indiaman Bridgewater, *which is probably the one built on the Thames in 1785 of 755 tons. Although she has a long driver boom, she also has a mizen yard as well as some unusual sails: from the main topmast she sets three staysails – two of which must be upper and lower middle staysails – instead of the normal two sails; and from the fore topmast she sets both inner and outer jibs. A sprit topsail is also set, but apparently no spritsail. Presumably these flying kites were the captain's fancy.* (Private Collection)

out of all proportion to the breadth.

The modern 800 ton ships have not only all the incumbrances aloft of the *Boddam*, but they are beginning to bring the gallies up on the upper deck altogether, until they are become, from this and other causes, so extremely crank, as to be unfit for the service they have to perform.

I understand there is no positive length or depth for the construction of East-India ships, and we are continually augmenting the weight upon the upper deck, without adding to the breadth to resist that weight. It is generally allowed, that a ship's length should be equal only to three times her breadth, and some of the best ships formerly in the service, were kept nearly to that proportion. I remember the *Princess Royal*, in particular: she was 864 tons, about 113 feet keel, and 38 feet in breadth. She always performed well, and was an excellent ship for the Company and the owners. I perfectly agree however, with a very able and experienced Member of the Court, that ships may be improved by a reasonable deviation from this rule; but I am equally convinced, we have gone greatly too far into the contrary extreme, particularly with our present 800 ton ships, as may be seen by the following dimensions:

118ft 0in Keel for tonnage
36ft 0in Breadth
14ft 9in Depth in hold
6ft 2in Height between decks

Now here is a class of ships, more numerous than any other, of 800 tons burthen, having all the accumulation of weight upon her upper deck, already described, with a keel 10 feet longer than three times her breadth. This really outrages all proportion, and I do most sincerely hope, will be remedied in future.

Although the 1200 ton ships go a little into the extrmee, and are likewise too long for their breadth, yet they do not exceed the proportion, by any means, so much as the 800 ton ships do, and they are certainly by far the best class that were ever built for the China trade; for we have had sufficient experience of the 1400 ton ships, to be thoroughly satisfied they will never answer.

It is the opinion of the best informed builders, that a ship of from 900 to 950 tons burthen, will require no more scantling than what is given to the present class of 800 tons; and, I am prepared to say, such a ship may be navigated with the same establishment of men (or at most five more) as the 800 ton ships, as they are certainly overmasted, and therefore the same dimensions would be sufficient. Though a ship of 900 tons will require some addition to the size of her anchors and cables, the kintledge will be the same; and if this class of ships, which I now presume to recommend, should be constructed upon a scale of good dimensions, I am confident they will draw no more water, when loaded, than the 800 ton ships now do. A ship of about 900 tons will have materially the advantage over one of 800 tons, in keeping her ports open longer at sea, in shifting her cargo in port, in affording better accommodation for troops, passengers, and ship's company, and, in short, whether the safety, the defence, the speedy and economical transit of goods (which is the soul of commerce), or the welfare

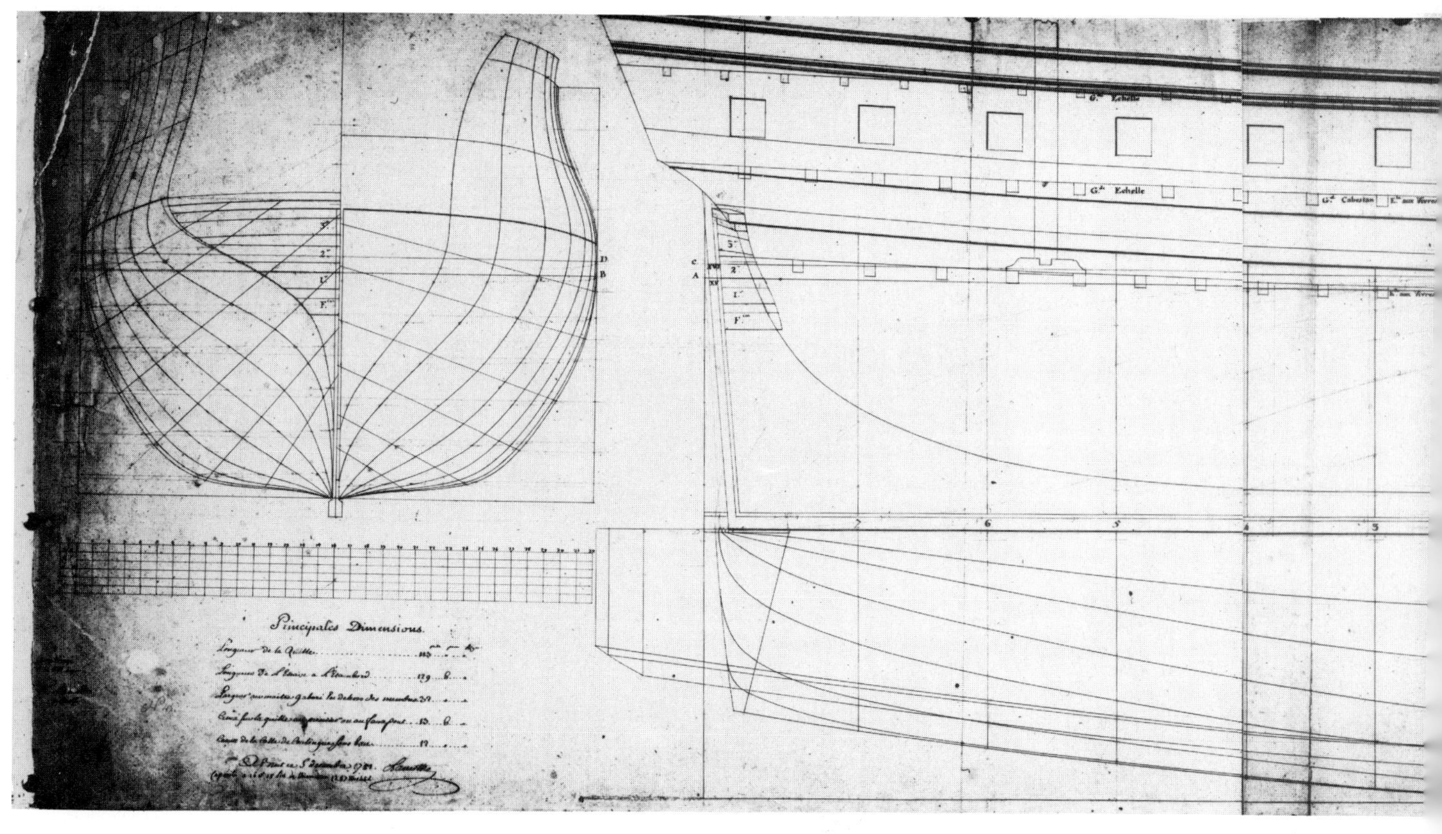

Fig 216. French East Indiaman. *Lines plan, unidentified, possibly a design drawing by Guibert Sr, dated 1781, and reproduced from the Guibert Collection at the Mariners Museum, Newport News. Dimensions on plan (and converted to English feet). 120.46ft (length of keel), 138.05ft (length from stem to sternpost), 34.11ft (moulded breadth at the midship frame), 14.39ft (depth of hold from keel to lower deck). Burthen at 16ft draught is 1289 French tons.*

Fig 218. A watercolour drawing by T E Lønning of the Danish East Indiaman Holsteen, *built in 1782, originally as a naval frigate.* (Maritime Museum, Kronborg)

of the Company or owners be considered, I can entertain no doubt of the advantages which would result, by abandoning the one class and adopting the other, whenever it shall be found right to supply the present deficiency of regular ships for the Indian trade.

I know there is a pretty general coincidence of opinion in favour of 900 ton ships, and upwards, among the owners, the maritime officers, and the builders, and I trust, therefore, it only remains to agree and to decide upon her dimensions; but it would absolutely be presumption in me to offer you my opinions, however it may be formed, upon a subject of this nature: I therfore take the liberty of submitting to you the propriety of causing a letter to be written to the principal builders (say Messrs Wells and Co, Messrs Barnards, and, if you think proper, Mr Brent, and Mr Pitcher) requesting they will each of them be so good as to furnish the Committee of Shipping with a plan for a ship of about 930 tons burthen, keeping in view the safety, the convenience, the capacity, the performance, the economy, and the duty, upon the whole, which it may be required of her to perform, both at sea in a tidesway, and in the harbours and rivers to which she may be destined, where length of keel and draft of water must necessarily be considered.

It seems strange, that there has never yet been any proportion given for the depth of a ship's hold. The depth does not enter into the calculation for tonnage to the builder, so that, whether a ship be deep or shallow, he is paid just the same; the ship-owners have, therefore, been continually adding to the depth of the hold, until the ships are certainly very much weakened thereby. For this cause, the Company's 1400 ton ships have been supplied with additional beams, to strengthen the immense space unsupported in their holds; but all this will not do, as they are certainly too large for the manner in which they are constructed. I cannot help feeling the necessity of fixing some boundary to the defect alluded to above, in whatever ships shall be built for the Company's service in future.

The method of calculating a ship's tonnage, is to multiply the keel for tonnage by the breadth of the ship, and that product, by the half breadth. This being divided by 94, is the tonnage required, so that the depth has nothing to do with the calculation.

Should the alteration which I have ventured to suggest, and which, indeed, is a good deal sanctioned by the sentiments of the Honorable Director before alluded to, be adopted, I shall be ready, at a future period, to submit my opinion upon the dimensions of the masts and yards, with the armament, and general equipment which such a ship would necessarily require.

In examining the foregoing subject, I have endeavoured to meet your wishes, as far as time and circumstances would enable me to do, and have the honor to be,

Sir,

Your most humble servant,

George Millett

NB I have not mentioned the extra ships, because they did not seem to me to form a part of the subject; but if economy alone were to be considered, their savings, in freight and expenses, to the Company, particularly in the Bengal trade, would be immense.

Charles Grant, Esq Chairman.

216

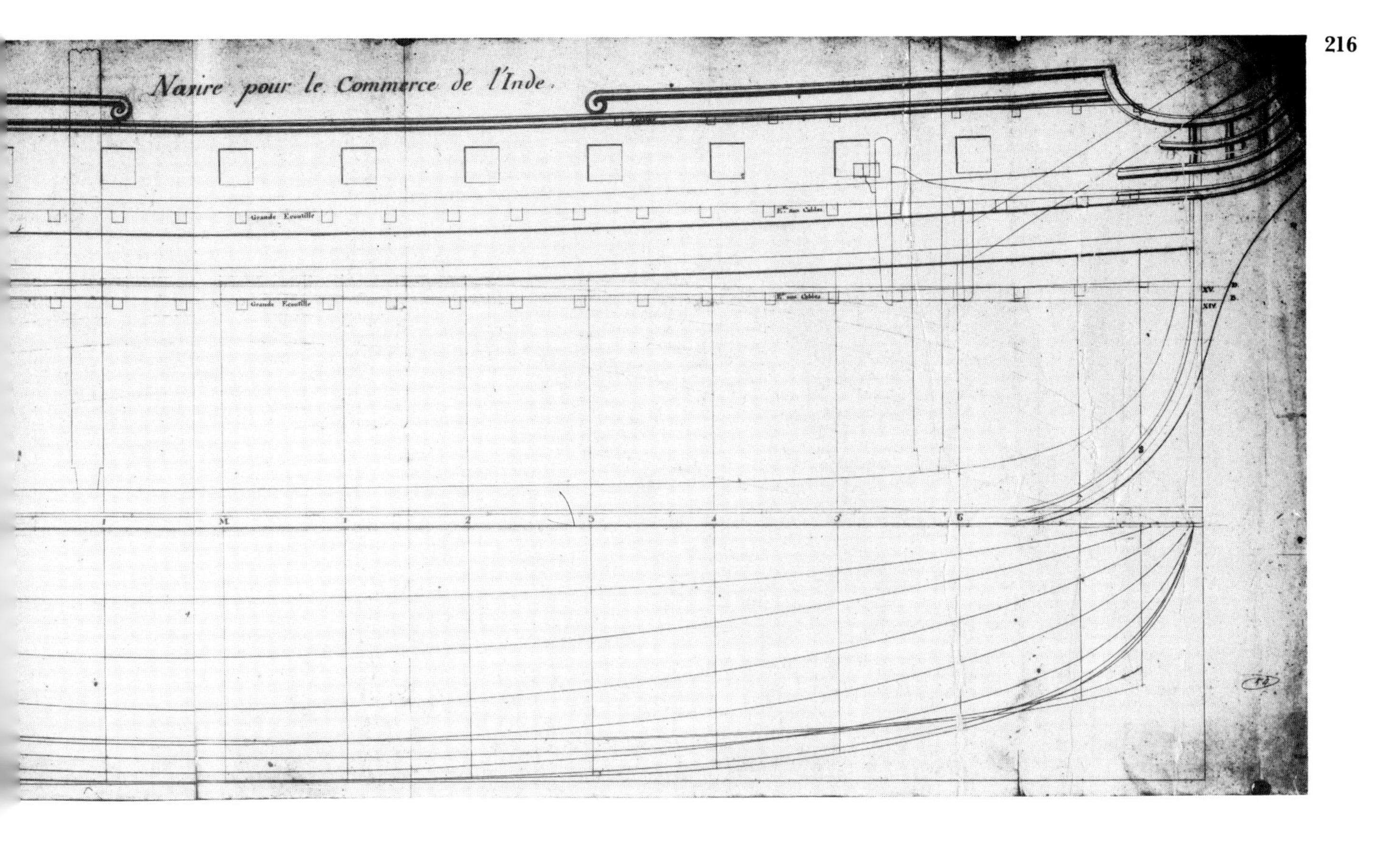
Navire pour le Commerce de l'Inde.
Grande Ecoutille
Grande Ecoutille

218

Det Danske Asiatiske Compagnies Skib HOLSTEEN Commanderet af Hr Capitaine Helsding

217

Fig 217. The Dutch East Indiaman Candia, *drawn by G Groenewegen and published in 1789.*

A letter sent from the Blackwall Yard in response to the suggestion in the above memorandum that leading shipbuilders be invited to submit plans of 900-ton ships is of interest:[37]

Sir, Blackwall, 11th August 1809.

We have been honored with the commands of the Committee of Shipping to send you a plan of a ship of about 950 tons, but we are of opinion, that we cannot improve on the construction of the *Warren Hastings*, of 1000 tons, which ship is of great stability and capacity, and draws less water than the ships of 800 tons.

With regard to the ships that may prudently be built with the same scantlings as the present ships of 800 tons, we are of opinion, that, with the exceptions of the beams, provided copper bolts be used instead of treenails, that the scantlings would be sufficiently large for ships of 1200 tons.

The most perfect ship of 600 tons, in our judgment, was the *Travers*, or similar to the *Sovereign*, and the only improvement that we can suggest is to reduce the depth from the gun-deck to the keelson 18 inches, and not to lay the lower deck, which alteration would give great increase of ability for stowage, and great stability, by the reduction of height.

We remain, Sir,
Your most obedient servants,
John Morice, Esq — Wells, Wigrams, and Green

In the Collection of Guibert plans at the Maritime Museum at Newport News, Virginia, there are three lines plans of East Indiamen: two are unnamed but are dated 1781 and 1786; the third is undated but may represent the *Sophie*. This collection covers the works of the French naval architects named Guibert, father and son, and embraces a period of about sixty years from 1760–1820. All three plans show vessels with much finer lines than the English East Indiamen, having the typical French pear-shaped cross section with a finer entrance and a long hollow run. There are only two continuous decks, and they carry their guns on the upper one, so that, as there is a deep waist, the ports are cut in the high bulwarks amidships.

The plan dated 1781 (figure 216) has short floors with very little deadrise, but as the bilge is placed about half-way out, the side soon rounds up to run with only small curvature up to the maximum breadth at the load waterline. From here there is a big tumblehome at the top of which the sides start to flare out again. In this plan, the diagonals are developed on the half-breadth plan which uses the underside of the keel as its centre line, and the waterlines are drawn in pencil above this, so that they are superimposed over the sheer elevation. Fifteen ports are cut in the side. The quarter-deck extends just forward of the mainmast, and as the forecastle runs a long way aft, the length of the deep waist is about 32ft. The dimensions on the plan, converted into English measure where 1 *pied* equals 1.0657 feet, give 120.46ft length of keel, 138.05ft length from foreside of stem to aftside of sternpost between perpendiculars drawn on plan, 34.11ft moulded beam at midship frame and 14.39ft depth of hold. No tonnage is given, but at a draft of 15–16ft the cargo capacity is given as 1287 French tons. There is a drag of about 1ft.

The plan dated 1786 shows a similar hull-form to the earlier one with a fine entrance and run. Twelve ports are cut in the side on the main deck, and a further four on the quarter-deck; alone among these three plans, this ship has a poop deck reaching to the mizen, giving her a great height at the stern. Deck beams and hold pillars are drawn, and three hatchways are indicated. This plan looks like a drawing used in a shipyard, with some alterations included. Although diagonals are drawn on th body plan, they have not been developed in the half-breadth plan.

The third plan is inscribed in pencil beside the measurements: '*origine du Navire* La Sophie...'; and below the border line it is written in ink: '*origine de la Corvette* La Sophie'. Nevertheless the plan is entitled across the top: 'Sheer draught of a ship for the Indian trade pierced for 20 guns', and she has only ten ports on her side, with none under her quarter-deck. The latter extends only a short distance forward of the mizen, which gives a longer waist than the other two plans described above. The plan shows a finer-lined vessel than the other two in which the floor begins to round up only a short distance outside the rabbet. The forefoot is more angular but then the stem curves all the way up. Dimensions written on the plan, converted into English feet, give the following: length between perpendiculars [length of lower deck] 125.79ft, length of keel 113.00ft, breadth amidships 32.86ft, depth of hold 13.68ft, cargo capacity at a draft of 14.66ft is 895 French tons.

In Albert Sebille's *Histoire de la Marine*, a lines plan of a French East Indiaman is reproduced, somewhat similar to the 1781 French plan just described above. The chief difference is that, although she is not much deeper, she carries a broadside of guns on her lower deck; this gave fourteen ports on this deck and fifteen on the main deck. From the reproduction, her dimensions appear to be 178.02ft length from stem to sternpost, 46.90ft breadth amidships, and 21.32ft depth of hold. There may be a date of 1775 underneath, beside the signature of Coulomb, who designed her.[38]

THE REGULAR SHIP *FARQUHARSON*

One of the big ships sold for breaking-up was the *Farquharson* of 1326 tons, which in 1834 fetched £6,000. She is the vessel chosen to illustrate an East Indiaman both in the matter of plans and in descriptive text. It is always desirable to employ an actual vessel as an example and she is the only large named Indiaman built after 1815 whose plans have so far been discovered. Dimensions scaled off the plan give 171ft 0in (foreside stem to after side of sternpost) × 42ft 9in (moulded breadth) × 31ft 6in (top of floors to underside of upper deck); the height between decks is 6ft 6in to underside of the deck above. The tonnage given on the lines plan is 1326, although on her seventh voyage her log book states it to be 1406, proving her to be of the largest class. She was launched in August 1820 from Gordon's yard on the Thames and began her first voyage in January 1821.

There are five plans of the *Farquharson* at the National Maritime Museum. They are beautifully drawn at ¼in scale by Charles Dandridge and are probably copied from the originals, as they are much too clean to have been used in the shipyard. In any case the lines plan is dated 1820 which would make it too late for a design drawing because that was the year in which the ship was launched. From these plans, the lines, longitudinal section and deck plans have been drawn (figures 219 and 221). As usual, no spar plan existed and so one has been reconstructed. The final form adopted by the big East Indiamen can be seen in the plans of the *Farquharson*.

Compared with published plans, it is at once apparent that there was a fairly standard form of design and that, even if the ships could be mistaken for a frigate or a two-decked ship-of-the-line in profile, it was easy to tell from their almost flat floors, rounded bilges and small tumblehome that they were in fact merchant ships. The *Farquharson* has a full convex hull-form which conforms to the standard pattern, but her great length at the load line derived from the huge hull gave her a large speed potential

219

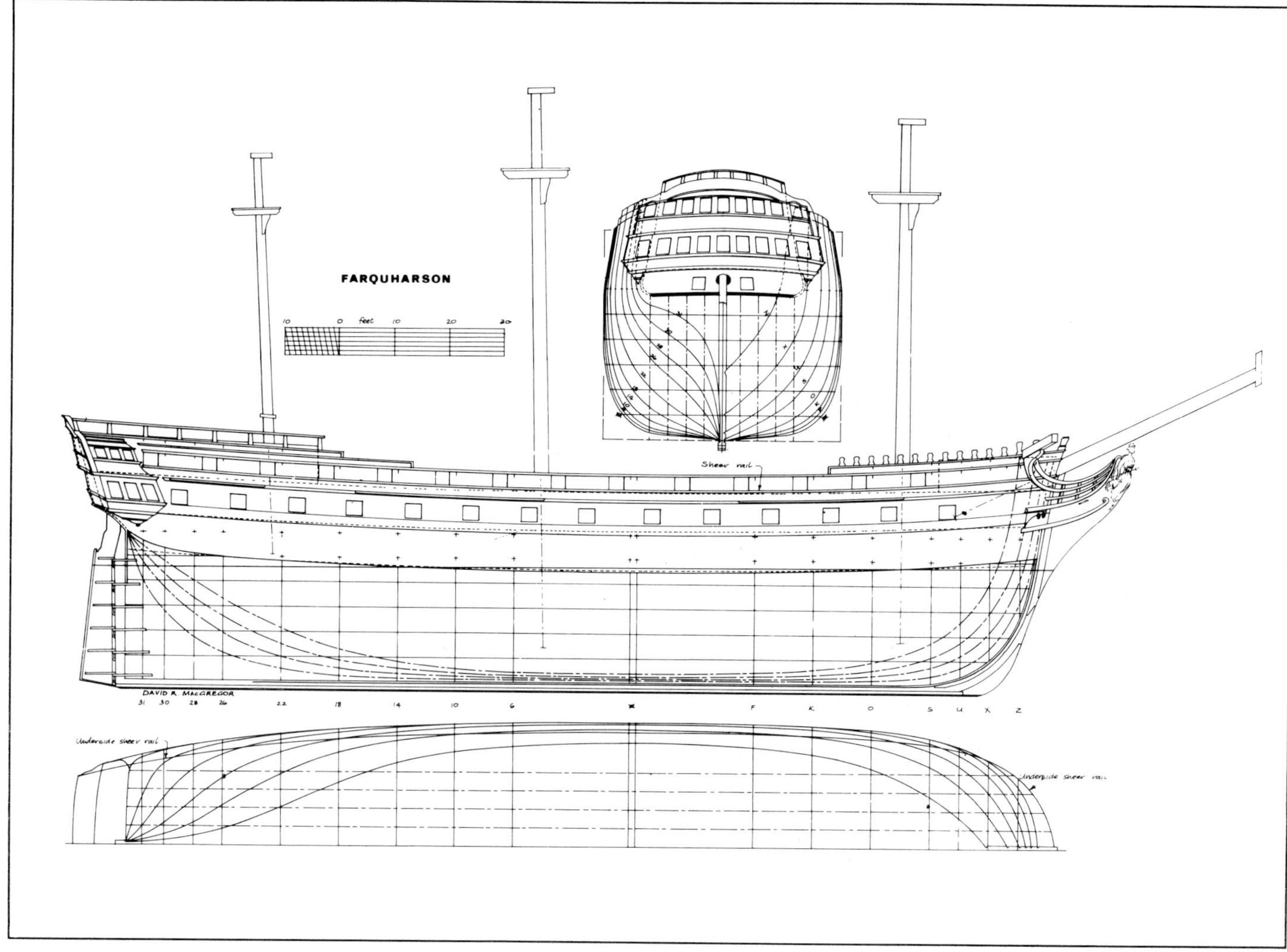

which was aided by the extensive sail plan and the big crew to operate it. Many small ships, such as Hedderwick's ship of 500 tons, are virtually smaller editions of an East Indiaman.

The lithograph of a stranded Indiaman (figure 220) reveals the fullness of hull and various features common to ships of this class, such as the heavy timber davits at the quarter and the double tier of stern windows which are without galleries. Internally, the chief difference between the Indiaman and a large warship lay in the deck arrangement. The warship still had an open waist, with the quarter-deck and forecastle merely connected at the sides with wide gangways, while in the Indiaman the waist was covered over and the quarter-deck and forecastle formed one continuous deck, called the upper deck; there was also a small topgallant forecastle for some of the crew placed right forward.

The Indiaman carried her principal armament on her middle deck. David Steel's draught shows a hull pierced for a broadside of 54 guns and the *Farquharson* is pierced for 56 guns, divided equally between the middle and upper decks. But a crew totalling about 130 could not possibly man such an armament and many of the upper deck ports were empty. In fact, Steel's draught states that the armament consisted of twenty-six 18-pounders on the middle deck and ten 18-pounders on the upper deck, together with two 18-pounders, eight feet long, to serve as stern chasers. Even with this armament of thirty-eight guns, the crew was barely sufficient to man one battery at a time.[39] Thomas Whitcombe's painting of *Farquaharson* shows only thirty-eight guns – twelve on the upper deck and twenty-six on the middle deck.

By 1815 square hances and high bulwarks had superseded the curved hances and lower bulwarks that Steel shows. The presence of a windlass on deck was the sure sign of a merchant ship but the Navy did not employ it except in cutters and schooners. Indiamen followed the naval practice of heaving in the anchor cable by means of an endless messenger taken to the capstan, a system to which the *Farquharson* confronted. On her middle deck are

Fig 219. Farquharson. *Lines plan. She was built in 1820 at Deptford by Gordon. The plan has been redrawn from one at the National Maritime Museum, Greenwich, dated 1820. Reconstruction: height of load waterline; lengths of lower masts and size of tops. Dimensions scaled off plan: 171ft 0in × 42ft 9in (moulded) × 31ft 6in (below upper deck). 1326 tons.*

Fig 220. Entitled 'An Indiaman Stranded', this lithograph was drawn by J R Jobbins whose work has a lyrical quality about it, but he never drew people on his ships. The outside of the hull is well-detailed.

Fig 221. Farquharson. *Section and decks. She was built in 1820 at Deptford of 1326 tons. These have been redrawn from plans at National Maritime Museum dated 1820 and 1821. Reconstruction: capstan and hatch coamings added.*

220

13.
AN INDIAMAN STRANDED
Published by Charles Tilt, Fleet Street, London.

221

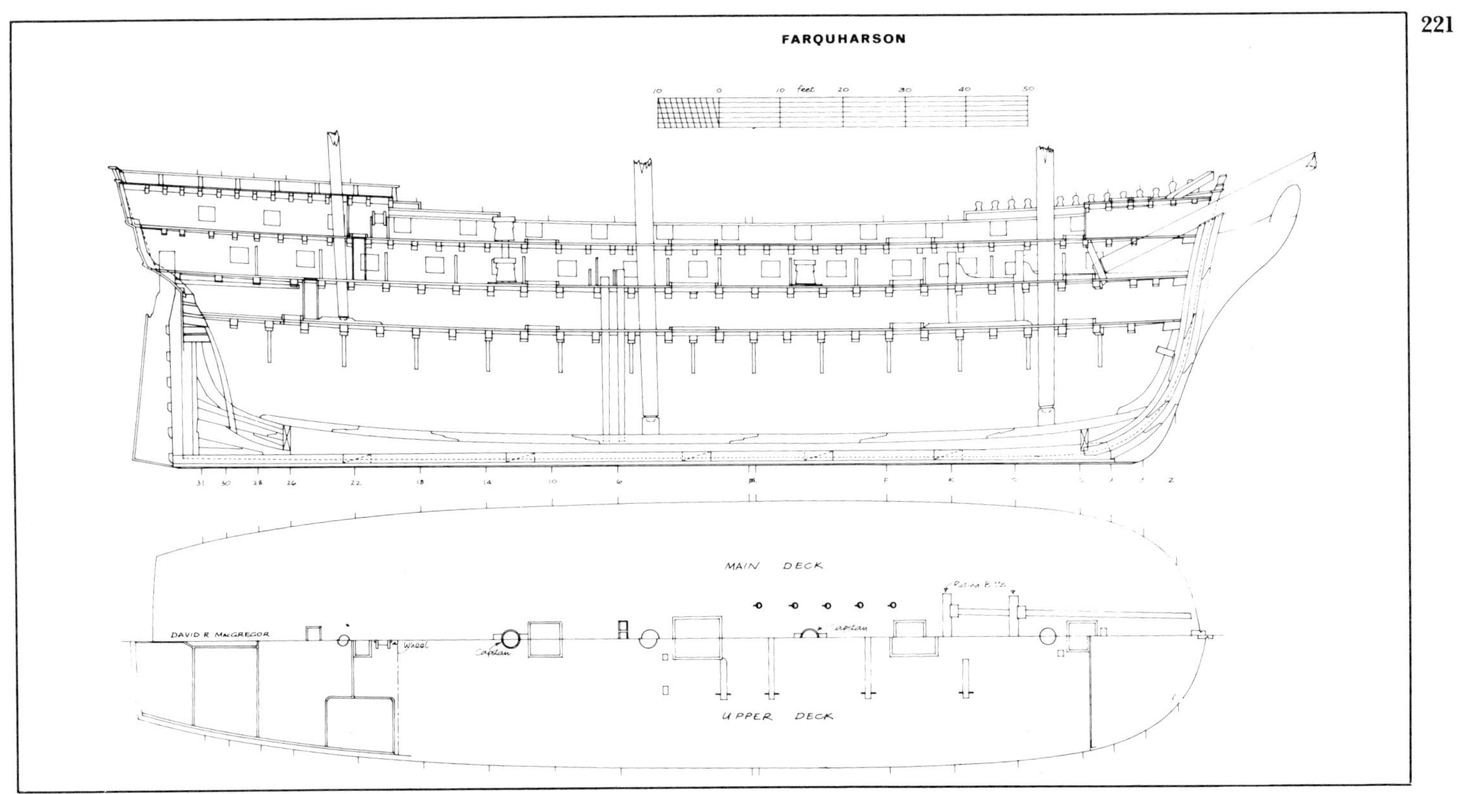
FARQUHARSON
10 0 10 feet 20 30 40 50
MAIN DECK
UPPER DECK
DAVID R MacGREGOR

222

Fig 222. Painting by Thomas Whitcombe (c1752–1824 or 1827) of an East Indiaman said to be the Farquharson, *off Table Bay. Whitcombe painted several ship portraits with the ship in these two positions, including the boat in the foreground. See the text for comments on the picture.* (Parker Gallery)

two capstans for this purpose and also two sets of massive riding bitts abaft the foremast to which the cable could be made fast when riding to anchor. The capstans are reconstructed because none was drawn in Dandridge's plans, although the capstan steps were marked; in addition one is placed on the upper deck on the same spindle as the aftermost one, because although no step is drawn on the plan it was standard practice to have one there.

The longitudinal section appearing in figure 221 has been reconstructed from the structural timbers which appeared on the lines plan, it being the convention to combine everything on a single drawing, and confusion was avoided by drawing the structural timbers in red ink and the sheer elevation in black. The hanging and staple knees appear to be of iron but the remaining structural work is timber, and other plans drawn by Charles Dandridge in 1821 and 1822 show the ship to be framed practically solid with immense timbers. On the lower and middle decks the beams are sided 15in and moulded 12in and are approximately 4ft 6in apart with a timber lodging knee at each deck, and are braced with six carlings sided 9in and moulded approximately 6in and 5ft 0in apart; further support is given by the ledges running between the carling and parallel to the beams.

In figure 222 the deck plans consist of the middle deck above the centre line and the upper deck drawn below it. Five ring bolts are drawn abreast of the forward capstan – there would be others to starboard – and stoppers could be attached to these for checking the cable when heaving in or letting go, in the same manner as a compressor on a chain cable. The long knees to the riding bitts are clearly seen. On the upper deck plan, the four beams with a pin at the outer ends are possibly placed there to receive the boats which could be lashed to them. The wheel is positioned just under the break of the poop and the tiller ropes would have taken several turns on the barrel before leading down to the deck below and aft to where the tiller is mounted. The capstan on the upper deck was used for hoisting the topsails and the lower yards, the fall from the tackles being led to the capstan through sheaves in bitts placed at the foot of the fore and main masts.

The only sail and rigging plan discovered for an Indiaman appeared in *Marine Models* in 1934 and is a reconstruction made by G W Munro, who stated that the hull was taken from a lines plan engraved in 1816. This suggests that he used the lines appearing in Rees's *Cyclopædia* which were dated 1816; he estimated the tonnage for this ship to be 955.[40]

In the case of the *Farquharson*, no spar dimensions are known, but there is an oil painting executed by Thomas Whitcombe who died in 1824 or 1827 and who, during his lifetime, painted many ship portraits. Unfortunately, the picture appears to represent a somewhat smaller ship than is shown in the pans. The Parker Gallery Ltd, through whose hands it passed, say it was signed and dated 'Thomas Whitcombe 1816'. This throws further doubt on the authenticity of the picture because the *Farquharson* was not built until 1820. The most reliable evidence on the ship is from her log books, perserved in the India Office Library.[41] These give a list of sails crried, but as no spar dimensions are listed, those given by David Steel for a merchant ship of 1300 tons have been used for the purpose of reconstructing a sail and rigging plan that could accompany the lines plan and deck layout.[42]

As the *Farquharson's* mizen steps on the lower deck, some adjustment to the length of Steel's lower mast was required, otherwise the mizen cap would be much too high. Conversely it would be too low if the dimension was taken from the keelson. Contemporary illustrations show that the crossjack yard and the fore yard were level and the length of the mizen lower mast has accordingly been adjusted to bring this about.

Although Whitcombe's painting does not depict fidded royal masts, the log book notes them quite clearly in numerous references. Other entries mention 'short royal masts' and 'royal masts with the long poles', depending on the state of wind and weather. It is surprising that the log does not mention the setting of skysails when referring to the 'long poles' as one would assume that this was the masts' function. The first reference to skysails does not occur until her fifth voyage which began in January 1829:

> 12 February. 'Up royal masts and crossed yards'.
> 20 February. 'Got the skysail masts up and royal studding sail booms on the yards'.[43]

The log records the skysails and royal stunsails being set and taken in and the respective masts, yards and booms being sent down and hoisted again on several occasions. From the above extracts, it might be said that the sail plan reconstructed here shows the ship as she was in 1829.

There are a number of illustrations showing Indiamen and other vessels with separate royal masts fidded either abaft or on the fore side of the topgallant masts, but on the *Farquharson's* reconstructed sail plan it seemed logical to step the royal masts on the foreside to allow the skysail masts to be fidded abaft. These slide through a cranse iron fixed to the royal mast head and the heel steps on the topgallant mast cap, the arrangement being similar to the anner of rigging out a flying jibboom. Several other plans show these sliding gunter masts rigged, such as the *Ziba (Merchant Sailing Ships 1850-1875*, figure 128).

David Steel's dimensions for the yards of a 1300-ton merchantman are identical in the 1794 and 1816 editions of

SPAR DIMENSIONS FOR A MERCHANT SHIP OF 1300 TONS AS LISTED BY STEEL IN *ART OF MAKING MASTS, YARDS ETC* (1816 ed) AND SPARS CALCULATED FOR *FARQUHARSON*

	1300-TON SHIP				*FARQUHARSON*				
	Mast or boom Length	Dia	**Yard** Length	Dia	**Mast or boom** Length	Dia	**Head** Length	**Yard** Length	Dia
Main mast and yard	96ft	31½in	86ft	20in	96ft	31½in	16ft	86ft	20in
Main topmast and yard	56ft	17½in	58ft	14in	56ft	17½in	6ft 3in	62ft	14in
Main topgallant mast and yard	27ft	9in	38ft	8½in	27ft	9in	3ft 6in	40ft	8½in
Main royal yard	20ft	6½in	24ft	5in	20ft	6½in		26ft	5in
Fore mast and yard	90ft	30in	82ft	20in	90ft	30in	15ft	82ft	20in
Fore topmast and yard	56ft	17½in	56ft	13½in	56ft	17½in	6ft 3in	60ft	13½in
Fore topgallant mast and yard	26ft	9in	36ft	8in	26ft	9in	3ft 3in	40ft	8in
Fore royal yard	18ft	6in	22ft	5in	18ft	6in	—	24ft	5in
Mizen mast and yard	78ft	21½in	72ft	13in	78ft	21½in	10ft 10in	43ft 9in	8in
Mizen topmast and yard	41ft	13in	40ft	9½in	41ft	13in	4ft 7in	42ft	9½in
Mizen topgallant mast and yard	21ft	7in	26ft	5½in	21ft	7in	2ft 6in	27ft 6in	5½in
Mizen royal yard	12ft	5in	16ft	4½in	12ft	5in	—	18ft	4½in
Bowsprit	60ft	31in	56ft	11½in	60ft	31in	18ft	56ft	11½in
Jib boom	44ft	12½in	38ft	8in	44ft	12½in	—	—	—
Driver boom	62ft	12in	—	—	62ft	12in	—	—	—
Crossjack yard			56ft	11in	—	—		56ft	11in
Lower studdingsail boom and yard	44ft	9in	30ft	7in	44ft	9ft	—	30ft	7in
Main topmast studdingsail boom and yard	43ft	8½in	24ft	6in	43ft	8½in		27ft	6½in
Main topgallant studdingsail boom and yard	29ft	6in	18ft	5in	29ft	6in		15ft	4½in
Fore topmast studdingsail boom and yard	41ft	8½in	24ft	6in	41ft	8½in		21ft	5½in
Fore topgallant studdingsail boom and yard	27ft	6in	17ft	5in	27ft	6in		14ft	4½in
Ensign staff	40ft	7in							
Jack staff	26ft	5½in							
Spars not listed by Steel: boom and yard									
Main royal studdingsail					21ft			10ft 6in	
Fore royal studdingsail					20ft			10ft	
Main skysail yard								15ft 6in	
Fore skysail yard								15ft	
Mizen skysail yard								12ft	
Jib boom outside cap					27ft 6in				
Flying jib boom oa					49ft 6in				

Note: Steel's mizen yard is fore-and-aft lateen yard

his book, but to avoid making the *Farquharson's* spars like those of a ship thirty years earlier it was necessary to lengthen the upper yards somewhat to avoid a too-narrow sail plan. The lower yards listed by Steel are sufficiently long – The mainyard measures 86ft 0in – but the length of the fore and main topsail yards is increased by 4ft and all the other upper yards by 2ft each with the exception of the of the mizen topgallant yard which is increased by only 18in. The spar dimensions that Edye gives for the 52-gun frigate form a useful comparison.[44] The increase in the length of the topsail yards has resulted in less curve to the leeches of the fore and main topsails and yet the cringle of the lowest reef band, still lies vertically under the sheave in the yard. At this date the outer leech of the stunsails ran in an almost continuous line from royal yard to lower yard.

A list of sails is bound into the *Farquharson's* logbook at the India Office Library, at the end of the third voyage. Written in an uneducated hand with atrocious spelling, it has been corrected:[45]

3 foresails
3 mainsails
3 fore topsails
3 main topsails
2 fore topgallant sails
2 main topgallant sails
1 mizen topgallant sail
1 fore royal
1 main royal
1 mizen royal

3 skysails

1 topgallant staysail
1 royal staysail
1 spindle staysail
3 lower stunsails
1 foretopmast stunsail
2 maintopmast stunsails
3 topgallant stunsails
3 royal stunsails
1 main 'monsail' [crossed out; should presumably read 'moonsail']
1st launch 5 sails

2 flying jibs
3 standing jibs
2 fore topmast staysails
2 mizen staysails
1 spanker
1 storm mizen

2nd launch 5 sails
2nd cutter 5 sails
1 quarter-deck awning
3 boats awnings
4 windsails

The spindle staysail ran on a stay from the royal masthead and the name may be derived from the spindle fixed at the masthead to carry a weather vane. On the foremast, the spindle staysail was later called a jib topsail. William Hutchinson says of the spindle staysails that 'by having two sheaves in each truck, at our long topgallant masts' heads, we hoisted the topgallant royals up to the trucks by the sheaves on one side, and the main and mizen spindle staysails by the sheaves on the other side of the trucks.[46]

There is no mention in the above list of a main topmast staysail, but she must undoubtedly have set one. Nor is a middle staysail listed although there is a reference in the log to one being set; the use of this sail was growing less frequent as the century advanced. The log records the setting of storm staysails, probably on the fore and main stays; also the setting of a trysail. The latter is perhaps the equivalent of the storm mizen given in the list, being an old style mizen course with a short gaff. Some ships had fore and main trysail gaffs with their own trysail masts; large ships sometimes had a trysail mast at the mizen to allow the hoops of the spanker to be fitted more easily and there is a reference in *Farquharsons's* log to the trysail mast being sprung, which presumably refers to that on the mizen.

A good illustration of the largest class of Indiamen under

223

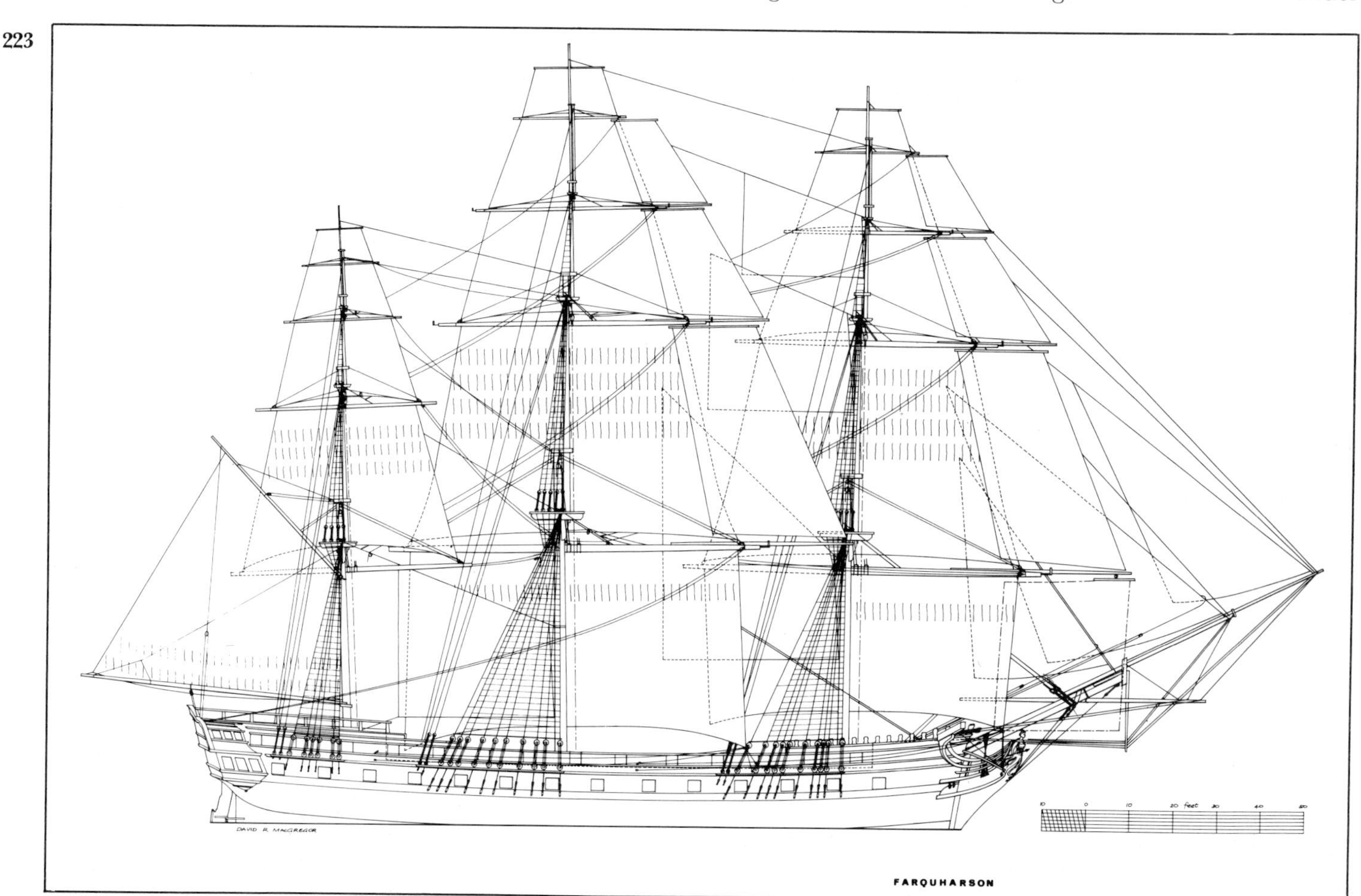

224

Fig 223. Farquharson. *Sail plan entirely reconstructed from the following sources: sheer elevation and rake of masts from the lines plan (figure 219); spare dimensions from Steel's* Rigging and Seamanship, *(1794 and 1816); sails carried as described in log-books; rigging from contemporary books and pictures.*

Fig 224. A fantastic suit of sails portrayed on the Essex *by W J Huggins. The two sails above the moonsails have been called 'star gazer' and 'angel's footstool'. The* Essex *was of 1352 tons and was built in 1812 in London.* (W Salisbury)

a press of sail may be seen in figure 59 of *Fast Sailing Ships* which depicts the *London* on a broad reach with all her flying kites set, including three mizen stunsails.

When one considers the extraordinarily large number of flying kites set on the *London*, it takes only a small leap of the imagination to picture the *Essex* as portrayed by W J Huggins with her incredible cloud of canvas (figure 224). This ship of 1332 tons was built in 1812 by Perry, Wells & Green. The evidence presented by both *Farquharson* and *London* proves that there were an infinite number of flying kites available for setting by imaginative commanders and Huggins has resourcefully combined them all in his engraving of the *Essex*. One can really accept every sail up to the moonsails on each mast – after all the tea clipper *Maitland* is reputed to have set them and they are shown on her sail plan in *Fast Sailing Ships* (figure 248) – but the two sails above are over-stretching one's credibility. Another tea clipper, the *Ariel*, set stunsails outside her regular ones. Huggins has chosen some idyllic occasion when every sail could draw in spite of being blanketed by several others, but it would be instructive to know how far he gave his fancy free rein and whether he really did draw the extra sails just to amuse his chidren, as Basil Lubbock suggests.[47]

It was not always possible to space the shrouds out so that the ran clear of the ports and for this reason deadeyes occasionally had no chain plates below them, as these

225

Fig 225. East Indiamen at the mouth of the Canton River, signed 'W J Huggins 1843' and painted two years before his death. Neither ship has been identified. Paintings of Indiamen with skysails set are none too common. Huggins has painted reef points across the stunsails, so that the topmast and lower stunsails have four rows of points each! Compare this with his flight of fancy in figure 224. (Parker Gallery)

would have had to run across a port. But this was not the case in the *Farquharson*; the painting suggests eight shrouds on the fore and main masts although the sheer elevation shows ten chain plates, as drawn here. An examination of other paintings and plans of Indiamen show that the plans allot about two chain plates more on the fore and main masts than the paintings do.

There are five topmast shrouds on fore and main masts and four on the mizen. Thirty years later a ship of this tonnage would have had only six lower and three topmast shrouds, but triple topmast backstays and double topgallant ones. The tops drawn here are to man-of-war proportions, namely one-third of the topmast length for the breadth athwartship, and three-quarters of this for the length fore-and-aft.[48] On *Farquharson's* main top these measurements work out to be 18ft 8in across and 14ft 0in fore-and-aft. The only brace leading directly to the deck is that from the mainyard, all the others leading first through a block lashed to a stay.

PASSAGES IN THE *FARQUHARSON*

Life aboard these lordly giants was quite unlike anything else in the merchant service and the largest ones of about 1400 tons were four times the size of most full-rigged ships. Discipline was modelled on naval practice and so was the whole outlook and running of the ships; the log-book of the *Farquharson* suggests this stiff-necked attitude and there are frequent references to men being placed in irons for 'mutinous conduct'. The crew was large for ships of similar size in later years, but elasticity in rigging and uncertainties in the strength of masts and stays led to the custom of sending down royal and topgallant yards and also royal masts, when fidded, during bad weather. Large crews were needed for this heavy work and in any case the Company's bye-laws laid down the size of crew to be carried. During the years of continuous warfare the ships were heavily armed and though the guns could not be manned at the strength prescribed by the Navy, at least it was essential to have sufficient men to work them efficiently and to defend the ship. By 1820 it was necessary to protect the ship only from pirates, but tradition died hard.

The *Farquharson* began her first voyage under the command of William Cruickshank, under whom came the chief mate and five other mates. The complete crew list

Fig 226. The Kent *on fire in the Bay of Biscay in a gale, after the cargo had shifted and become ignited. The 200-ton brig* Cambria *(right) bound for Vera Cruz with Cornish miners aboard rescued 547 people and took them back to Falmouth. 82 lives were lost in the* Kent, *which was carrying the 31st Regiment to India together with their families. She had been built at Blackwall in 1820 and was of 1315 tons.* (MacGregor Collection)

when the ship left Gravesend in December 1820, was given by the captain, in the following order:[49]

Commander
6 mates
surgeon
purser
boatswain
gunner
master at arms
carpenter
6 midshipmen
surgeon's mate
caulker
cooper
captain's cook
ship's cook
captain's steward
ship's steward
2 boatswain's mates
2 gunner's mates
carpenter's 1st &
2nd mates
caulker's mate
cooper's mate
6 quarter masters
sailmaker
armourer
butcher
baker
poulterer
70 seamen
12 ordinary seamen
captain's servant
chief mate's servant
2nd mate's servant
surgeon's servant
2 seamen

The total complement numbered 133 souls

She also embarked 181 troops, 19 women and 6 children, besides 6 passengers, and it is interesting to note that she was towed down to Gravesend by two steamers. The ship was probably more comfortable than an emigrant or passenger ship of the same size, which might be crowded with eager persons bound for the Australian gold fields a mere thirty years later, when the whole passenger-carrying operation was frequently improvised. Considerable expertise was displayed by the Company in transporting large numbers of troops about the world, frequently in specially chartered ships, yet the face remained that having 345 persons aboard to feed and sleep and exercise was quite a problem. The *Farquharson's* log contains frequent references to the quantity of water drunk and how the ship's trim was affected by the stores consumed.

Often the log-books give little data on the day-to-day work aboard, so monotonous to the log-keeper but now so interesting. The *Farquharson* usually trimmed by the head and at the beginning of her third voyage with stores and provisions aboard she drew 22ft 3in forward and 21ft 10in aft. On her first voyage she started with 37,525 gallons of water and 200 tons of iron kentledge.

The log often records a speed of 10 knots and occasionally 11 knots. With a load line length of 170ft 6in a speed of 11 knots results in a speed-length ratio of 0.84 which is possibly the maximum one can expect for a vessel of her type, although under a skilful master and with good gear she could probably stand considerable driving. The biggest day's run found in her log-book was 244 miles during which the fore topmast stunsail was split. This was made in 1826, shortly after a series of big consecutive runs when the ship was homeward bound from China in the south-east trades;

227

228

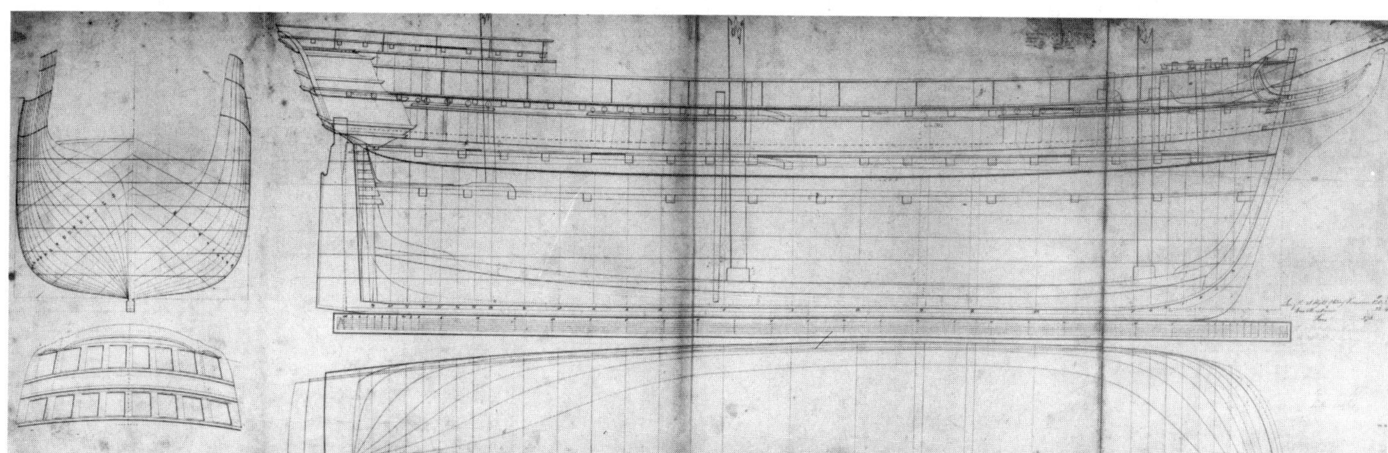

between 24 January and 1 February these runs were: 208, 214, 242, 220, 171, 148, 197, 207 and 212. Her fastest homeward passage from China was on this occasion. She left Lintin on 6 January 1826, saw Gaspar Island on 14 January, remained at St Helena from 5 to 8 March, crossed the Line on 17 March and took her pilot in the Channel on 22 April. Next day she was off Portland, 107 days out from China. Sailing ten days after her, the *Lowther Castle* of 1427 tons took 103 days to Deal.[50]

The *Farquharson's* log contains no account of taking in canvas at dusk and setting it again at daybreak, as is so often claimed to have been the practice in such ships. The removal of the convoy system after the end of the Napoleonic Wars and the spur of competition contributed largely to the faster passages made by Indiamen after 1815. Hopes of financial remuneration as the result of a fast passage proved a great incentive at all times, as the Rev William Money confirms in an extract from his journal aboard the *Walthamstow*:[51]

June 14, 1800. Having effectually parted from our dilatory commodore and his party, we were of course making the best

Fig 227. Animals occupied an important place in life aboard a ship carrying passengers and here William Ward has drawn the longboat full of hen coops, with pigs and sheep in stalls below, and a stubborn cow in the foreground.

Fig 228. Coromandel. *Lines plan. She was built in 1820 on the Thames. Reproduced from plan in the Hilhouse Collection in the possession of Charles Hill & Sons, Bristol. Dimensions on plan: 128ft 2in (length at height of wing transom), 32ft 4in (extreme breadth), and 576 tons. The* Lady Raffles *was also built on the Thames three years earlier to the same lines.*

Fig 229. Model of an Extra ship similar in size to Coromandel *but unidentified. The date is about 1820 and her tonnage would be 550 to 650 tons. The yards are seen end-on and so hardly show in the photograph.* (Liverpool County Museums)

229

of our way for Madras, which place, should we reach before the rest of the fleet, our exertions would be amply repaid by the considerable advantage of having the first of the market for European investments. In this attempt the wind was determined to lend us every assistance blowing still a fair and very stiff gale. Last night there was an amazing degree of motion, and this morning the heaviest sea we had yet witnessed. The swell at a distance exactly resembled a chain of immense mountains, which following with superior speed overtook and raised us to an immense height, when suddenly shifting from under our elevated bark, down we rushed into a valley proportionably low. During the voyage we had been particularly unfortunate in springing masts, which proceeded from two causes, having badly seasoned timber and encountering bad gales. About 10 am in continuation of the old story, we sprang our fore topmast, but replaced the damage without loss of time. At noon, 202 miles; lat. 36.46 S, long 62.4 E.

EXTRA SHIPS AND THE *COROMANDEL*

An example of reducing sail at night and setting it again at daybreak is given by the extra ship *Coromandel*, built on the Thames in 1820 and of 645 tons. Her log in 1828 contains too many such references for it to be dismissed as stress of weather. The most consistent references are to royals, flying jib and staysails being taken in at about 10 pm and set at daybreak.[52]

The *Coromandel* was an East Indiaman in miniature as can be judged from the reproduction of a contemporary plan in figure 228 if it be compared with that of the *Farquharson*.[53] Again we find the double tier of stern windows, the three decks, the mizen stepped on the lower deck rather than the keelson, the double riding bitts, and the absence of a windlass. The *Coromandel* has a full-bodied hull and is rather more bluff at the entrance than *Farquharson*; the headroom on her lower and middle decks is approximately 4ft 6in and 5ft 0in respectively, compared with 6ft 6in in each case on the bigger ship. On her upper deck she would undoubtedly have had a capstan, and it is only on this deck that gunports are drawn. A note on her plan states a length of 128ft 2in at the height of the wing transom and a maximum beam of 32ft 4in. The *Lady Raffles* was also built from the same draught three years earlier. A model at one time in the Science Museum of a small East

Indiaman represents a vessel very similar to *Coromondel* and gives a good idea of what her rigging might have been like and the relationship of hull to spars (figure 229).

An interesting point about the lines plan is that it comes from the Hilhouse Collection at Bristol. This gives an inkling of the interchange of ideas between shipbuilders in different parts of the country. Amongst the Hilhouse plans are several copies of Admiralty draughts of British-built ships and take-offs of captured French vessels. While not insisting that James Hilhouse was influenced by such plans, I think it worth observing the additional knowledge such plans afforded.

The *Coromondel* was chartered by the Company in 1820 at a rate of £10 19s per ton and again in 1828. She did not set skysails, but she fidded royal masts above her topgallants and she had a flying jibboom. There is no mention of royal stunsails, but on 2 August 1828 the log records: 'Hauled down larboard mizen topmast studding sail'. Another flying kite is mentioned on the previous day, 'Bent the spare flying jib for a spindle sail' and again on 9 August, 'Set the fore topgallant studdingsails, mizen royal and spindle jibb'. Here it must have been set like a jib topsail, high up on the fore royal stay. A middle staysail is also mentioned.[54]

Of course she had a smaller complement than a regular ship like the *Farquharson*, there being a captain, four mates and fifty-one other persons. At the start of her first voyage she drew 16ft 8in on an even keel. On her first outward passage to Madras in 1820 she had almost four weeks of fair winds to give her a wonderful average of 197½ miles per day over 27 days, 22 June to 18 July inclusive, mostly in the south-east trades in the Indian Ocean. The maximum speed was 10 knots, which on a load line length of 128ft gives a speed-length ratio of 0.88 which is good for such a full-bodied hull. The highest day's run was 230 miles and the lowest 103, only four runs being below 170 miles. High intrinsic speed was not part of the make-up of these ships, but a steady performance like this often produced more satisfactory results and shorter passages.[55]

George Millet, whose memorandum on the design of East Indiaman was quoted earlier in this chapter, penned another such piece on the subject of the Extra Ships, and after comparing the rates of freight between them and the Regular ships, part of which is quoted in Chapter 1, he has this to say about their design:[56]

> I now beg leave to draw your attention to the construction of the extra ships, upon which the success of their voyage must essentially depend; and having observed that many of those now employed are but ill calculated for the service, it will perhaps be expected of me to point out their imperfections, which, in my opinion, are these:-
>
> Some of the three-decked ships carry their guns below, and are hardly ever able, when laden, to keep their ports open at sea, which not only renders them defenceless in general; but it being almost impossible for their ports to be fitted tight enough to keep the decks sufficiently dry for the preservation of the cargo, damage frequently ensues. Some of them, too, are burthened with poops and high forecastles, which makes them extremely crank leewardly, and less seaworthy: others have more the form of chests than ships, and detain every thing they are in company with, whilst some have performed extremely well for the public and the owners. To obviate, therefore, these various imperfections, in whatever ships shall be built for the Company's extra-service in future, is, I conceive, an object most worthy of the Court's attention; and I therefore earnestly recommend, that one specific plan of construction (which shall combine, as much as possible, the various properties of safety, burthen, expedition, moderate draft of water, defence, and economy) should be adopted in all future engagements for building. The class which, in my opinion, will come the nearest to this description, is a ship with three flushed decks, of about 600 tons burthen, unincumbered with either poops or high forecastle; her guns to be carried on her upper deck, by which she will decidedly be far more capable of attack and defence, both against artillery and boarders, than if the guns were below; the ship herself will be stronger, by not being pierced for ports, and her cargo will be better preserved. A two decked ship would certainly be cheaper, both to the Company and owners, but her cargo would not be so well preserved; neither could she, upon an emergency, be converted into a transport, and the accomodation of troops cannot, in course, be lost sight of.

An inspection of the *Coromandel's* plan in figure 228 suggests that she conformed fairly closely to the desideratum which George Millett proposed for extra ships as her tonnage was close to 600, she did have three flush decks, the gunports were on the upper deck, and the poop and forecastle were not too large.

LATER LIFE OF AN INDIAMAN

An interesting sidelight on the later career of one of the Indiamen is provided by the *Herefordshire* of 1342 tons, built at Bombay in 1813. After her sale, she was employed in the India trade, mostly carrying troops. An example of the speed at which Indiamen could sail under favourable conditions and with commercial competitions as the spur, is shown by this series of very fast passages which she made across the Atlantic in four stages in 1851, when carrying troops:

sailed Spithead	25 May	arrived Gibraltar	5 June	11 days
sailed Gibraltar	13 June	arrived Barbados	3 July	20 days
sailed Barbados	10 July	arrived Quebec	28 July	18 days
sailed Brandy Pot (St Lawrence River)	15 Aug	arrived Leith	30 Aug	15 days

She reached Leith 13 days after landing her pilot and with 17 of her crew in irons for mutiny.[57]

Two years later under the same master, George Richardson, she went out to Sydney from Southampton in a passage that lasted 108 days, from 24 August to 10 December 1853, returning to London the following year. On her arrival in Australia, the *Sydney Morning Herald* gave her a short write-up. The paper said that she carried a full complement of passengers, invalid officers and troops. (Another paper said she carried 401 emigrants and 7 passengers.) When she was examined in London in 1853 by Government and Insurance surveyors she was, in spite of her age, 'found in every respect to be as perfectly sound as it was possible for a ship to be, and in as good condition as if she had been only launched a twelvemonth.[58] The newspaper also commented on her large beam, which measured 42ft 6in and her loaded draft which was 25ft 0in. On her gun deck she had 18 large cabins and the remaining space was occupied by steerage passengers and troops. Her full crew numbered 100 but on this voyage there were only 80. Although pierced for 36 guns, these were mostly dismantled and stowed below as ballast. The ship carried,

230

100 tons of water on her lower deck and altogether 600 tons of iron and stone ballast as deadweight. Captain Richardson owned shares in the ship and had been her master for fifteen years, during which time he had been engaged in transporting troops across the world. She still had her original masts. The *Sydney Morning Herald* claimed that her original cost in Bombay came to £86,000, which works out at just over £64 per ton on 1342 tons.[59] This amount would have to include the cost of fitting out for the first voyage with all the various stores, and even acknowledging that building costs were much higher in India for the basic hull and spars, it still leaves a wide gap unaccounted for.

Although much maligned, the Indiamen gave excellent service for many years, and not least in the days after the abolition of the Honourable Company's Trading monopoly in 1834, when the dearth of large ships for troop transports much have been acute.

Fig 230. An engraving by Henry Moses, published in 1822, of Indiamen rigged down in the basin at Blackwall. It was customary to strip off the upper masts and rigging leaving only the lower masts standing. The sterns on the left belong to ships of the 800 or 1200 tons class, but the stern on the right is of an extra ship or a packet. (MacGregor Collection)

231

Fig 231. The hulk of the old Java, *photographed at Gibraltar in 1918 when she was 107 years old. Built in 1811, she passed into British registry in 1813 and was owned in London by Paxton & Co. She was of 1175 tons and was licensed to trade to India. She must have been one of the largest merchantmen afloat that was not chartered by the East India Co. She became a coal hulk at Gibraltar in 1865 and was still in use there in 1936.*

APPENDIX 1

DIMENSIONS & TONNAGES &c OF VESSELS BUILT BY STEELE & CARSWELL, GREENOCK, 1796-1816

This yard list was loaned to me in 1954 by the late James Steele and copied out by hand. In the dimensions, all lengths consist of 'keel and fore rake'. Sometimes no fractions are given in the tonnage, and the owner's name is not always stated. At one time 'N B' stood for 'North Britain'.

Yard No	Name	Rig	Dimensions (ft in)	Tons OM	Date Launched	Owner
1	*Clyde*	bg	71 0 × 21 9 × 14 5	145 76/94	29 Apr 1797	—
2	*Moina*	slp	37 4 × 13 0½ × 6 9½	26 65/94	13 Oct 1779	—
3	*Diana*	sch	57 0 × 18 0½ × 9 8½	79 89/94	5 Mar 1798	—
4	*Dart*	bg	68 10 × 21 3½ × 13 6	135 16/94	19 May 1798	
5	*Trim*	slp	49 8 × 17 0½ —	60 87/94	13 Jan 1799	—
6	*Ariadne*	S	85 10 × 24 0½ × 16 4 'tween deck ht 4 9	219 51/94	12 Jan 1799	—
7	*Leander*	S	77 1 × 23 8½ × 14 9½ 'tween deck ht 4 6	187 87/94	22 Jul 1799	—
8	*Swan*	bg	64 8 × 20 1 × 11 0	117	14 Jan 1800	—
9	*Clio*	bg	58 1 × 18 6½ × 10 3	86	28 Apr 1800	Steele & Carswell
10	*Brilliant*	S	96 4 × 27 6 × 17 0 'tween deck ht 5 1	321	9 Aug 1800	Q Leitch
11	*Cato*	slp	[not stated]	22	Sep 1801	Steele & Carswell
12	*Sisters*	S	95 6 × 27 3 × 18 10½ 'tween deck ht 6 3	312 48/94	Oct 1801	—
13	*Garland*	sch	62 4 × 20 1 × 7 10½	107 81/94	Nov 1801	—
14	*Mary*	S	102 6 × 28 4 × 19 0	364	19 Apr 1803	—
15	*Dispatch*	slp	47 0 × 15 0 × 8 0	50	Mar 1803	—
16	*Spinster*	bg	80 0 × 23 2 × 16 2 'tween deck ht 5 2	188 51/94	25 Apr 1804	—
17	*Herald*	bg	80 2 × 23 2 × 16 1½ 'tween deck ht 5 2	189	12 Jun 1804	—
18	*Mariner*	S	91 2½ × 26 2½ × 18 5 'tween deck ht 6 1	278 3/94	Jul 1805	—
19	*Princess of Wales*	—	45 8 × 16 10 × 8 4	53 57/94	Oct 1807	Excise yacht
20	*Nereid* [sic]	S	93 2 × 26 3½ × 17 11 'tween deck ht 5 6	284 52/94	26 Aug 1808	—
21	*Maria*	—	46 8 × 16 10½ × 8 3½	55 18/94	7 Nov 1808	Excise yacht
22	*Trinidad*	S	102 9 × 28 4 × 19 1½	365	4 Jan 1810	Robt Eccles & Co
23	*Amazon*	S	111 0 × 30 3 × 21 1 length aloft 113 0	442 4/94	26 Jan 1811	Robt Eccles & Co
24	*Cervantes*	S	102 3 × 28 5 × 18 10 length aloft to taffrail 112 2	365	19 Nov 1811	H Hamilton
25	*Shawfield*	slp	47 0 × 15 1 × 7 11	45 86/94	17 Jan 1812	—
26	*Grace*	slp	49 9 × 15 7 × 8 0	52	21 Mar 1812	—
27	*Clyde*	S	104 5 × 29 6 × 19 3 'tween deck ht 6 4	401	3 Jun 1813	—
28	*Eliza*	slp	48 9 × 16 8 × 8 10	57 19/94	13 Aug 1814 (note suggests 1813)	—
29	*Vittoria*	bg	68 6 × 21 5½ × 12 6	136	Jul 1813	—
30	*Norval*	bg	79 9 × 23 10 × 14 11	198	25 Jan 1814	Baine, Johnston & Co
31	*Wellington*	—	66 0 × 22 9 × 10 8	144	15 Nov 1814	Custom house yacht
32	*Bengal*	S	103 11 × 29 7½ × 19 8 'tween deck ht 6 3	402	25 Feb 1815	Cropper, Benson & Co
33	*Trader*	slp	37 10 × 13 7 × 7 2	29 12/94	11 Aug 1815	—
34	*Oscar*	bg	82 0 × 24 7 × 15 9 'tween deck ht 5 1	216 16/94	4 Oct 1815	—
35	*Crescent*	bg	62 5 × 19 8 × 11 1	—*	4 Mar 1816	—

* tonnage not stated in Yard List but *Lloyd's Register* (red) 1818 gives it as 104.
After the partnership with Carswell was dissolved, the yard numbers re-commenced at no 1 in 1816.

APPENDIX 2

LIST OF EAST INDIAMEN BUILT IN THE BLACKWALL YARD 1774–1825

This MS list in the National Maritime Museum, Greenwich, (ref GRN/1 ff102–04) begins in 1759 when the price was £10 10s per ton. The price per ton has been added to the original in red ink; dividing the cost by the tons does not always produce the correct price per ton, and so perhaps it was the contract price. The column headed 'amount' is presumably the cost of building; the last column headed 'extra' could be the launch expenses, gratuities to workmen, moving ship to owner's berth, etc.

Year	*Ship's name*	Husband	Price per ton	Tons	'Amount'	'Extra'
1774	*Hillsborough*	Chas Fowlis	£12	723	£8628	£100
1777	*Southampton*	Chas Fowlis	£12	723	£9096	£143
1777	*Atlas*	Chas Raymond	£13 10s	758	£10,358	£295
1778	*Oxford*	Chas Raymond	£13 10s	758	£10,333	£279
1778	*Talbot*	Chas Raymond	£13 10s	827	£10,333	£308
1779	*London*	John Webb	£13 10s	758	£11,167	£310
1779	*Pigot*	Chas Fowlis	£13 10s	799	£10,239	£366
1780	*Essex*	Henry Bolton	£14	799	£11,195	£338
1780	*Assia* [sic]	Thos Newte	£14 10s	796	£11,595	£305
1780	*Earl of Hertford*	Chas Fowlis	£14	799	£11,195	£374
1780	*Chesterfield*	Donald Cameron	£14 14s	799	£11,754	£329
1781	*Busbridge*	Robt Preston	£14 14s	753	£11,111	£395
1781	*Winterton*	Henry Phillip	£15 5s	755	£11,526	£367
1781	*Europa*	Thos Newte	£14 14s	755	£11,111	£376
1782	*Raymond*	Henry Boulton	£14 14s	755	£11,426	£370
1782	*Elliott*	Robt Preston	£14 14s	755	£11,111	£524
1782	*Macartney*	Robt Preston	£14 14s	755	£11,111	£329
1782	*Fowlis*	Robt Preston	£14 14s	755	£11,111	£417
1783	*Hillsborough*	Robt Preston	£14 14s	755	£11,111	£428
1784	*Henry George*	Henry Pelly	£12 5s	799	£9400	£723
1785	*William Pitt*	Robt Preston	£11 15s	799	£9396	£546
1785	*Worcester*	Henry Boulton	£11 15s	799	£9396	£316
1785	*Minerva*	Jer Royde	£12	799	£9588	£358
1786	*Dundas*	Donald Cameron	£12	802	£9595	£380
1786	*Hawke*	Henry Boulton	£11 15s	799	£9392	£368
1786	*Ceres*	Donald Cameron	£13	1162	£15,111	£717
1787	*Albion*	Richard Lewin	£13	961	£12,502	£440
1788	*Warley*	Henry Boulton	£13	1170	£15,210	£558
1790	*Woodford*	Robt Preston	£12 10s	1180	£14,775	£445
1792	*Brunswick*	Thos Newte	£12 10s	1219	£15,247	£607
1795	*Earl Spencer*	James Duncan	£14 10s	630	£9343	£259
1796	*Thames*	Thos Newte	£17 10s	1416	£24,784	£485
1796	*Warley*	Henry Boulton	£17 19s	1449	£25,364	£363
1796	*Talbot*	Thos Newte	£17 10s	1416	£24,784	£421
1797	*Ceres*	Donald Cameron	£17 10s	1416	£24,784	£378
1798	*Walpole*	Robert Wigram	£17	818	£13,906	£268
1798	*Lord Duncan*	John Woolman	£17	830	£14,120	£458
1799	*Lady Burgess*	Princip & Co	£16	818	£13,088	£450
1800	*Wyndham*	Robert Wigram	£16 10s	818	£13,497	£176
1801	*Alnwick Castle*	John Locke	£19 10s	1257	£24,517	£708
1801	*Marquis of Ely*	Robert Wigram	£19 10s	1257	£24,517	£708
1801	*United Kingdom*	John Atkins	£20	818	£16,366	£429
1802	*Harriott*	John Woolman	£19	544	£10,318	£157
1802	*Royal George*	Robt Anderson	£22	1257	£27,661	£433
1803	*Europe*	Pr & Wm Mellish	£22	818	£17,996	£191
1803	*Essex*	Henry Bonham	£22	1257	£27,661	£633
1806	*Britannia**	East India Co	£28	1273	£35,664	£669
1808	*Warren Hastings*	J P Larkins	£27	997	£26,937	£304
1808	*Carnatic*	Wm Agnew	£25	818	£20,451	£454
1810	*Rose*	Jas Begbie	£26 10s	955	£25,176	£423
1811	*Cabalva*	Wm Davies	£26 10s	1257	£33,318	£417
1811	*Prince Regent*	Henry Bonham	£27	950	£25,651	£432
1811	*Bengal*	Gabriel Gillet	£27	950	£25,651	£376
1812	*Marchioness of Ely*	Sir R Wigram	£27	950	£25,651	£647
1813	*Lady Melville*	Sir R Wigram	£28	1257	£35,204	£845
1814	*St Helena* (sch)	East India Co	£21	135	£2835	£55
1816	*Waterloo**	East India Co	£22 10s	1315	£29,588	£466
1817	*Duke of York*	S Majoribanks	£23 10s	1315	£30,903	£364
1817	*Canning**	East India Co	£22	1315	£28,930	£432
1817	*Dunira*	G Palmer	£23 10s	1315	£30,903	£262
1819	*Royal George*	J F Timmins	—	1315	—	—
1819	*Repulse*	J F Timmins	—	1315	—	—
1819	*Kent*	S Majoribanks	—	1315	—	—
1820	*Duchess of Athol*	W Ferrers	—	1315	—	—
1825	*Edinburgh*	Fairlie Bonham & Co	—	1315	—	—

* Hardy's *Register of Ships* confirms that these three ships belonged to the Company but they only made 2 voyages each instead of the usual 4 or more. The *St. Helena* is listed by Hardy as a 'Schooner Packet' and her plans are given in *Fast Sailing Ships*. The last 5 ships in the list have no costs entered against their names.

APPENDIX 3

LIST OF SHIPS BUILT AT THE BLACKWELL YARD THAT WERE NOT EAST INDIAMEN

This list begins in 1749 and ends in 1818 (NMM ref GRN/1, ff124–25)

Year	Ship's name	Managing owner	Service	Tons	'Amount'
1749	*Ruby*	Mr Kimble	W Indies	—	£1675
1749	*Diamond*	Mr Kimble	W Indies	—	£1675
1751	*Pearle*	Mr Kimble	W Indies	—	£1540
1772	*Warners*	Mr Warner	W Indies	294	£2652
1773	*Friendship*	Mr Hibbert	W Indies	294	£2572
1773	*Thynne*	Capt Leslie	Packet	182	£1640
1774	*Jamaica*	Mr Long	W Indies	291	£2708
1774	*Hillsborough*	Mr Parry	Packet	74	£710
1775	*Amity*	Mr Morse	W Indies	314	£3440
1774	*Clarimont*	Mr Taylor	Packet	74	£710
1774	*Landovery* [sic]	Mr White	W Indies	291	£3622
1782	*Betsey*	Mr Curling	W Indies	326	£3237
1784	*Duck Hall* [sic]	Mr Nesbitt	W Indies	364	£3372
1784	*Braithwaite*	Mr Blackman	W Indies	287	£2500
1785	*Baillies*	Mr Baillie	W Indies	371	£2615
1787	*Delaford*	Mr Boddington	W Indies	393	£3739
1786	*Turners*	Mr Turner	W Indies	371	£3529
1787	*Justinian*	Mr Young	W Indies	371	£3536
?	*Swift*	E I Company	—	97	£918
1788	*Three Sisters*	Mr Robt Mangles	W Indies	329	£2967
1794	*Thames*	Mr Trenham	W Indies	364	£3480
1789	*Amity Hall*	Mr Tarbutt	W Indies	314	£2708
1792	*Constance*	Smith & Barbe	'Streights trade'*	284	£2556
1797	*St Vincent*	Mr Saml Boddington	W Indies	340	£3570
1799	*Walker*	Mr Robt Wigram	South [sea] whaler	341	£3753
1799	*Willoughby*	Mr Robt Dale	W Indies	429	£5177
1799	*Sir Geoffrey Webster*	Plummer & Bonham	W Indies	511	£6549
1799–1802	11 ballast lighters	Trinity Corp	—	55 each	av price = £420
1788	*Fort William*	Newte & Cameron	sloop	87	£913
1789	*Crowley*	Mr Millington	collier	183	£2486
1810	*Guildford*	Mr Mangles	W Indies	506	£9632
1810	*Caesar*	Mr C H Turner	W Indies	604	£13,908
1815	*Eliza*	Capt J Huddert	yacht	22	£350
1818	*Catherine*	Mr Henry Blanshard	'Ex E M'	502	£8535

*probably indicates an Arctic whaler
Fort William and *Crowley* placed in this order

REFERENCES

CHAPTER 1

[1] Ralph Davis, *The Rise of the English Shipping Industry* (London 1962), p 64.
[2] *Ibid*, p 68.
[3] *Ibid*, p 68.
[4] *Account, presented to the House of Commons, of Ships and Vessels built in Great Britain, 1790–1806*, PP, 1806, XIII, (243), pp 739–57; quoted in Stephanie Jones, *A Maritime History of the Port of Whitby, 1700–1914* (unpublished Ph D thesis, London University 1982), p 54, Table 4b.
[5] Jones, *Maritime History of Whitby, op cit*, p 29.
[6] Davis, *Rise of English Shipping Industry, op cit*, p 77.
[7] *Ibid*, p 71.
[8] Aubrey F Burstall, *A History of Mechanical Engineering* (London 1965), paperback edition pp 258–60.
[9] *Ibid*, pp 267–8.
[10] Edgar C Smith, *A Short History of Naval and Marine Engineering* (Cambridge 1937), pp 97–8.
[11] W A Baker, *From Paddle-Steamer to Nuclear Ship* (London 1965), p 13.
[12] *Ibid*.
[13] Davis, *Rise of English Shipping Industry, op cit*, Chapter XIV.
[14] 12 Charles II c18.
[15] 7 & 8 William III c22.
[16] 26 George III c60; see Charles Abbott, *A Treatise of the Law Relative to Merchant Ships and Seamen* (London 1808, 3rd ed), pp 488–92.
[17] For summary of provisions of Navigation Acts, see Lawrence A Harper, *The English Navigation Laws* (New York 1939, reprint 1964) pp 387–414; John Reeves, *A History of the Law of Shipping and Navigation* (London 1792), pp 515–41; Davis, *Rise of English Shipping Industry, op cit*, pp 306–11.
[18] See Herbert S Klein, *The Middle Passage* (Princeton, NJ 1978), pp 163–64 and Walter E Minchinton 'The Triangular Trade Revisited', reprinted from *The Uncommon Market* (nd) pp 331–52.
[19] Gomer Williams, *History of the Liverpool Privateers and Letters of Marque with an Account of the Liverpool Slave Trade* (London 1897), pp 603–04.
[20] Klein, *Middle Passage, op cit*, p 143.
[21] *Ibid*, Chapter 7.
[22] *Ibid*, pp 169–70.
[23] George F Dow, *Slave Ships and Slaving* (Marine Research Society, Salem, Mass 1927, reprint), p xxvii.
[24] David Syrett, *Shipping and the American War 1775–83* (London 1970), p 90.
[25] *Ibid*, p 249.
[26] Charles Wright and C Ernest Fayle, *A History of Lloyd's* (London 1928), p 156.
[27] Jones, *Maritime History of Whitby, op cit*, p 381.
[28] *Ibid*, p 400, Table 8a.
[29] Basil Lubbock, *The Arctic Whalers* (Glasgow 1937), p 120; and S G E Lythe, 'The Dundee Whale Fishery' *Scottish Journal of Political Economy*, vol XI, pp 158–9.
[30] Lythe, 'Dundee Whale Fishery', *op cit*, pp 159–61.
[31] Jones, *Maritime History of Whitby, op cit*, p 286.
[32] *Ibid*, based on Table 5a, p 306.
[33] William Scoresby, *An Account of the Arctic Regions with a History and Description of the Northern Whale-Fishery* (Edinburgh 1820, reprint 1969) vol II, pp 138–71.
[34] Edouard A Stackpole, *The Sea-Hunters* (Philadelphia 1953) Chapters XI and XII.
[35] 'Evidence given by Mr Snodgrass before a Committee of the House of Commons, appointed in March 1771, to consider how His Majesty's Navy might be better supplied with Timber', *A Collection of Papers on Naval Architecture originally communicated through the channel of the European Magazine* (London 1798), vol II, part 2, pp 29–32.
[36] *Ibid*, pp 29–32.
[37] *Ibid*, pp 33–34.
[38] *List of Marine Records of the late East India Company... in the India Office Library* (London 1896), p xiii.
[39] *Ibid*, pp xii–xiii.
[40] *Ibid*, p xiv.
[41] *Ibid*, p xv.
[42] *Ibid*, p xv.
[43] *Ibid*, p xiv.
[44] *Proceedings Relative to Ships Tendered for the Service of the United East-India Company 2nd July 1806 to 27 September 1809* (London 1809), Appendix No 4679, p 3996.
[45] *Ibid*, Appendix No 4395, p 3769.
[46] Jean Sutton, *Lords of the East; the East India Company and its Ships* (London 1981), p 21.
[47] 'Copy of Letter from Mr Ferguson...to Gab Snodgrass Esq', *Collection of Papers on Naval Architecture, op cit*, p 54, No LVIII.
[48] R Stewart-Brown, *Liverpool Ships in the Eighteenth Century* (Liverpool 1932), p 42.

CHAPTER 2

[1] Fredrik af Chapman, *Architectura Navalis Mercatoria* (Stockholm 1768); at least four reprints have been published but all to a smaller size, the last, *c*1970.
[2] Frederick Henry de Chapman, translated by Revd James Inman, *A Treatise on Ship-Building* (Cambridge 1820) p 187.
[3] L G Carr Laughton, *Old Ship Figure-Heads & Sterns* (London 1925), p 106.
[4] *Ibid*, p 107.
[5] William Falconer, *An Universal Dictionary of the Marine* (London 1769); also in 1780 edition.
[6] *Ibid*, plate VIII fig 4.
[7] G Groenewegen, *Verzameling van Vier en tachtig Stuks Hollandsche Schepen* (Rotterdam 1789, facsimile reprint 1967).
[8] John R Stevens, *An Account of the Construction, and Embellishment of Old Time Ships* (Toronto 1949), p 91.
[9] Mungo Murray, *A Treatise on Ship-Building and Navigation* (London, 2nd ed. 1765), p 182 and plate IX.
[10] William Salisbury, 'Merchantmen in 1754', *M M* 1936, vol XXII, pp 347 and 349–50.
[11] *Industry:* NMM, Admiralty Draughts, plan 6429 box 63; sloop: Science Museum, Sailing Ship Collection, plan C/3/21.
[12] Falconer, *Dictionary, op cit*.
[13] Antoine Lescallier, *Vocabulaire des Termes de Marine Anglois et François* (Paris 1777) pp 182–3.
[14] Richard Weatherill, *The Ancient Port of Whitby and its Shipping* (Whitby 1908) pp 34–88.
[15] Björn Landström, *The Ship* (London 1961), p 187, fig 436; and Nederlandsch Historisch Scheepvaart Museum, *Beschrijvende Catalogus der Scheepsmodellen en Scheepsbouwkundige Teekeningen 1600–1900* (Amsterdam 1943) p 26 and plate 35.
[16] Nederlandsch Sheepvaart Museum, *Catalogus, op. cit*, pl 27.
[17] Vice-Admiral Pâris, *Collection de Plans ou Dessins de Navires et de Bateaux Anciens ou Modernes* (Paris 1884), Part II, plate 62.
[18] Groenewegen, *Hollandsche Schepen, op cit*.
[19] David Steel, *The Elements and Practice of Rigging and Seamanship* (London 1794), vol I, between pp 208 and 209.
[21] Lescallier, *Vocabulaire, op cit*, figs 138 and 263.
[21] Chapman, *Architectura Navalis, op cit*, plate LXII, fig 1.
[22] Steel, *Rigging and Seamanship, op cit*, vol 1, p 105.
[23] William Hutchinson, *A Treatise on Naval Architecture* (Liverpool, 4th ed, 1794), p 54.
[24] *Ibid*, p 57.
[25] Darcy Lever, *The Young Sea Officer's Sheet Anchor; or, a Key to the Leading of Rigging, and to Practical Seamanship* (London 1808), p 65.
[26] John Harland (illustrated by Mark Myers) *Seamanship in the Days of Sail* (London 1984), pp 155–72.
[27] Lever, *Sea Officer's Sheet Anchor, op cit*, p 80.
[28] For reconstructed sail plans of *Codrington* and *London*, see Howard I Chapelle, *The Search for Speed under Sail 1700–1855*, (New York 1967), plates 22 and 27. For reconstructed spar and rigging plan of *Oliver Cromwell* see V R Grimwood, *American Ship Models and How to Build Them* (New York 1942), plate XI; but the presence of a dolphin striker in a ship of 1778 cannot be correct. The topgallant poles are omitted on the plan: their lengths were 10ft (fore), 14ft (main), 8¾ft (mizen) in round figures.
[29] Groenewegen, *Hollandsche Schepen, op cit*.
[30] G La Roërie and J Vivielle, *Navires et Marins de la Rame à L'Hélice* (Paris 1930), vol II, pp 144, 145 and 148.
[31] Falconer, *Dictionary of the Marine, op cit*, entry 'Bark'.
[32] Gustaf Halldin and others, *Svenskt Skeppsbyggeri* (Malmö, Sweden 1963), plate facing p 204.

[33] Groenewegen, *op cit*; Baugean, *Recueil de Petites Marines*, (nd, boxed, loose oblong plates), plate 46. The publication date is assigned to 1817.
[34] Lescallier, *Vocabulaire, op cit,* p 189, fig 76.
[35] E W Petrejus, 'The Dutch Flute', *The Great Age of Sail*, editor Joseph Jobé (Lausanne, Switzerland 1967), p 84.
[36] Howard I Chapelle, 'Dolphin Strikers', *MM*, 1957, vol XLIII, p 166.
[37] Hans Szymanski, *Deutsche Segelschiffe* (Berlin 1934, reprint Hamburg 1972), plate 2, fig 97.
[38] Collection of George P B Naish (in 1980).
[39] L G Carr Laughton, '*HMS Victory*: Report to Technical Committee', *MM*, 1924, vol X, p 190.
[40] Hutchinson, *Naval Architecture, op cit,* pp 55–56.
[41] Carr Laughton, 'HMS *Victory Report*', *op cit,* p 190.
[42] Lever, *Sea Officer's Sheet Anchor, op cit,* pp 6–7 and fig 357.
[43] Basil Lubbock, *The Arctic Whalers* (Glasgow 1937), p 150; and F Holm-Petersen and A Resondahl, *Fra Sejl Til Diesel* (Copenhagen *c*1950), vol I, p 85.
[44] H C Knight, 'HM Bark *Endeavour*', *MM*, 1933, vol XIX, p 293.
[45] *Ibid*, pp 295–9.
[46] *Ibid*, p 294.
[47] Admiralty Draughts at NMM, plan nos 3814a and b, box 66.
[48] Stephanie Jones, *A Maritime History of the Port of Whitby 1700–1914* (unpublished Ph D thesis, London University 1982), Chapter 1.
[49] *Ibid*, p 37.
[50] Knight, 'Bark *Endeavour*', *op cit,* p 296.
[51] Hutchinson, *Naval Architecture, op cit,* p 67.
[52] Alan Villiers, *Captain Cook* (London 1967), p 77.
[53] Knight, 'Bark *Endeavour*', *op cit,* p 296.
[54] I am grateful to David Lyon for help in sorting out the name changes.
[55] Knight, 'Bark *Endeavour*', *op cit,* p 297.
[56] Chapman (translated by Inman), *Treatise on Ship-Building, op cit,* pp 79–80.
[57] Duhamel du Monceau, *The Elements of Naval Architecture: or, a Practical Treatise on Ship-Building*, abridged by Mungo Murray (London 1764), pp 46–49, bound in at end of Murray, *Treatise on Shipbuilding op. cit.*
[58] Chapman (translated by Inman), *Treatise on Ship-Building, op cit,* p 109.
[59] J W Damer Powell, *Bristol Privateers and Ships of War* (Bristol 1930), pp 309–10
[60] Gomer Williams, *History of Liverpool Privateers and Letters of Marque with an Account of the Liverpool Slave Trade* (London 1897), p 678, Appendix No VIII.
[61] Hutchinson, *Naval Architecture, op cit,* pp 22–23.
[62] *Ibid*, p 42.
[63] *Ibid*, pp43–44.
[64] NMM, Admiralty Draughts, boxes 59–62.
[65] John Charnock, *History of Marine Architecture* (London 1801), vol III, p 266.
[66] J J Colledge, *Ships of the Royal Navy: an Historical Index*, (Newton Abbot 1969), vol I p 94.
[67] Blackwall Yard: 'List of Ships Built for other than E I Service', NMM, GRN/1, fr 124.
[68] Thomas Richardson, *Mercantile Marine Architecture* (London 1833), plate V.
[69] Danish Maritime Museum, *Søhistorisk Billedbog* (Helsingør 1967), plate 62.
[70] Chapelle, *Search for Speed under Sail, op cit,* plate 21 and 22.
[71] *Ibid*, plate 27.
[72] NMM, Admiralty Draughts, plan 3311 box 49.
[73] *Ibid*; redrawn plan in Chapelle, *Search for Speed under Sail, op cit,* pl 26.
[74] Chapman, *Architectura Navalis, op cit,* pl LXII, figs 2 and 4.
[75] NMM, Admiralty Draughts, plan 6671 box 66.
[76] NMM, Admiralty Draughts, plan 6671 box 66.
[77] Mungo Murray, *Treatise on Ship-Building, op cit,* pp 179–84; William Salisbury, 'Merchantmen in 1754', *MM*, 1936, vol XXII, pp 346–55.
[78] NMM, Admiralty Draughts, plan 6769 box 59.
[79] John Lyman, 'The Bilander', *MM*, 1963, vol 49, p 143.
[80] W Salisbury, 'Bilanders, Brigantines and Snows', *MM*, 1964, vol 50, p 61.
[81] Lescallier, *Vocabulaire, op cit,* pl 3, fig 19 and p 165.
[82] Mungo Murray, *Supplement to the Treatise on Ship-building*, (London 1865), p 108; bound in at end of Murray *Treatise on Ship-Building*, op.cit. Although this Supplement includes a translation from Bouguer's *Traité du Navire* it seems that the items on spar dimensions were contributed by Murray himself.
[83] William Salisbury, 'Bilanders, Brigantines, and Snows', *MM* 1964, vol 50, p 61.
[84] E P Morris, *The Fore-and-Aft Rig in America* (New Haven, Connecticut 1927), pl XXVIII B, reproduced from Labat, *Nouveau Voyage aux Isles de L'Amérique* (1724), vol II, p 256.
[85] See E A Dingley, 'Brigantines', *MM* 1920, vol 6, p 298; here Dingley has redrawn the plates of a brig and a brigantine from Nicholas P Ozanne, *Marine Militaire ou Recueil des différents Vaisseaux* (Paris 1762).
[86] Morris, *Fore-and-Aft Rig in America, op cit,* pl XXX B; also reproduced in Alexander Laing, *American Sail* (London 1961), p 58.
[87] NMM, sketch book by Edward Gwyn (artists *c*1780, size I).
[88] NMM, sketch book by Thomas Luny (artists 1837, size I).
[89] NMM, Admiralty Draughts, plan 6429 box 63.
[90] Chapelle, *Search for Speed under Sail, op cit,* pp 53–4.
[91] *Ibid*, plates 5 and 6 and pp 54–59.
[92] Morris, *Fore-and-Aft Rig in America, op cit,* p 191.
[93] Howard I Chapelle, *The History of American Sailing Ships* (New York 1935), figs 5,6 and 7.
[94] Chapelle, *Search for Speed under Sail, op cit,* plates 13 and 14.
[95] Chapman, *Architectura Navalis, op cit.*
[96] Groenewegen, *Hollandsche Schepen, op cit,* plate G (?) 8.
[97] Lescallier, *Vocabulaire, op cit,* p 225.
[98] NMM, Admiralty draughts, plan 4523 box 64.
[99] Steel, *Rigging and Seamanship, op cit,* vol I, p 221.
[100] NMM, sketch books by Thomas Luny (artists 1837, size I).
[101] William A Baker, *Sloops and Shallops* (Barre, Mass 1966).
[102] R Morton Nance, 'Ketches', *MM*, 1912, vol 2, pp 362–70.
[103] Morris, *Fore-and-Aft Rig in America, op cit,* pp 142–3.
[104] Chapman, *Architectura Navalis, op cit,* pl LXII, figs 3, 7, 8, 9 and 11.
[105] Sir Alan Moore and R Morton Nance, 'Round-Sterned Ships', *MM*, 1911, vol. 1, p 109.
[106] John Lyman, 'Gibraltar Shipping in 1783', *M M*, 1965, vol 51, pp 183–4.
[107] Science Museum, Sailing Ship Collection, plan C/3/21.
[108] 34 George III, *c*47, was the first of several smuggling Acts.
[109] Chapelle, *Search for Speed under Sail, op cit,* plates 10 and 11.

CHAPTER 3

[1] The third edition (1822) was edited by John Knowles and an additional plan added.
[2] NMM, GRN/1, MS. list of ships built at Blackwall Yard up to 1818.
[3] *Ibid.*
[4] Davis Steel, *Naval Architecture*, revised by John Knowles (3rd ed, London 1822), p 181.
[5] *Ibid*, Tables, p 24.
[6] David Steel, *Elements and Practise of Rigging and Seamanship* (London 1794), vol I, p 52.
For further comments see R C Anderson, 'The Dolphin Striker', M M, 1956, vol 42, p 282; Howard I Chapelle, 'The Dolphin Striker', M M, 1957, vol 43, p 166; John Lyman, 'Dolphin Strikers', M M, 1958, vol 44, p 147.
[8] John C G Hill, *Shipshape and Bristol Fashion* (Liverpool 2nd ed *c*1958), p 3 *et seq.*
[9] Damer Powell, *Bristol Privateers and Ships of War* (Bristol 1930), p 318.
[10] Hill, *Shipshape and Bristol Fashion, op cit,* p 92.
[11] C Ernest M Fayle, *A Short History of the World's Shipping Industry* (London 1933), p 218.
[12] N M M, Admiralty Draughts, No 4533 Box 64.
[13] Published 1953, 2 vols.
[14] *Ibid*, Appendix I, vol I.
[15] William A Baker, *Sloops & Shallops* (Barre, Mass 1966), p 96.
[16] N M M, Artists, Thomas Luny sketchbook dated 1799 size I.
[17] Richard Weatherill, *The Ancient Port of Whitby and its Shipping* (Whitby 1908), p 26; see also lists of ships built in Whitby pp 89 *et seq.*
[18] I am grateful to the Whitby Literary and Philosophical Society which owns the Museum, for permission to copy some of the plans.
[19] Revd George Young, *A History of Whitby* (Whitby 1817) vol II, p 553 footnote. I am grateful to Stephanie Jones for providing me with photocopies of the shipping section.
[20] Basil Lubbock, *The Arctic Whalers* (Glasgow 1937) pp 148–49.
[21] Cost account books of John Brockbank in Lancaster Museum; extracts from transcription made by William Salisbury.

[22] Data supplied by Daniel Hay, Librarian, Whitehaven Library.
[23] *Cumberland Pacquet* 25 October 1803. This extract was made by W Stewart Rees and communicated to William Salisbury.
[24] J W Smith and T S Holden, *Where Ships are Born; Sunderland 1346–1946* (Sunderland 1947), pp 8–12.
[25] *Ibid*, p 10.
[26] I am indebted to James Steele (died 1955) for allowing me to make a transcript of the list of ships built by his firm. There are a number of accounts of the history of the firm, e.g. *The Greenock Telegraph* 14 March 1914, with portraits of four generations of the partners; more recently in February and March 1956 the same paper ran a series of articles on the shipyard.
[27] Robert Steele, *Report on the Admeasurement of Shipping for Tonage* (Greenock 1834), p 15.
[28] Jean J Baugean, *Recueil de Petites Marines* (Paris 1817), plate 77.
[29] *Ibid*, plate 63. Plate 62 is also called 'schooner-brig' but has *no* square sails on mainmast!
[30] Jean J Baugean, *Collection de Toutes les Espèces de Bâtiments de Guerre et de Bâtiments Marchands* (Paris 1814), plate 58. She is flying a Red Ensign.
[31] N M M, Admiralty draughts, plan No 4036 a, box 57.
[32] N M M, Admiralty draughts, plan No 3986 b, box 57.
[33] E A Digley, 'Brigantines', M M, 1920, vol 6, pp 28 & 297. A photograph of this brigantine is reproduced in Harold A Underhill, *Deep-Water Sail* (Glasgow 1952), p 40.
[34] N M M, Sketh book by Copley Fielding, p 18 (artists 1853–9, box I).
[35] Henry Moses, *Sketches of Shipping* (London 1837) published Ackermann, (4to size).
[36] David Steel, *Rigging and Seamanship, op cit*, vol I, p 220.
[37] Baugean, *Collection de... Bâtiments Marchands, op cit*, plate 9.
[38] Alexander Hall & Sons, yard book transcribed by James Henderson.
[39] *List of Shipping Registered in the Different Ports of Scotland* (Glasgow 1828), 3rd ed.
[40] A Hall & Sons, yard book, *op cit*.
[41] The specification referred to consists of the scantlings given for the collier brig of 170 tons in David Steel's *Naval Architecture* (1805) and repeated in John Knowles's 3rd edition of this work (1822), folios I to LVII (which follow chapter 7).
[42] N M M, GRN/1, MS list of ships built at the Blackwall Yard up to 1818.
[43] Steel, *Rigging and Seamanship, op cit*, vol I, p 52.
[44] Darcy Lever, *The Young Sea Officer's Sheet Anchor* (London 1808).
[45] Plan no 1761. Copy of this plan loaned to me by W Salisbury.
[46] N M M, sketch book by Copley Fielding, *op cit*, p 2.
[47] E W Cooke, *Fifty Plates of Shipping and Craft* (London 1829); in particular, plates 'Collier Discharging' and 'Collier & Calm'.
[48] Darcy Lever, *Young Sea Officer's Sheet Anchor, op cit*, p 61.
[49] Steel, *Rigging and Seamanship, op cit*, vol I; pp 98–105 cover square sails.
[50] N M M, Admiralty Draughts, plan No 4533, box 64. The design was amended to schooner rig.
[51] The four plates are referred to in some detail early in the Chapter; the book and plates were first published in 1805.
[52] Writing in the *Mechanics' Magazine*, *c*1825.
[53] Thomas Simpson, '*Edward*, snow and emigrant ship', *Sea Breezes*, Oct 1927, vol 10, pp 174–7.
[54] For information on the *Balfour* see John F Gibson, *Brocklebanks 1770–1950* (1953), vol I, in particular pp 62 and 201. For plan of the brig, see Brocklebank archives.
[55] Howard I Chapelle, *The Search for Speed under Sail 1700–1855* (New York 1967), p 189.
[56] Henry M Jones, *Ships of Kingston* (Plymouth, Mass 1926), pp 41–43.
[57] *Ibid*, p 44.
[58] Finch Coxe, 'An Essay of the Present State of the United States of America' extracted from the *Pennsylvanian Packet* 7 May 1790, and reprinted in *A Collection of Papers on Naval Architecture, originally communicated through the channel of the European Magazine* (London 1791, 2nd ed), part I, pp 38–39.
[59] N M M, Admiralty Draughts, plan No 4533 box 64.
[60] A Hall & Sons, Yard Book, *op cit*.
[61] John Fincham, *A Treatise on Masting Ships and Mast Making:...* (London 1843) pp 73 and 76. This is the second edition referred to but the tables and contents are identical, alterations being the addition of new material.
[62] Hans Szymanksi, *Deutsche Segelschiffe* (Berlin 1934, reprint Hamburg 1972), plates 9–18.
[63] J W D Powell, 'The *Jenny* of Bristol, 1791–7', M M, 1956, vol 42, pp 327–9.
[64] Chapelle, *The Baltimore Clipper, op cit*, p 44.
[65] Charles S Morgan, 'New England Coasting Schooners', *American Neptune*, 1963, vol 23, p 7.
[66] Howard I Chapelle, *The Search for Speed under Sail 1700–1855* (New York 1967), pp 165 and 167.
[67] N M M, Admiralty Draughts, plan no 4547 box 64.
[68] Chapelle, *Search for Speed under Sail, op cit*, plate 39.
[69] Lancaster Library MSS, Contract Book of John Brockbank 1789–1822; taken from transcript made by W Salisbury.
[70] Richard Hall Gower, *A Supplement to the Practical Seamanship* (London 1807), 2 plates between pp 20 and 21.
[71] John Fincham, *A History of Naval Architecture* (London 1851), plate 22 facing p 181.
[72] Gower, *Supplement to Practical Seamanship, op cit.*, plate facing p 11.
[73] W H Chaplin, 'The Four-Masted Ship *Transit*', *M M*, 1933, vol 19, p 316; also David R MacGregor, *Fast Sailing Ships, their Design and Construction 1775–1875* (Lymington, Hants, 1973), pp 50–52.
[74] Frederik Henrik af Chapman, *Architectura Navalis Mercatoria* (Stockholm 1768), plate LXII.
[75] Alan Moore and R Morton Nance, 'Round-Sterned Ships: No II The Hooker', *M M*, 1911, vol I, p 296.
[76] Szymanski, *Deutsche Segelschiffe, op cit*, plate 14, fig 118.
[77] *Ibid*, plate 16, fig 123.
[78] Baugean, *Recueil de Petites Marines, op cit*, plate 84.
[79] *Ibid*, plate 39.
[80] Original in Bristol Museum and Art Gallery. Later published as an aquatint entitled 'Floating Harbour in Bristol and Tower of St. Mary Redcliffe Church'. (cf Witt Library, Courtauld Institute of Art.)
[81] Chapman, *Architectura Navalis Mercatoria, op cit*, pl. LXII, fig No 7.
[82] Thomas Agnew's advertisement of their 47th annual exhibition, *Contry Life*, 31 Jan 1947.
[83] Grahame Farr, 'Ketch Rig', *M M*, 1950, vol 36, p 269.
[84] Frank C Bowen, *The Sea, its History and Romance* (London 1926), vol III, p 233.
[85] N M M, sketch book by Thomas Luny, No 1, 1799 (artists 1837, size D).
[86] C F Partington, *The Ship-Builder's Complete Guide; Theory and Practice of Naval Architecture* (London 1826), p 108.
[87] M A N Marshall, 'Whitstable and Faversham Hoymen; early Nineteenth Century', *M M*, 1962, vol 48, pp 65 *et seq*.
[88] Peter Hedderwick, *A Treatise on Marine Architecture containing the Theory and Practice of Shipbuilding* (Edinburgh 1830), p 363.
[89] Nautical Museum, Castletown, I O M: letter from Thomas Quayle to his brother George, dated London May 1791, describing talk he had had with Capt Schank. I am grateful to Basil Greenhill for showing me a transcript he had made of this letter.
[90] John Knowles, *Naval Architecture* (3rd ed, London 1822), pp 158–171.
[91] *Encyclopaedia Britannica* (1797), article 'Shipbuilding', p 376.
[92] A H Clarke, *History of Yachting* (New York 1904), pp 147–52.

CHAPTER 4

[1] C Northcote Parkinson, *Trade in the Eastern Seas 1793–1813* (Cambridge 1937), pp 164–8.
[2] Sir Evan Cotton, ed Sir Charles Fawcett, *East Indiamen: the East India Company's Maritime Service* (London 1949), p 43.
[3] Jean Sutton, *Lords of the East; the East India Company and its Ships* (London 1981) pp 21–24 and 31.
[4] *List of Marine Records of the late East India Company...in the India Office Library* (London 1896) p xii.
[5] Sutton, *Lords of the East, op cit*. p 22.
[6] *Proceedings Relative to Ships Tendered for the Service of the United East-India Company, from the 2nd July 1806 to the 27th September 1809* (London 1809), p 2846.
[7] *Reports and Papers on the Impolicy of Employing Indian Built Ships in the Trade of the East India Company and of Admitting them to British Registry* (London 1809), p 183.
[8] John Leather, 'The Shipbuilding Bayleys', *MM*, 1965, vol 51, p 135.
[9] *Proceedings Relative to Ships, op cit*, Appendix 4518, p 3844.
[10] *Ibid*, Appendix 4560, p 3869.
[11] *Ibid*, Appendix 4567, pp 3873–76.
[12] *Ibid*, Appendix 4568, pp 3877–80.
[13] *Ibid*, Appendix 4595, pp 3911–12.

[14] *Ibid*, Court of Directors 3 August 1808, pp 2871–72.
[15] *Ibid*, Appendix 4559, p 3868.
[16] Charles Hardy, *A Register of Ships Employed in the Service of the Honourable East India Company, 1760 to 1819* (London 1820), p 364 and Appendix pp 156–8.
[17] Cotton, *East Indiamen, op cit*, p 47.
[18] Parkinson, *Trade in the Eastern Seas, op cit*, p 131.
[19] 'Evidence given by Mr Snodgrass before a Committee of the House of Commons, appointed in March 1771, to consider how his Majesty's Navy might be better supplied with Timber', *A Collection of Papers on Naval Architecture, originally communicated through the channel of the European Magazine* (London 1798), vol II, part 2, p 29.
[20] 'Letter from Gabriel Snodgrass Esq to the Right Hon Henry Dundas. . .and to the Chairman . . .of the East India Company, on the Mode of Improving the Navy of Great Britain. . .' *ibid*, pp 8–9. The letter was dated 9 Nov 1796.
[21] 'A list of Ships in the East India Company's Service, built with all Iron Knees. . .' *ibid*, p 55.
[22] Private journal kept aboard *Walthamstow* by Revd William Money, 18 Mar to 29 Oct 1800. Kindly made available to me by T E P Gilpin.
[23] See Parkinson, *Trade in the Eastern Seas, op cit*, pp 167–70; C N Parkinson, 'The East India Trade'; C N Parkinson editor, *The Trade Winds* (London 1948), pp 143–5.
[24] Hardy, *Register of Ships in the East India Company, op cit*; especially pp 291–9; and *ibid* (4th ed, London 1835), supplement pp 25–35.
[25] Knud Klem, 'The Danish Chartered Companies', *Ships and Shipyards, Sailors and Fishermen* (Copenhagen 1972), pp 152 and 154.
[26] Henry Green and Robert Wigram, *Chronicles of the Blackwall Yard* (London 1881), part I, pp 26 *et seq*. Part II was never published.
[27] Cotton, *East Indiamen, op cit*, p 125.
[28] Hardy, *Register of Ships in East India Company, op cit*, (4th ed., 1835), appendix to supplement, pp 25–7; W H Coates, *The Good Old Days of Shipping* (Bombay 1900), pp11–12.
[29] Green and Wigram, *Chronicles of the Blackwall Yard, op cit*, Part I, p 27.
[30] William Salisbury, 'Merchantmen in 1754', *MM*, 1936, vol XXII, pp 347–8.
[31] Fredrik Henrik af Chapman, *Architectura Navalis Mercatoria* (Stockholm 1768), plate L1.
[32] N M M, Merchant Ship Draughts, plan No T 2013.
[33] Parkinson, *Trade in the Eastern Seas, op cit*, p 167.
[34] David Steel, *The Elements and Practice of Naval Architecture* (London 1805), plate XX.
[35] Abraham Rees, *The Cyclopædia*; or, *Universal Dictionary of Arts, Sciences and Literature* (London 1820); the plans of ships appear in Vol III of the plates under 'Naval Architecture'.
[36] *Proceedings Relative to Ships, op cit*, Appendix 4678, pp 3992–95.
[37] *Ibid*, Appendix 4684, p 4001.
[38] Albert Sebille (editor), *Histoire de la Marine* (Paris 1939), p 174.
[39] Parkinson, *Trade in the Eastern Seas, op cit*, p 158.
[40] G W Munro, 'East Indiamen', *Marine Models*, June 1934, vol 7, No 3, pp 64–5. I am grateful to B W Bathe for drawing my attention to this article and lending me his copy of it.
[41] India Office Library, log-books Nos 40 A-H.
[42] David Steel, *Art of Making Masts and Yards* (London 1816, 2nd ed), p 100.
[43] India Office Library, log-book No 40 E.
[44] John Edye, *Calculations of Ships and Vessels of War* (London 1832), especially pp 100–1.
[45] India Office Library, log-book No 40 C.
[46] William Hutchinson, *Treatise on Naval Architecture* (Liverpool 1794, 4th ed), p 56. See also David R MacGregor, 'Spinaker and Spindle', *MM*, 1965, vol 51, p 342, for further information on the subject.
[47] B L [? Basil Lubbock], 'Flying Kites', *MM*, Dec 1911, vol I, p 350. Also p 190 (in July 1911).
[48] David Steel, *The Elements and Practice of Rigging and Seamanship*, vol I (London 1794), p 37.
[49] India Office Library, log-book No 40 A.
[50] *Lloyd's List*, 2 May 1826, for date of arrival.
[51] Revd William Money's private journal, *op cit*.
[52] India Office Library, log-book Nos 205 B & C.
[53] Original inspected when in Hilhouse Collection, at offices of Charles Hill & Son, Bristol.
[54] India Office Library, log-book No 206 C.
[55] *Ibid*, log-book No 206 B.
[56] *Proceedings Relative to Ships, op cit*, Appendix 4679, pp 3998–99.
[57] *The Times*, 4 Sept 1851, p 3.
[58] *Sydney Morning Herald*, 9 Mar 1854.
[59] *Ibid.*

Note: *MM* = *Mariner's Mirror*; *NMM* = *National Maritime Museum*.

SOURCES

PLANS, MODELS, AND RELATED ARCHIVES

The backbone of the book consists of the plans derived from models and shipbuilders' draughts, which are measured and reconstructed to produce the plans used here. Comments on any Collection are usually given in the text or the references, so no additional data is listed here.

National Maritime Museum, Greenwich. Admiralty Collection of Draughts; plans of merchant ships contained in such collections as Longstaff and Charnock, as well as in the general collection; also ship models. In the Print Room, artists' sketch books and watercolour drawings. Various manuscripts including a list of ships built in the Blackwall Yard.
Science Museum, London. Plans and models of merchant ships.
Charles Hill & Sons. Hilhouse Collection of plans (*c*1760 onwards).
Liverpool County Museums. Brocklebank Collection of plans, and Yard Data book; models; shipbuilding lists.
Howard I Chapelle. Numerous plans reconstructed from contemporary draughts (inspected during his lifetime).
Whitby Museum. (Whitby Literary and Philosophical Society). H W Smales Collection of ships plans.
India Office Library. Log-books.
W. Salisbury. Ship plans; models; shipbuilding lists; analysis of Hilhouse plans.
James Henderson. Cost accounts and spar dimensions of ships built by A Hall & Sons.
James Steele. Half-models; Shipyard list (inspected during his lifetime).
Author's Collection. Plans; log-books; illustrations.
Mariners Museum, Newport News. Guibert Collection of French ships.
Historisch Scheepwaart Museum, Amsterdam. Plans and models.
Musée de Marine, Paris. Models; drawings by Ozanne.

PRINTED WORKS

The following are the principal books consulted but it is not intended to be an exhaustive list on the period. Articles in journals are given in the References and so are omitted. A number of the books listed were used in reconstructing the plans.

Abell, Sir Wescott, *The Shipwright's Trade* (Cambridge 1948)
Baugean, Jean, *Collection de toutes les Espèces de Bâtimens de Guerre et de Bâtimens Marchands* (Paris 1814)
Baugean, Jean, *Recueil de Petites Marine* (Paris 1817)
Benham, Hervey, *Once upon a Tide* (London 1955)
Biddlecombe, George, *The Art of Rigging* (London 1848)
Bowen, Frank C, *The Golden Age of Sail* (London 1925)
Brewington, M V and Dorothy Brewington, *The Marine Paintings and Drawings in the Peabody Museum* (Salem 1968)
Burstall, Aubrey F, *A History of Mechanical Engineering* (London 1965)
Chapelle, Howard I, *The History of American Sailing Ships* (New York 1935)
Chapelle, Howard I, *The National Watercraft Collection* (Smithsonian Museum, Washington 1960)
Chapelle Howard I, *The Search for Speed under Sail* (New York 1967)
Chapman, Fredrik Henrik af, *Architectura Navalis Mercatoria* (Stockholm 1768, reprinted London *c*1970)
Chapman, Frederick Henry de, *A Treatise on Ship-Building* translated by Rev James Inman (Cambridge 1820)
Clowes, G S Laird, *Sailing Ships* (Science Museum catalogues, 2 vols, London 1932)
Coates, W H, *The Good Old Days of Shipping* (Bombay 1900)
Collection of Papers on Naval Architecture originally communicated though the channel of the European Magazine (London 1798)
Colledge, J J, *Ships of the Royal Navy: an Historical Index* (Newton Abbot 2 vols 1969 and 1970)
Cooke, E W, *Fifty Plates of Shipping and Craft* (London 1829)
Cotton, Sir Evan, *East Indiamen* (London 1949)
Court, W H B, *A Concise Economic History of Britain from 1750* (Cambridge 1954)
Davis, Ralph, *Rise of the English Shipping Industry* (London 1962)
Falconer, William, *An Universal Dictionary of the Marine* (London 1769 and 1780)
Finberg, H P R (editor), *Approaches to History* (London 1965)
Finch, Roger, *Coals from Newcastle* (Lavenham 1973)
Fincham, John, *An Outline of Ship-Building* (2 vols text and plates London 1852)
Fincham, John, *A Treatise on Masting Ships and Mast Making,* (2 vols text and plates, London 1st ed 1829 and 3rd ed 1854)
Gibson, John F, *Brocklebanks 1770–1950* (2 vols Liverpool 1953)
Gower, Richard Hall, *A Supplement to the Practical Seamanship* (London 1807)
Green, Henry, and Wigram, *Chronicles of the Blackwall Yard* (part I London 1881)
Groenewegen, G, *Verzameling van Vier en tachtig Stuks Hollandsche Schepen* (Rotterdam 1789, reprint 1967)
Hardy's Register of Ships Employed by the East India Co (London 3rd ed 1820 and 4th ed 1835)
Harland, John, illustrated by Mark Myers, *Seamanship in the Age of Sail* (London 1984)
Harper, Lawrence A, *The English Navigation Laws* (reprint of 1939 ed, New York 1964)
Hill, John C G, *Shipshape and Bristol Fashion* (Liverpool *c*1955)
Hutchinson, William, *A Treatise on Naval Architecture* (4th ed Liverpool 1794)
Kipping, Robert, *The Elements of Sailmaking* (2nd ed London 1851)
Klein, Herbert S, *The Middle Passage* (Princeton, New Jersey 1978)
Laughton, L G Carr, *Old Ship Figure-Heads & Sterns* (London 1925)
Lescaller, Antoine, *Vocabulaire des Termes de Marine* (Paris 1777)
Lescallier, Antoine, *Traité Pratique du Gréement des Vaisseaux* (2 vols Paris 1791)
Leslie, Robert C, *Old Sea Wings, Ways and Words* (London 1930)
Lever, Darcy, *Young Sea Officer's Sheet Anchor* (London 1808)
Lindsay, W S, *History of Merchant Shipping 1816–1874* (2 vols, London *c*1874)
List of Marine Records of the late East India Company ... in the India Office Library (London 1896)
Lloyd's Register of Shipping (annually, London)
Lloyds's Register, *Annals of Lloyd's Register* (London 1934)
Lubbock, Basil, *The Blackwall Frigates* (Glasgow 1922)
Lubbock, Basil, *The Arctic Whalers* (Glasgow 1937)
MagGregor, David R, *Fast Sailing Ships 1775–1875* (Lymington 1973)
Moorsom, George, *A Brief Review and Analyses of the Laws for the Admeasurement of Tonnage* (London 1952)
Morgan, William, and Augustin Creuze (editors), *Papers on Naval Architecture* (4 vols, London 1826, 1828, 1830, 1832–65)
Morris, E P, *The Fore-and-Aft Rig in America* (New Haven, Conn, 1927)
Moses, Henry, *Sketches of Shipping and Craft* (London 1824)
Murphy, John M, and W N Jeffers jnr, *Spars and Rigging from Nautical Routine* (reprint of 1849 ed, Providence, RI 1933)
Murray, Mungo, *A Treatise on Ship-Building and Navigation* (London 1765)
Pâris, Vice-Adml Edmond, *Souvenirs de Marine* (original 6 vols reprinted as 3, Grenoble 1975)
Parkinson, C Northcote, *The Trade Winds: British Oversea Trade 1793–1815* (London 1948)
Petrejus, E W, *Modelling the Brig of War 'Irene'* (Hengelo, Holland 1970)
Powell, J W Damer, *Bristol Privateers and Ships of War* (Bristol 1930) *Proceedings Relative to Ships Tendered for the Service of the United East-India Company, from the 2nd July 1806 to the 27th September 1809* (London 1809)
Rees, Abraham, 'Naval Architecture', *Cyclopaedia* (London 1820)
Richardson, Thomas, *Mercantile Marine Architecture* (London 1833)
Shields, John, *Clyde Built* (Glasgow 1949)
Shipbuilder's Repository or, A Treatise on Marine Architecture (London nd *c*1788)
Smith, J W, and T S Holden, *Where Ships are Born: Sunderland 1346–1946* (Sunderland 1947)
Stackpoole, Edouard A, *The Sea-Hunters* (Philadelphia 1953)

Starbuck, Alexander, *History of the American Whale Fishery* (reprint of 1878 ed 2 vols, New York 1964)
Steel, David, *The Elements and Practice of Rigging and Seamanship* (2 vols London 1794)
Steel, David, *Elements and Practice of Naval Architecture,* editor John Knowles (2 vols text and plates, London 2nd 1822)
Steel David, *The Shipwright's Vade-Mecum* (2 vols text and plates, London 1805)
Stevens, John R, *Old Time Ships* (Toronto 1949).
Stewart-Brown, R, *Liverpool Ships in the Eighteenth Century* (Liverpool 1932)
Sutton, Jean, *Lords of the East; the East India Company and its Ships* (London 1981)
Szymanski, Hans, *Deutsche Segelschiffe* (Berlin 1934)
Weatherill, Richard, *The Ancient Port of Whitby and its Shipping* (Whitby 1908)
Williams, Gomer, *History of Liverpool Privateers and Letters of Marque with an Account of the Liverpool Slave Trade* (London 1897)
Winchester, Clarence (editor), *Shipping Wonders of the World,* (2 vols, London *c*1936)
Young, Arthur, *Nautical Dictionary* (1st ed Dundee 1846, 2nd ed London 1863)

INDEX

Figures in italics refer to page numbers of illustrations.